THE GREAT DISMAL SWAMP

THE GREAT DISMAL SWAMP

Edited by Paul W. Kirk, Jr.

Published for the Old Dominion University Research Foundation
by the University Press of Virginia, Charlottesville

THE UNIVERSITY PRESS OF VIRGINIA
Copyright © 1979 by the
Old Dominion University Research Foundation, Inc.

First published 1979

Proceedings of a Symposium Sponsored by Old Dominion University and
United Virginia Bank–Seaboard National
14 March 1974

Endpapers: LANDSAT I false color infrared multispectral scanner image
of the Great Dismal Swamp and vicinity, taken from an altitude of
approximately 800 km. (EROS Data Center, Sioux Falls, SD 57198).

Library of Congress Cataloging in Publication Data

Main entry under title:

The Great Dismal Swamp.

  Includes bibliographies and indexes.
  1. Natural history—Dismal Swamp—Congresses.
2. Dismal Swamp—Congresses. I. Kirk, Paul W.,
1931– II. Old Dominion University. III. United
Virginia Bank–Seaboard National.
QH105.V8G73   500.9′755′523   79-375   ISBN 0-8139-0759-4

Printed in the United States of America

CONTENTS

Preface   ix

Contributors   xi

Geologic Setting and Origin of the Dismal Swamp,
Southeastern Virginia and Northeastern North Carolina
Robert Q. Oaks, Jr., and *Donald R. Whitehead*   1

Developmental History of the Dismal Swamp   *Donald R.
Whitehead* and *Robert Q. Oaks, Jr.*   25

Evidence of Aboriginal Utilization of the Bola in the Dismal
Swamp Area   *Edward Bottoms* and *Floyd Painter*   44

Man and the Swamp: The Historical Dimension   *Peter C.
Stewart*   57

Public Use Policy of the National Wildlife Refuge System
James W. Pulliam, Jr.   74

Remote Sensing Applications to the Dismal Swamp
Virginia Carter   80

Forest Dynamics in the Dismal Swamp of Virginia   *Gerald
   F. Levy* and *Susan W. Walker*   101

Log Ferns (*Dryopteris celsa*) and Their Relatives in the Dismal
   Swamp   *W. H. Wagner, Jr.,* and *Lytton J. Musselman*   127

Hydrology of the Dismal Swamp, Virginia–North Carolina
   William F. Lichtler and *Patrick N. Walker*   140

Lake Drummond: With a Discussion Regarding Its Plankton
   Composition   *Harold G. Marshall*   169

Notes on the Overlying Substrate and Bottom Contours of
   Lake Drummond   *Harold G. Marshall* and *W. Wright
   Robinson*   183

Hydrocarbon Background Levels at Two Rural Sites in
   Tidewater Virginia   *R. S. Davis, P. J. Maroulis, Robert B.
   Denyszyn,* and *A. R. Bandy*   188

Aquatic Insects of the Dismal Swamp   *James F. Matta*   200

The Ecology of the Two Dominant Tick Species in Relation
   to the Dismal Swamp National Wildlife Refuge in Virginia
   Mary Keith Garrett and *Daniel E. Sonenshine*   222

A Provisional Checklist of Amphians and Reptiles in the
   Dismal Swamp, with Comments on Their Range of
   Distribution   *David E. Delzell*   244

An Analysis of the Birdlife of the Dismal Swamp   *Brooke
   Meanley*   261

Contents

A Simulation Model of a *Peromyscus leucopus* Population in an
Area of the Dismal Swamp   *James E. Paschal, Daniel E.
Sonenshine*, and *John H. Richardson*   277

Mammals of the Dismal Swamp: A Historical Account
Charles O. Handley, Jr.   297

Essay on the Literature of the Dismal Swamp   *Peter C.
Stewart, Paul W. Kirk, Jr.*, and *Harold G. Marshall*   358

Scientific and Technical Literature concerning the Dismal
Swamp Area   *Paul W. Kirk, Jr., Harold G. Marshall,*
and *Peter C. Stewart*   378

Author Index   405

Organism Index   411

Subject Index   417

PREFACE

The first symposium to concern the natural history of the Dismal Swamp was held in a joint meeting of the Washington Academy of Science and the Washington Society of Engineers on 9 June 1911 aboard the steamer *Southland* en route from Washington, D.C., to Norfolk, Virginia. It had been decided to combine the lectures with an excursion through the fabled Swamp to Lake Drummond, which was attended the following day by 135 persons. Six topics were discussed, some by noted authorities of that period: the geography and geology of the Swamp (E. W. Shaw); peat deposits (C. A. Davis); forest types (R. Zon); plant life (F. V. Coville); ground animals, although "many varieties" of fish were also mentioned in addition to mammals, including bears "in abundance" and snakes in "super-abundance" (F. W. True), and birds (C. Hart Merriam, whose specialty was mammals). Merriam's talk reportedly also gave much attention to snakes in response to the audience enthusiasm generated by True's preceding discussion (see *Science* 33:909–910 for a brief but lucid account of this event by the recording secretary, W. J. Humphreys). During the ensuing 67 years these topics and many others concerning the natural and cultural history of the Dismal Swamp have continued to hold the interest of the academic and lay communities, as the extensive bibliographic materials at the end of this volume will attest.

The interest in this enigmatic wildlands area was intensified recently by the Union Camp Corporation's gift of nearly 50,000 acres, including Lake Drummond, to The Nature Conservancy, and subsequent establishment of the Dismal Swamp National Wildlife Refuge. In order to examine the past, present, and future of this great resource, experienced government scientists and university shcolars converged for a second symposium on the Dismal Swamp, 14 March 1974, under the joint sponsorship of Old Dominion University and the United Virginia Bank–Seaboard National. Thirteen speakers addressed a general audience, interpreting recent and ongoing comprehensive investigations into geological, chemical, biological, and historical aspects of the Swamp. The heterogeneity of this audience reflects the widespread interest and concern for this unique habitat—actually a vast peat formation consisting of at least 11 distinct plant communities and supporting a diversity of animal species. The symposium attracted almost 200 teachers and students from high schools and colleges, conservationists, representatives of governmental agencies, the news media, and researchers in a number of disciplines.

Undoubtedly several portions of this work, which is comprised of five contributed papers and two bibliographic essays in addition to the invited symposium presentations, will be of interest and value to the many people who, for one reason or another, are intrigued by the Dismal Swamp of eastern Virginia and North Carolina.

Appreciation is expressed to Dr. Robert L. Ake and Dr. Daniel Sonenshine for editorial assistance, and to Mrs. Terry Smarr for typing the manuscript. This publication was made possible by a grant from the Old Dominion University Research Foundation.

Department of Biological Sciences   PAUL W. KIRK, JR.
Old Dominion University

CONTRIBUTORS

Alan R. Bandy, Department of Chemistry, Drexel University, Philadelphia, Pa. 19104

Edward Bottoms, 2016 Powell Circle, Chesapeake, Va. 23323

Virginia Carter, U.S. Geological Survey, 467 National Center, Reston, Va. 22092

Robert S. Davis, 9429 Wells Parkway, Norfolk, Va. 23503

David E. Delzell, Department of Biological Sciences, Old Dominion University, Norfolk, Va. 23508

Robert B. Denyszyn, Research Triangle Park, N.C. 27709

Mary Keith Garrett, Dismal Swamp National Wildlife Refuge, Suffolk, Va. 23508

Charles O. Handley, Jr., Smithsonian Institution, Washington, D.C. 20560

Paul W. Kirk, Jr., Department of Biological Sciences, Old Dominion University, Norfolk, Va. 23508

Gerald F. Levy, Department of Biological Sciences, Old Dominion University, Norfolk, Va. 23508

William F. Lichtler, U.S. Geological Survey, 901 N. 17th Street, Lincoln, Neb. 68508

Peter J. Maroulis, Department of Chemistry, Drexel University, Philadelphia, Pa. 19104

Harold G. Marshall, Department of Biological Sciences, Old Dominion University, Norfolk, Va. 23508

James F. Matta, Department of Biological Sciences, Old Dominion University, Norfolk, Va. 23508

Brooke Meanley, Patuxent Wildlife Research Center, Laurel, Md. 20810

Lytton J. Musselman, Department of Biological Sciences, Old Dominion University, Norfolk, Va. 23508

Robert Q. Oaks, Jr., Department of Geology, Utah State University, Logan, Utah 84332

Floyd Painter, 7507 Pennington Road, Norfolk, Va. 23507

James E. Paschal, Jr., 841 Harrison Avenue, Salt Lake City, Utah 84105

James W. Pulliam, Jr., U.S. Fish and Wildlife Service, Washington, D.C. 20240

JOHN H. RICHARDSON, Department of Biological Sciences, Old Dominion University, Norfolk, Va. 23508

W. WRIGHT ROBINSON, Department of Biological Sciences, Old Dominion University, Norfolk, Va. 23508

DANIEL E. SONENSHINE, Department of Biological Sciences, Old Dominion University, Norfolk, Va. 23508

PETER C. STEWART, Department of History, Old Dominion University, Norfolk, Va. 23508

WARREN H. WAGNER, JR., Department of Botany, University of Michigan, Ann Arbor, Mich. 48104

PATRICK N. WALKER, U.S. Geological Survey, 200 West Grace Street, Richmond, Va. 23220

SUSAN W. WALKER, 670 Wesley Dr., N.W., Atlanta, Ga. 30305

DONALD R. WHITEHEAD, Division of Biological Sciences, Indiana University, Bloomington, Ind. 47401

THE GREAT DISMAL SWAMP

GEOLOGIC SETTING AND ORIGIN OF THE DISMAL SWAMP, SOUTHEASTERN VIRGINIA AND NORTHEASTERN NORTH CAROLINA

Robert Q. Oaks, Jr., and Donald R. Whitehead

INTRODUCTION

General Statement

This report summarizes an investigation of the geologic units that directly underlie and surround the Dismal Swamp and their bearing on the origin of the Swamp; the geometry and surface morphology of peat in the Swamp; and possible reasons for original and continued ponding before interference by man. The location, extent, area, and morphology of the Swamp are first reviewed. This is followed by a discussion of the geologic units that underlie the peat. Characteristics of peat in the Dismal Swamp and the configuration of the base of the peat are next discussed, followed by a consideration of the age and origin of the Swamp.

Location, Extent, and Area

The name "Dismal Swamp" originated in colonial days for the swampy, undrained area that lies between the James River and its tributaries in southeastern Virginia and the Albemarle Sound and its tributaries in northeastern North Carolina. The drainage divide lies within a few miles of the James River, and passes through the northern part of the Dismal Swamp (Fig. 1). The western boundary of the Swamp lies along the abrupt and linear, eastward-facing Suffolk Scarp (Fig. 2). Peat of the Dismal Swamp extends west of the scarp in several short valley systems which begin in the plains above the scarp but terminate abruptly in peat at the base of the Suffolk Scarp. In other directions the boundaries of the Dismal Swamp are irregular and indistinct, commonly merging with swamps that extend down dis-

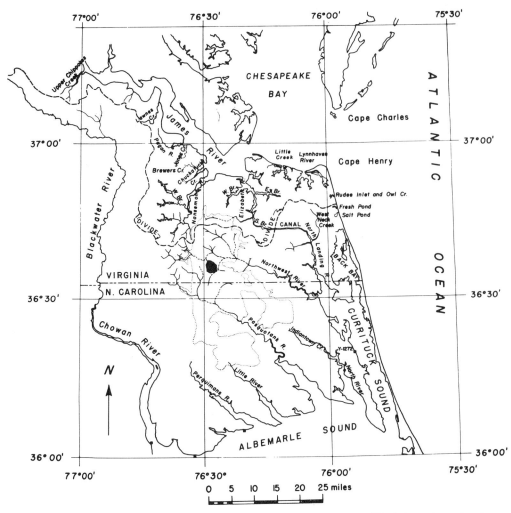

Fig. 1. Locality map showing drainage of southeastern Virginia and northeastern North Carolina. Dots outline Dismal Swamp; drainage divide and pre-peat drainage shown within Swamp are based in Fig. 9. From Oaks and Coch 1973 (fig. 4), courtesy Virginia Division of Mineral Resources.

tributary stream valleys to tidewater and extending through large, irregular low areas along interfluves on either side of such rivers (Fig. 1).

Because of man's activities before the earliest topographic mapping in the area (1902 Norfolk sheet, surveyed 1888–91), the original extent of the Dismal Swamp may never be known accurately, although the synoptic view provided by imagery from satellites may provide additional clues (see Carter, this volume). Shaler (1890, p. 318) estimated that the size of the Dismal Swamp in 1890 was about 1500 square miles (3900 sq. km) and that the original size

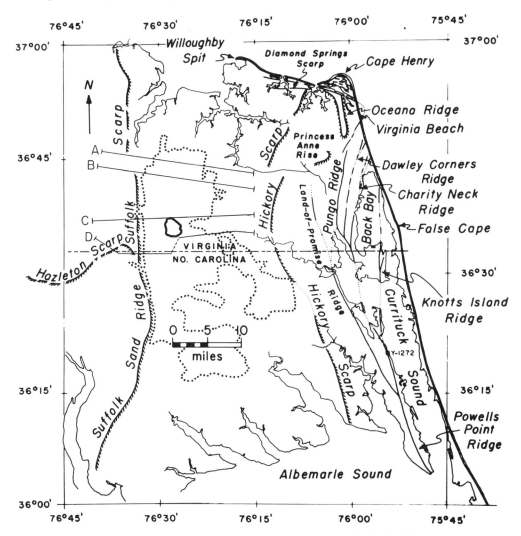

Fig. 2. Scarps and ridges in southeastern Virginia and northeastern North Carolina. Dots outline Dismal Swamp. Lettered lines show locations of geologic sections in Fig. 3. Modified from Oaks and Coch 1973 (fig. 5), courtesy Virginia Division of Mineral Resources.

probably was about 700 square miles (1800 sq. km) greater. Shaler (1890, p. 319) also pointed out that spoil banks from dredging of the Dismal Swamp Canal, opened about 1836 (Henry et al. 1959), interfered with eastward drainage in the Swamp and thereby permitted much of the acreage eastward to be "improved." Kearney (1901) estimated that the Dismal Swamp originally occupied approximately 2000 square miles (5700 sq. km), and Osbon (1919) merely repeated the figures of Shaler quoted above. Lewis and Cocke (1929) estimated that the total Swamp area had dwindled to only about 700 square miles (1800 sq. km) by 1929. All authors fail to note whether the swampy areas estimated were then contiguous or included areas assumed to have been contiguous before man's intervention. Certainly the greatly reduced estimate of Lewis and Cocke could have resulted as much from lost contiguity as from drainage and reclamation.

Outlines of the Dismal Swamp shown in the figures herein are based on the 1:250,000 and 1:62,500 topographic maps available in 1961–63 supplemented by 1:24,000 topographic maps then available and by soil surveys of Nansemond County (Devereux et al. 1936) and Norfolk County (Henry et al. 1959) in Virginia, and Camden and Currituck counties (Perkins et al. 1928), Perquimans and Pasquotank counties (Lapham and Lyman 1905), and Pasquotank County (Shearin et al. 1957) in North Carolina. Because the outline is hybrid and based primarily on maps made during the 1940s and 1950s, no calculations of area were made.

Continuous parts of the Dismal Swamp extended from a point east of Suffolk, Virginia, to an irregular southern boundary that reaches 10 to 20 miles (16 to 32 km) into North Carolina (Fig. 1). In Virginia the Swamp is 10 to 11 miles (16 to 18 km) wide, east to west, and about 15 miles (24 km) long, north to south (Oaks and Coch 1973, p. 19). Most of the work in this study was concentrated in Virginia and the northern 3 miles (5 km) of North Carolina.

Morphology

East of the Suffolk Scarp, southeastern Virginia and northeastern North Carolina are characterized by low altitude and low relief. Only a few localities rise above +25 feet (8 m) datum mean sea level. These areas include those that surround the Dismal Swamp. Several areas up to 5 miles (8 km) in diameter, including most of the Dismal Swamp, have less than 5 feet (1.5 m) of relief. East of the Suffolk Scarp both erosional and depositional topography are present, but the latter predominates. Between the James River and Albemarle Sound the subdued topography exhibits a nearly north-south grain closely related to the original morphology of sediments deposited in coastal environments (Oaks 1965, Oaks and Coch 1973). In the northern half of the Swamp two stream valleys trending east-west cut across the regional grain to drain the Dismal Swamp. In the southern half of the Swamp, other valleys follow original depositional lows parallel to the regional grain (Figs. 1 and 2).

The slightly irregular surface of peat in the Dismal Swamp (see Shaler 1890, p. 321) slopes gently eastward from one feather edge at the Suffolk Scarp near +27 feet (8 m) to another feather edge near

+15 feet (4.5 m) at the west side of the Deep Creek Swale (Fig. 3; see Oaks and Coch 1973, p. 104 and Figs. 3 and 6). Near the Virginia–North Carolina state line this slope is slight between the Suffolk Scarp and +20 feet (6 m), but somewhat steeper (5 feet in 0.2 to 0.5 mile) between +15 and +20 feet. Farther north this difference in slope is not so pronounced, but the slope is still greater between +15 and +20 feet than between +20 feet and the Suffolk Scarp (Fig. 9).

Natural drainage is poor in the Dismal Swamp because none of the streams are well developed. Before extensive ditching in the late 1950s and early 1960s the groundwater level was at the peat surface much of the year through large areas of the Swamp (Sharon Miller, pers. comm.). However, Shaler (1890, p. 319) speculated that spoil banks along the Dismal Swamp Canal had artificially raised the water table westward in the Swamp.

Lake Drummond is a nearly circular lake about 2.3 miles (3.7 km) wide, east to west, and about 2.7 miles (4.3 km) long, north to south. The lake occupies a position within the central portion of the Swamp, although slightly north of the Virginia–North Carolina state line, which perhaps is closer to the exact center (Fig. 1).

The 1940 topographic survey and 1954 revision show the contour for +20 feet (6 m) curving westward around the lake, and the lake level at +18 feet (5.5 m) and +17 feet (5.2 m), respectively, whereas the much more generalized 1888–91 topographic survey shows the contour for +20 feet east of the lake, and the lake level at +22.2 feet (6.8 m). Inasmuch as each of the three topographic maps has a different scale, direct comparison of successive borders of the lake is difficult. However, measurements from points of entry of canals show no significant differences in the size of the lake during the different surveys, despite an apparent fall of 5 feet (1.5 m) in the lake level. A fall of 2 to 3 feet (0.6 to 0.9 m) in the level of Lake Drummond was noted in August 1963 relative to the base of a pier at the north end of the lake during the severe drought of that summer. The shoreline was displaced only about 50 feet (15 m) lakeward from the pier. Buildings related to the pier occur on the 1940 survey but not on the 1888–91 survey. Therefore, fluctuations in the lake do occur despite the presence of a controlling spillway 0.5 mile (0.8 km) east of the lake.

The altitude of the spillway controlling the lake level is shown 2 feet higher (+20 feet) for 1888–91 than for 1954 (+18 feet). Although this discrepancy of 2 feet perhaps results from subsidence of the Swamp surface, possibly due to peat compaction, the change in 1927 to the new North American datum for sea level appears a more likely

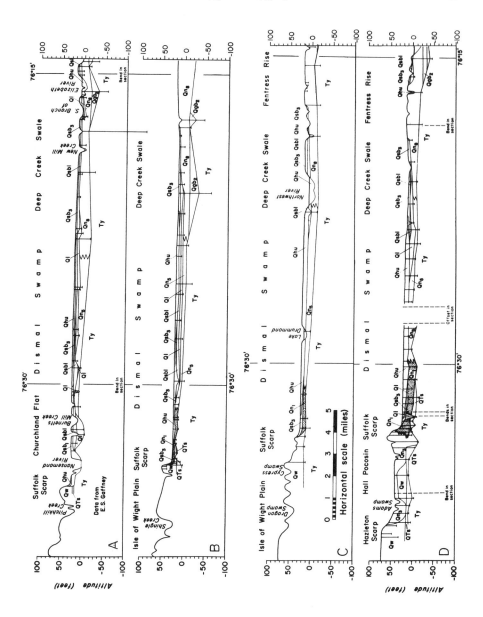

Fig. 3. Geologic sections through Dismal Swamp. Locations of sections shown in Fig. 2. Qhu = Dismal Swamp Peat; Qsb_1 = Sand Bridge Formation (Fm), upper member, clayey-sand facies; Qsb_3 = silty-clay facies; $Qsbl$ = lower member; Ql = Londonbridge Fm.; Qn_1 = Norfolk Fm., coarse-sand facies; Qn_3 = silty-clay facies; Qn_5 = medium-sand facies; Qn_8 = fine-sand facies; Qgb_2 = Great Bridge Fm., silty-clay facies; Qw = Windsor Fm.; QTs = Sedley Fm.; Ty = Yorktown Fm. From Oaks and Coch 1973 (plate 2), courtesy Virginia Division of Mineral Resources.

explanation why the position of the contour for +20 feet is east of the lake in the 1888–91 survey and west of the lake thereafter.

GEOLOGIC SETTING

Previous Work

The first systematic observations of geologic strata east of the Suffolk Scarp apparently were made during W. B. Rogers's geologic survey of Virginia from 1835 to 1840. In 1835 Rogers (1884, p. 30) recognized a fossiliferous Miocene "marl" unit, subsequently named the Yorktown Formation, west of Suffolk and through short distances eastward. In 1839 Rogers (1884, pp. 252–259) recognized the great linear extent of the Suffolk Scarp and its origin as a marine shoreline; he identified east of that scarp a pre-peat sequence of lightly colored, fine-grained sands and clays lacking pebbles (probably Nansemond facies of upper member of Sand Bridge Formation of Oaks and Coch 1973, p. 58) overlying the "marl" unit; and he tentatively assigned a Miocene age to marine shells found near Great Bridge (probably Pleistocene Norfolk Formation of Oaks and Coch 1963, 1973). Inasmuch as Rogers (1884, p. 255) envisioned a rapid shift in the shoreline from the Suffolk Scarp directly to its present position, he must have believed that the unit overlying the Miocene "marl" unit was marine in origin and synchronous with the formation of the scarp.

Shaler (1890, pp. 314, 329–330) independently recognized the marine origin of the Suffolk Scarp, which he called the "Nansemond escarpment," and the presence of a pre-peat marine unit overlying a widespread fossiliferous "Pliocene" deposit (Yorktown Formation). He believed that the pre-peat marine unit above the Yorktown was derived during wave erosion of the Suffolk Scarp, that stream valleys which enter the Dismal Swamp in the west were cut during the preceding emergent episode, that streams which leave the Dismal Swamp in the east were cut during the later emergent episode, and that a recent submergence has caused peat of the Dismal Swamp to accumulate. Fluctuations in relative sea level were ascribed to glacial control, although cyclic movements of the land were not dismissed entirely. Shaler (1890, p. 317) noted, "There may be . . . within the limits of the Dismal Swamp a number of stream valleys which have been so encumbered by the accumulation of vegetable matter that they are no longer evident to the eye." Also (1890, p. 314), "The eastern boundary of the swamp district is determined by certain low elevations, apparently dune-like in their nature . . . which attain a height of only a few feet, [and] serve in a measure to retain the swamp waters."

Darton (1902) observed that, east of the Suffolk Scarp, late Miocene sediments (Yorktown Formation) were overlain by fossiliferous "Pliocene" sands and "marls" 10 to 20 feet (3 to 6 m) thick that did not crop out but were known from wells and from canal excavations (probably Pleistocene Norfolk and Great Bridge formations of Oaks and Coch 1963, 1973). He assigned a thin sheet of loams and sands, overlying the "Pliocene" beds, to the Columbia Formation of Pleistocene age (probably chiefly Sand Bridge Formation of Oaks and Coch 1963, 1973), for which he inferred a fluvial or deltaic origin. Darton recognized that the Columbia Formation was cut through later by deep stream valleys and therefore inferred an emergent episode followed by submergence to the present position, which resulted in accumulation of peat in the Dismal Swamp.

Clark and Miller (1906) initially assigned the name "Norfolk Formation" to the fossiliferous, post-Yorktown sediments east of the Suffolk Scarp ("Pliocene" beds of Darton). Later, they (1912) and Wentworth (1930) named such units on the basis of altitudes above sea level and assigned to each of them a marine origin (cf. Oaks et al. 1974). Subsequently Moore (1956, 1957) ascribed a lagoonal origin to extensive, thin, clay-rich surficial sediments (Nansemond Formation) west of a relict barrier beach near the present coast (Pungo Ridge). This is the Sand Bridge Formation of Oaks and Coch (1973).

Osbon (1919) reported the presence of white sand and alternating layers of white sand and blue clay at the base of the peat at two localities in the Dismal Swamp and also recognized the presence of Pleistocene deposits beneath, from shells in spoil dredged from the Dismal Swamp Canal. Cocke et al. (1934, pp. 377–378) recognized the presence of two laterally persistent units beneath peat along the Dismal Swamp Canal, a marine clay or sand and clay overlying a sand (Sand Bridge and Norfolk formations, respectively, of Oaks and Coch 1973). The presence of distinct pre-peat channels that cut entirely through the upper clayey unit is shown by the second figure of Cocke et al. (1934, p. 377).

Present Study

Numerous borings east of the Suffolk Scarp (Oaks and Coch 1973, Oaks et al. 1974) have established the configuration of the top of the Yorktown Formation and the presence above it of five formations of Pleistocene age that underlie the peat. Beneath the Dismal Swamp, the Yorktown Formation is chiefly compact, impermeable fossiliferous clay. Locally, permeable coquina and sand may be present as Coch (1968) has shown in the area to the north. The top of the Yorktown Formation slopes eastward only about 1 foot per mile (0.2 m per km) beneath the Dismal Swamp. It is within 15 feet (4.5 m) of the surface through much of the western part of the Swamp and within 25 feet (7.5 m) of the surface in the eastern part of the Swamp (Fig. 4).

The Great Bridge Formation is the oldest unit overlying the Yorktown Formation east of the Suffolk Scarp. It is entirely subsurface and is present only locally beneath the eastern edge of the Swamp (Fig. 3). Each of the four younger units is composed of highly permeable, sandy shoreline deposits, moderately permeable nearshoremarine deposits east of the shoreline, and moderately permeable to impermeable, local to widespread lagoonal deposits west of the shoreline. From oldest to youngest these units are the Norfolk, Kempsville, Londonbridge, and Sand Bridge formations. An age greater than 40,000 C^{14} years B.P. (before present) from the Sand Bridge, U-equilibrium ages of 62,000 and 86,000 years B.P. from the Norfolk and

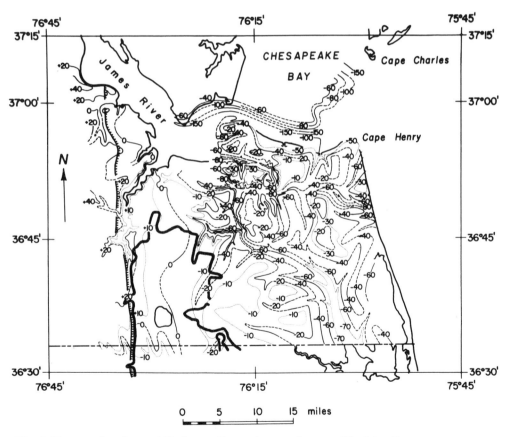

Fig. 4. Topography of top of Yorktown Formation, southeastern Virginia. Contour interval: above –100, 20 feet; below –100, 50 feet; supplementary contours at intervals of 10 feet. Modified from Oaks and Coch 1973 (fig. 13), courtesy Virginia Division of Mineral Resources.

Kempsville, fossil assemblages of the Great Bridge, Norfolk, and Kempsville, slight degree of weathering, and modest degree of dissection establish a late Pleistocene age, perhaps entirely Sangamon, for all of these units (Oaks and Coch 1973).

The Norfolk shoreline was along the Suffolk Scarp (Fig. 2). The presence of clayey lagoonal deposits west of the Suffolk Scarp near the James River and south of the Hazelton Scarp, and also in short stream valleys that cross the Suffolk Scarp, suggests that Shaler's inference of prior subaerial erosion at the Suffolk Scarp probably was largely correct. Nearshore-marine sediments of the Norfolk Formation, spread eastward across the area now beneath the Dismal Swamp, are only moderately permeable even near the Suffolk Scarp due to a considerable admixture of clay chunks reworked from the underlying York-town Formation. A coarse basal member of the Norfolk, 1 to 8 feet (0.3 to 2.5 m) thick, is very permeable and is apparently present continuously beneath the Swamp except within two miles of the Suffolk Scarp. The entire Norfolk Formation beneath the Dismal Swamp averages about 20 feet (6 m) thick and ranges from 0 to 30 feet (0 to 9 m) thick (Fig. 3).

The Kempsville shoreline was along the Hickory Scarp (Fig. 2), and lagoonal deposits apparently did not extend westward to the area of the Dismal Swamp. During the emergent episode following the Kempsville period a low area was excavated in the top of the Norfolk Formation, in the present position of the Dismal Swamp, by streams draining northeast, east, and south (Fig. 5). Remnants of the Norfolk Formation, in the Fentress Rise, today form a barrier to eastward drainage from the Swamp.

The Londonbridge shoreline was along Oceana Ridge and the Diamond Springs Scarp (Fig. 2), and impermeable clayey silt accumulated westward in a lagoon lying both east and west of the high-standing remnants of the Norfolk Formation in the Fentress Rise (Fig. 6). Beneath the Dismal Swamp, these impermeable lagoonal sediments extend entirely to the Suffolk Scarp south of the Virginia–North Carolina state line but are absent in sparse borings near Lake Drummond and north-westward near the Suffolk Scarp. Whether the topography in the latter area was too high for deposition to occur or whether subsequent erosion stripped once-present deposits cannot be determined with assurance from the sparse data. The Londonbridge Formation averages 5 feet (1.5 m) thick and ranges from 0 to 23 feet (0 to 7 m) thick beneath the Dismal Swamp (Fig. 3).

The lower member of the Sand Bridge Formation, permeable sand, is also present in approximately the same areas as the London-bridge (Fig. 7). The lower member of the Sand Bridge averages 3

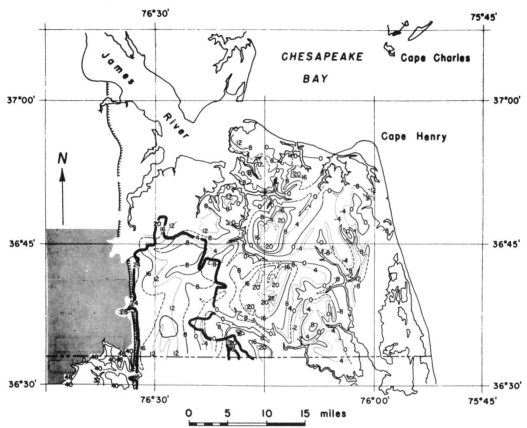

Fig. 5. Topography of top of Norfolk Formation, southeastern Virginia. Stipples show areas where unit is absent; contour interval 8 feet; supplementary contours at intervals of 2 and 4 feet. Modified from Oaks and Coch 1973 (fig. 22.), courtesy Virginia Division of Mineral Resources.

feet (1 m) thick and ranges from 0 to 8 feet (0 to 2.5 m) thick beneath the Dismal Swamp (Fig. 3).

The Sand Bridge shoreline successively occupied Land-of-Promise Ridge and Princess Anne Rise, Pungo Ridge, and other ridges east-ward that merge southward to form Powells Point Ridge in North Carolina (Fig. 2). Impermeable silty clay of the upper member accumu-lated westward in a lagoon occupying low areas east of the Fentress Rise and in the present location of the Dismal Swamp (Fig. 8). Northward, silty and clayey sand were deposited along the James River to a level (Churchland Flat) between +20 and +26 feet (Coch 1965, 1971). These sandy deposits apparently blocked northward drainage from the area of the Dismal Swamp. Such leveelike deposits along a river influenced by tides probably also caused the similar blockage at the southern limit of the Dismal Swamp, along Albemarle Sound, where the Sand Bridge Formation is exposed through large areas. The upper

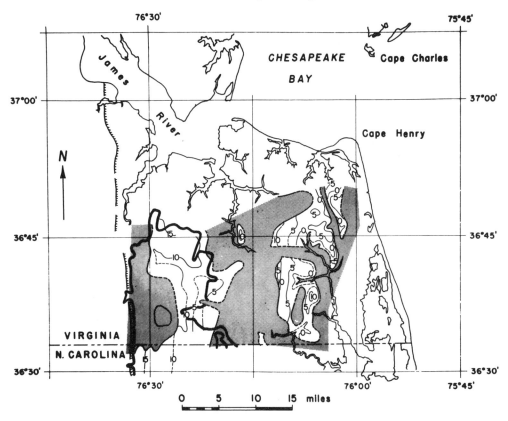

Fig. 6. Topography of top of clayey-silt facies of Londonbridge Formation, southeastern Virginia. Stipples show areas where facies absent; contour interval 5 feet. Modified from Oaks and Coch 1973 (fig. 26), courtesy Virginia Division of Mineral Resources.

member of the Sand Bridge Formation beneath the Dismal Swamp averages 3 feet (1 m) thick and ranges from 0 to 7 feet (0 to 2 m) thick (Fig. 3).

DISMAL SWAMP PEAT

Definition and Distribution

The formal stratigraphic name, "Dismal Swamp Peat," was proposed by Oaks and Coch (1963) for peat in the Swamp itself. The type section was established by Oaks (1965, p. 170) at a boring on Hamburg Ditch 0.5 mile (0.8 km) east of Sherrill Ditch, in North Carolina (lat. 36°00'47"N, long. 76°00'52"W), an easily accessible point where the peat is 12.8 feet (3.9 m) thick. The Dismal Swamp Peat is coextensive with all originally contiguous parts of the Dismal Swamp, including

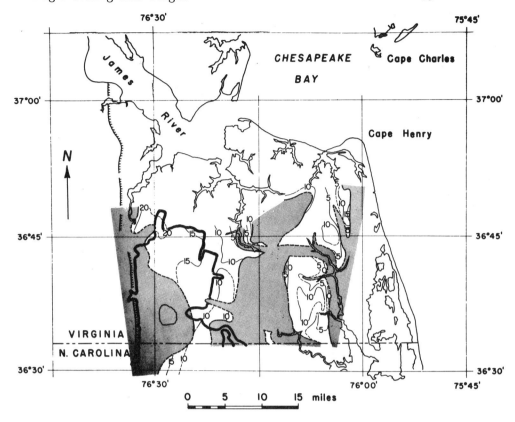

Fig. 7. Topography of top of lower member of Sand Bridge Formation, southeastern Virginia. Stipples show areas where unit is absent; contour interval 5 feet. Modified from Oaks and Coch 1973 (fig. 29), courtesy Virginia Division of Mineral Resources.

swamps of valleys tributary to the Dismal Swamp from the west and swamps of distributary streams to the east and southeast to Tidewater (Oaks and Coch 1973, p. 104). The Dismal Swamp Peat consists of a soft, wet, spongelike mass of decaying organic material, chiefly leaves, twigs, fallen logs, and rooted stumps. The color varies from dark brown (7YR3/2) near the surface to brownish black (5YR3/1) with depth. A thick tangle of logs, stumps, and roots occurs about 3 feet (1 m) below the surface through much of the western part of the Swamp (Oaks and Coch 1973, p. 106).

Thickness and Stratigraphic Relations

Although its surface shows little relief, the thickness of the Dismal Swamp Peat is highly variable. We determined thicknesses by direct observation where the peat is thin and fully exposed in ditches (Fig. 9). Elsewhere we determined thickness by 267 borings (Fig. 9), as

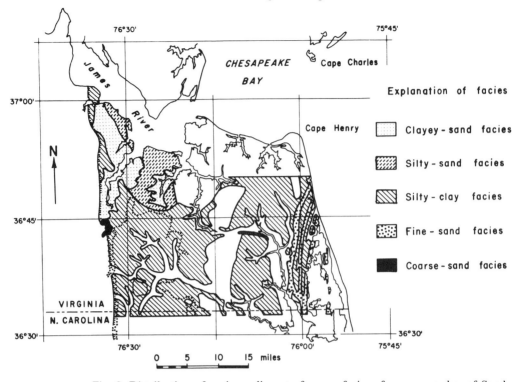

Fig. 8. Distribution of major sediment of upper facies of upper member of Sand Bridge Formation, southeastern Virginia. Area north and northwest of Dismal Swamp mapped by N. K. Coch (1965, 1968, 1971). Modified from Oaks and Coch 1973 (fig. 30), courtesy Virginia Division of Mineral Resources.

follows: Iwan hand auger (48), jet rig (21), USGS (Davis type) peat sampler (118), Hiller peat sampler (80).

Results of 50 borings (29 in North Carolina) made by Lewis B. Williams with an Iwan hand auger were kindly furnished by Fred Gall for holdings of the American Land Company, Virginia Beach, in the northeast and south parts of the Swamp. Results of numerous probes in the northwest part of the Swamp were generously supplied by Sharon Miller of Union Bag–Camp Paper Company, Franklin. Published results of peat thicknesses by Osbon (1919), Lewis and Cocke (1929), and Cocke et al. (1934) also were plotted and field checked wherever possible. Few data exist for the midsection of the Swamp because of general inaccessibility (Fig. 9). Moreover, the northeast corner of the Swamp was not studied in detail because it had been burned over to depths of as much as 6 feet during a fire in 1930 (William Rogers, Richmond Cedar Works, Portsmouth, pers. comm. and photographs).

Although the greatest thickness encountered was 12.8 feet (3.9 m), at the type section, Osbon (1919) reported that peat as much as 18 feet (5.5 m) thick was exposed in recent excavations east and northeast

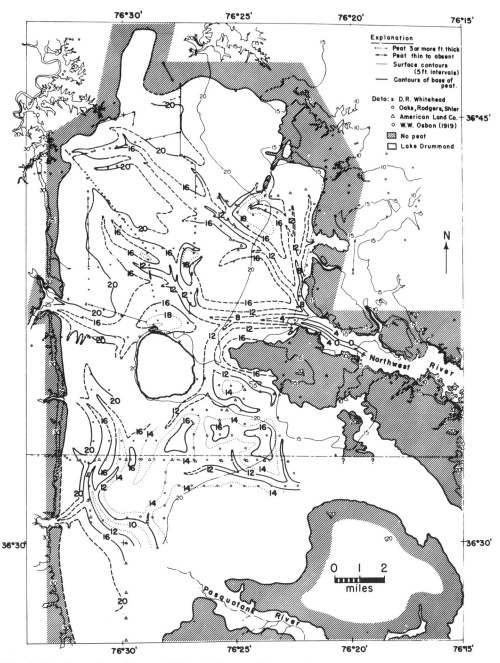

Fig. 9. Configuration of base of Dismal Swamp Peat, southeastern Virginia and northeastern North Carolina. Contour interval 4 feet; supplementary contours at intervals of 2 feet. From Oaks and Coch 1973 (fig. 33), courtesy Virginia Division of Mineral Resources.

of Lake Drummond. In the present study, borings spaced 0.5 mile (0.8 km) apart or less along two ditches north and northeast of Lake Drummond failed to reveal any thickness greater than 11.5 feet (3.5 m), the amount encountered on Jericho Ditch 2.5 miles (4 km) north of Lake Drummond.

Where the peat is no more than 3 feet (1 m) thick it generally overlies the upper member of the Sand Bridge Formation, or, more rarely, the lower member. Commonly where the peat is more than 5 feet (1.5 m) thick it is underlain for about 1 foot by two particular types of sediments, first recognized by Osbon. At the base is a white, angular, fine to medium sand, presumably of stream origin, interfingered with and overlain by a soft, pale blue (5B7/2) clay with organic fragments and freshwater histrichosphaerids, presumably of lake origin. Where the peat is thick, these two units and the Dismal Swamp Peat unconformably overlie older stratigraphic units, primarily the Yorktown, Norfolk, and Londonbridge formations. Which of these nearly flat-lying units lies directly beneath depends chiefly on the total thickness of peat, clay, and sand (Oaks and Coch 1973, pp. 104–105).

Base of the Peat

A map of the base of the peat was constructed on 15-minute topographic maps (contour interval of 5 feet) by interpolating 1-foot topographic contours over the plotted peat thickness data. The resulting map shows a subdued pre-peat topography with a well-developed dendritic pattern of anastomosing, elongate low areas separated by irregular high areas (Fig. 9). The map pattern, and the stratigraphic evidence that lows are underlain by probable stream sands and lake clays that unconformably overlie all older units, indicate a probable stream origin, in part at least, for the surface upon which the Dismal Swamp Peat accumulated.

The map of the base of the peat permits the following conclusions (Oaks and Coch 1973, p. 106). (1) The majority of drainage north, northeast, and perhaps southeast of Lake Drummond discharged through a narrow opening into Northwest River (Fig. 9). (2) Except near this outlet, where various streams converged, stream gradients were low, on the order of 1 foot per mile (0.2 m per km). (3) Near the outlet of the Swamp at Northwest River (Fig. 1), stream gradients became steeper, up to 4 feet per mile (0.8 m per km); similarly, the surface topography is rather steep in the same area compared to flatter areas west of the +20 foot contour. (4) Drainage south of Lake Drummond probably discharged through a narrow opening into Pasquotank River, and possibly into Little River or Indiantown Creek or both (Fig. 1).

ORIGIN AND AGE

Origin

Detailed pollen analysis by Whitehead (1965, p. 428; 1972) shows that peat in the northern and western Dismal Swamp is entirely of freshwater origin. Thus a freshwater environment has persisted continuously throughout accumulation of the peat at altitudes above +11 feet (3.5 m), and presumably in lower areas eastward at least to the Dismal Swamp Canal, but obviously not to tidewater. Where the peat is thick, pollen near the base shows that abundant sedge, grass, and aquatic plants were present in the initial stages of swamp formation, in close proximity to better-drained vegetation such as pine, spruce, and fir. The pollen evidence indicates an overall open environment with areas of standing water, adjacent areas of high ground, and ample precipitation. The map of the base of the peat supports this interpretation.

The adequacy of existing precipitation to maintain the Swamp is shown by the nearly continuous record of accumulation for the past 2500 years (Whitehead 1972), and is due largely to the water-holding capacity of the peat. As Lewis and Cocke (1929) pointed out, the Swamp is sensitive to differences in precipitation, for water level is lower in summer than it is in winter when precipitation is slightly increased and evaporation is lowest. Osbon (1929) reported an annual rainfall of about 52 inches (132 cm) with 73 percent relative humidity for the Dismal Swamp area. Records taken in the Norfolk area indicate an average rainfall of 40 to 50 inches (102 to 127 cm), and mean winter and summer temperatures near 44°F and 76°F (7°C and 24°C), respectively (Simmons and Shulkcum 1945, p. 5).

Although present precipitation appears adequate to maintain continued development of the Swamp, at least before major intervention by man, initial ponding is considered important to the inception of peat accumulation. Ponding would afford the conditions necessary for preservation of peat. Once a sufficient thickness of peat accumulated, the conditions promoting peat formation would tend to become self-perpetuating due to the resistance of the peat to desiccation.

The Yorktown Formation undoubtedly was important to the development of ponding, due to its impermeable nature, wide extent, and proximity to the surface. Additionally, where the Yorktown is deeper in the eastern part of the Swamp, clay-rich lagoonal deposits of the overlying Londonbridge and Sand Bridge formations produce widespread, imprevious layers wherever they were not removed by preswamp erosion. Also, the Norfolk Formation is only moderately permeable, and the permeable lower member of the

Sand Bridge pinches out eastward against the Fentress Rise, where it is overstepped by the impermeable upper member (Fig. 3). The Fentress Rise forms a major barrier to eastward drainage, with breaches only at narrow transverse stream valleys (Oaks and Coch 1973, p. 106). The Churchland Flat, analogous to a levee, forms an effective barrier to outflow northward. A similar feature, breached by narrow stream valleys, presumably impedes outflow southward.

Age

The greatest age of 5 dated samples from the base of thick sections of Dismal Swamp Peat is 8900 $\pm$ 160 C^{14} years B.P. Harrison et al. (1965) reported freshwater peats and clay deposits with oyster shells and brackish-water diatoms between −70 and −89 feet (21 and 27 m) in borings for the Chesapeake Bay Bridge-Tunnel. These indicate a position of sea level (relative to the land) no higher than −60 to −80 feet (18 to 27 m), when maximum possible compaction is considered, between 8135 $\pm$ 160 and 15,280 $\pm$ 200 C^{14} years B.P. (Harrison et al. 1965, pp. 217–221), during the period that peat began accumulating in the Dismal Swamp. Also, the freshwater clay beneath thicker parts of the Dismal Swamp Peat contains a late-glacial to full-glacial pollen flora that correlates closely with pollen flora from the freshwater peats beneath the mouth of Chesapeake Bay, studied by Terasmae (Harrison et al. 1965). Therefore initial ponding in the area of the Dismal Swamp must have occurred while relative sea level was 60 feet (18 m) *or more* below its present position (Oaks and Coch 1973, pp. 106–107).

Furthermore, results of Newman and Rusnak (1965) from peats at the base of the Holocene section, overlying Pleistocene substrates in the Eastern Shore Peninsula, indicate that sea level was near −20 feet (6 m) 4350 $\pm$ 70 C^{14} years B.P. and approached −10 feet (3 m) only between 3390 $\pm$ 75 and 2550 $\pm$ 70 C^{14} years B.P. (Fig. 10).

Possible Mechanisms

If ponding began in the Dismal Swamp during a glacial episode or during the late glacial retreat, when sea level was well below its present position, such ponding probably was unrelated to the position of sea level. However, Whitehead (1972, p. 313) has suggested that a rapid rate of sea level rise at the end of the last glaciation may have caused ponding by raising the water table inland along streams. Hence, the *rate* of rise of sea level may have been important, in contrast to the exact position of sea level.

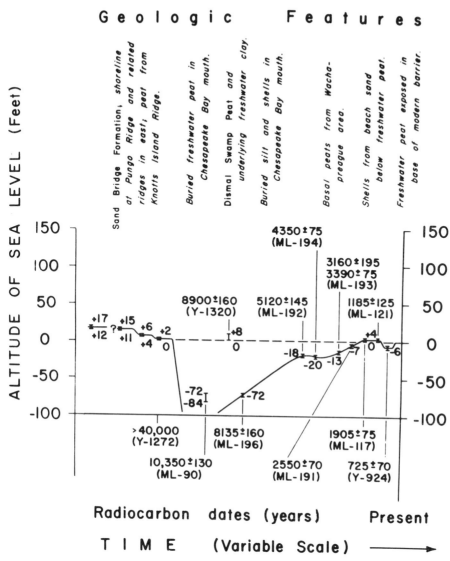

Fig. 10. Postglacial eustatic rise of sea level in Virginia relative to inception of the Dismal Swamp, based on C[14] dates. From Oaks et al. 1974 (fig. 12), reproduced by permission of Utah State University Press, Logan.

Former stream gradients are crucial to this hypothesis: if stream gradients are appreciably steeper east of the Fentress Rise than to the west, this mechanism probably would not work. The Northwest River is tributary to North Landing River (Fig. 1). A boring along Northwest River 10 miles (16 km) upstream from this junction reached the bottom of Holocene valley-fill sediments near –45 feet (Oaks and Coch 1973, Plate 2, Section GG–GG′). The North Landing River is tributary to Albemarle Sound. Swift et al. (1973, Fig. 215) show the probable former offshore continuation of the Albemarle River Valley. The present sea floor along this valley lies near –80 feet (24 m) approximately 70 to 75 miles (115 to 120 km) downstream from the junction of Northwest River and North Landing River. Swift et al. (1973, pp. 538–543) imply that their seismic work indicates little or no fill along older valleys now submerged. If so, North Landing River would have had a gradient of only 0.4 to 0.5 foot per mile (0.1 to 0.2 m per km), and Northwest River, from the Fentress Rise to North Landing River, about 2.5 feet per mile (0.5 m per km).

Such low gradients would be conducive to widespread flooding during a rapid rise of sea level, even if sea level were well below its present position. Conversely, the rate of rise of sea level decreased abruptly about 6000 C^{14} years B.P., near the time that peat began to accumulate in low areas in the Okefenokee Swamp in Georgia, more than 100 feet (30 m) above present sea level and 135 to 140 feet (41 to 43 m) above sea level at that time (Cohen 1973, pp. 146 and 150).

Another possibility is that restriction of distributary streams caused ponding in the Dismal Swamp. Restriction of distributary streams at their narrow outlets through the Fentress Rise would cause ponding through a large part of the Swamp. Possibly only Northwest and Pasquotank rivers would have to be blocked. Blockage could have been accomplished by the accumulation of numerous fallen trees. Another possible natural method of producing such ponding is beaver dams. Both methods are independent of the position or rate of rise of sea level.

In this connection, the previously abundant beaver, *Castor canadensis canadensis* Kuhl, proved such a nuisance to farmers in Virginia that they were trapped and hunted to extermination by 1911. Handley and Handley (1950, p. 261) reported of the beaver: "It is an animal which requires not only streams of low gradient, but also forested stream margins. . . . Also dams may be constructed which flood bottomland fields." The original range of the beaver included the entire James River Basin, of which much of the Dismal Swamp is considered a part (Handley and Handley 1950, p. 262; see also Handley, p. 319 this volume, and note p. 24).

Furthermore, Kaye (1962) noted the tendency of beavers to occupy low, poorly drained areas in New England within a short time after the retreat of glaciers there about 12,000 C^{14} years B.P. Such rapid invasion indicates the ability of beavers to migrate across an area the size of the Dismal Swamp within a very short time.

In addition, beaver dams would afford a reason for the sloping upper surface of the peat. If beaver dams controlled the water level in the east, an eastward-sloping groundwater table and peat surface would result. The gradual rise of the beaver dams through time would control the rate of peat accumulation. For effective ponding at any one time, dams would be needed only in the lowest places, as in many modern river valleys, and so might have been modest in size. Climatic change to warmer, drier conditions during the Hypsithermal might have influenced the water table also and by itself account for a decreased rate of peat accumulation beginning about 6000 C^{14} years ago (Whitehead 1972, p. 314).

However, beaver dams would be difficult to prove without extensive dredging, and perhaps not even with such drastic and destructive action.

In conclusion, the mechanism for ponding is not known. Possibly both the rate of rise of sea level and restriction of distributary streams, perhaps by beaver dams, played an important role.

SUMMARY

Clay-rich layers of the Yorktown Formation and the lagoonal deposits of overlying Pleistocene units form an impermeable, nearly horizontal substrate beneath the Dismal Swamp. The Pleistocene units also form low barriers to drainage northward, eastward, and southward. The depression in which peat of the Dismal Swamp accumulated was excavated, at least in part, by dendritic streams that discharged through narrow breaches in these low, surrounding barriers.

The former stream channels are floored by angular sand overlain by freshwater clay containing a late-glacial or full-glacial pollen flora. Accumulation of freshwater peat began about 8900 C^{14} years B.P., at a time when sea level was at least 60 to 80 feet (18 to 24 m) below its present position. As much as 13 feet (4 m) of peat have accumulated at an average rate of 0.1 to 0.3 foot (0.03 to 0.05 m) per century. The eastward slope of the surface of the peat suggests control of the groundwater level by gradually rising dams in the narrow breaches, perhaps as the result of beaver activity.

ACKNOWLEDGMENTS

Oaks was supported by Office of Naval Research Contract NONR 609 (40), Task Order NR 388-064, during 1961–63, and by the Virginia Division of Mineral Resources in 1963–64. Whitehead was supported by National Science Foundation Grants G-17277, GB-1963, GB-6400, and GB-12672.

Virginia Carter, N. K. Coch, R. F. Flint, Patricia Gammon, Mary Keith Garrett, W. F. Lichtler, W. H. Rodgers, J. E. Sanders, and D. E. Shier made many useful suggestions and constructive criticisms during the course of this study. Rodgers and Shier assisted Oaks during 1963 and 1962, respectively, and J. H. Thomas and D. H. Hamilton III assisted Whitehead during 1961 and 1962, respectively. J. E. Sanders suggested that beavers might have been present, which was easily confirmed.

Access to their holdings in the Dismal Swamp was graciously provided by the American Land Company, Virginia Beach (Fred Gall), and the Union Bag–Camp Paper Company, Franklin (Sharon Miller). The Virginia Game and Wildlife Commission (B. E. Walters) aided access to another part of the Swamp. USGS (Davis) peat samplers were lent to Oaks by E. S. Deevey and W. S. Newman. Much of the material herein formed part of a doctoral dissertation by Oaks (1965) at Yale University.

REFERENCES CITED

Clark, W. B., and B. L. Miller. 1906. A brief summary of the geology of the Virginia Coastal Plain. Pp. 11–24 *in* H. Ries. The clay deposits of the Virginia Coastal Plain. *Va. Geol. Survey, Geol. Series, Bull.* 2.

_____. 1912. The physiography and geology of the coastal plain province of Virginia. *Va. Geol. Survey, Geol. Series, Bull.* 4. 274 pp.

Coch, N. K. 1965. Post-Miocene stratigraphy and morphology, inner coastal plain, southeastern Virginia. U.S. Office of Naval Research, Geography Branch, Contract NONR 609 (40), Task Order NR 388-064, Tech. Rpt. 6. Ph.D. Diss. Yale Univ. 97 pp.

_____. 1968. Geology of the Benns Church, Smithfield, Windsor, and Chuckatuck quadrangles, Virginia. *Va. Div. Mineral Resources, Rpt. Inv.* 17. 39 pp.

_____. 1971. Geology of the Newport News South and Bowers Hill quadrangles, Virginia. *Va. Div. Mineral Resources, Rpt. Inv.* 28. 26 pp.

Cocke, E. C., I. F. Lewis, and Ruth Patrick. 1934. A further study of Dismal Swamp peat. *Amer. J. Bot.* 21:374–395.

Cohen, A. D. 1973. Possible influences of subpeat topography and sediment type upon the development of the Okefenokee swamp-marsh complex of Georgia. *Southeastern Geol.* 15:141–151.

Darton, N. H. 1902. Description of the Norfolk quadrangle. *Geol. Atlas of United States, Norfolk folio,* no. 80. U.S. Geol. Survey. 4 pp.

Devereux, R. E., E. Shulkcum, and G. W. Patteson. 1936. Soil survey of Nansemond County, Virginia. *U.S. Dept. Agric., Soil Survey Series* 1932, no. 6. U.S. Govt. Print. Off., Washington. 39 pp.

Handley, C. O., Jr., and C. O. Handley, Sr. 1950. Mammals. Pp. 235–276 in *The James River Basin: past, present and future.* Va. Acad. Sci., Richmond.

Harrison, W., R. J. Malloy, G. A. Rusnak, and J. Terasmae. 1965. Possible late Pleistocene uplift, Chesapeake Bay entrance. *J. Geol.* 73:201–229.

Henry, E. F., J. Chudoba, and H. C. Porter. 1959. Soil survey, Norfolk County, Virginia. *U.S. Dept. Agric., Soil Survey Series* 1953, no. 5. U.S. Govt. Print. Off., Washington. 53 pp.

Kaye, C. A. 1962. Early post glacial beavers in southeastern New England *Science* 138:906–907.

Kearney, T. H. 1901. Report on a botanical survey of the Dismal Swamp region. *Contrib. U.S. Natl. Herbarium* 5:321–550.

Lapham, J. E., and W. S. Lyman. 1905. Soil survey of Perquimans and Pasquotank counties, North Carolina. *U.S. Dept. Agric., Soil Survey Rpt. U.S. Govt. Print. Off., Washington.* 22 pp.

Lewis, I. F., and E. C. Cocke. 1929. Pollen analysis of Dismal Swamp peat. *J. Elisha Mitchell Sci. Soc.* 45:37–58.

Moore, W. E. 1956. Pleistocene terraces south of the James River, Virginia. Guidebook to Spring field trip, May, 1956. Va. Acad. Sci., Richmond.

———. 1957. Stratigraphy of Pleistocene terrace deposits in Virginia (abs.). *Geol. Soc. Amer., Bull.* 67:1755.

Newman, W. S., and G. A. Rusnak. 1965. Holocene submergence of the Eastern Shore of Virginia. *Science* 148:1464–1466.

Oaks, R. Q., Jr., 1965. Post-Miocene stratigraphy and morphology, outer coastal plain, southeastern Virginia. U.S. Office of Naval Research, Geography Branch, Contract NONR 609 (40), Task Order NR 388–064, Tech. Rpt. 5. Ph.D. Diss. Yale Univ. 240 pp.

Oaks, R. Q., Jr., and N. K. Coch. 1963. Pleistocene sea levels, southeastern Virginia. *Science* 140:979–983.

———. 1973. Post-Miocene stratigraphy and morphology, southeastern Virginia. *Va. Div. Mineral Resources, Bull.* 82. 135 pp.

Oaks, R. Q., Jr., N. K. Coch, J. E. Sanders, and R. F. Flint. 1974. Post-Miocene shorelines and sea levels, southeastern Virginia. Pp. 53–87 *in* R. Q. Oaks, Jr. and J. R. DuBar (eds). *Post-Miocene stratigraphy, central and southern Atlantic Coastal Plain.* Utah State Univ. Press, Logan.

Osbon, C. C. 1919. Peat in the Dismal Swamp, Virginia and North Carolina. *U.S. Geol. Survey, Bull.* 711-C:41–59.

Perkins, S. O., W. D. Lee, G. B. Shivery, and S. F. Davidson. 1928. Soil survey of Camden and Currituck counties, North Carolina. *U.S. Dept. Agric., Soil Survey Series* 1923, no. 2. U.S. Govt. Print. Off., Washington. 56 pp.

Rogers, W. B. 1884. *A reprint of annual reports and other papers, on the geology of the Virginias.* D. Appleton and Co., New York. 832 pp.

Shaler, N. S. 1890. General account of the fresh-water morasses of the United States, with a description of the Dismal Swamp district of Virginia and North Carolina. *U.S. Geol. Survey, Ann. Rpt.* 10:255–339.

Shearin, A. E., J. P. Covington, and J. H. Vaden. 1957. Soil survey of Pasquotank County, North Carolina. *U.S. Dept. Agric., Soil Survey Series* 1949, no. 3. U.S. Govt. Print. Off., Washington. 58 pp.

Simmons, C. S., and E. Shulkcum. 1945. Soil survey of Princess Anne County, Virginia. *U.S. Dept. Agric., Soil Survey Series* 1939, no. 3. U.S. Govt. Print. Off., Washington. 56 pp.

Swift, D. J. P., J. W. Kofoed, F. P. Saulsbury, and P. Sears. 1973. Holocene evolution of the shelf surface, central and southern Atlantic shelf of North America. Pp. 449–574 *in* D. J. P. Swift, O. B. Duane, and D. H. Pilkey (eds). *Shelf sediment transport: process and pattern.* Dowden, Hutchinson and Ross, Stroudsburg, Pa. 656 pp.

U.S. Geological Survey. 1902. Norfolk quadrangle, Virginia–North Carolina, topographic map surveyed in 1888–91 by W. R. Atkinson and R. M. Towson. Scale 1:125,000, contour interval 5 feet.

_____. 1945. Lake Drummond quadrangle, Virginia–North Carolina, topographic map surveyed in 1940 by C. W. Buckey, L. S. Howe, Jr., and J. W. Pumpelly. Scale 1:62,500, contour interval 5 feet.

_____. 1954. Lake Drummond quadrangle, Virginia–North Carolina, topographic map of 1940 revised from aerial photographs in 1954. Scale 1:24,000, contour interval 5 feet.

Wentworth, C. K. 1930. Sand and gravel resources of the coastal plain of Virginia. *Va. Geol. Survey, Bull.* 32. 146 pp.

Whitehead, D. R. 1965. Palynology and Pleistocene phytogeography of unglaciated eastern North America. Pp. 417–432 *in* H. E. Wright, Jr., and D. G. Frey (eds). *The Quaternary of the United States.* Princeton Univ. Press, Princeton, N.J.

_____. 1972. Developmental and environmental history of the Dismal Swamp. *Ecol. Monographs* 42:301–315.

[Editor's note: In September 1978, Donald Schwab reported the return of a few beavers to the Dismal Swamp. Cecil Frost earlier told me of beaver dams 1000 and 2000 feet long and about 6–8 years old at nearby Merchants Mill Pond, and suggested that dams this extensive should produce appreciable geological effects.]

DEVELOPMENTAL HISTORY OF THE DISMAL SWAMP

Donald R. Whitehead and Robert Q. Oaks, Jr.

INTRODUCTION

The Dismal Swamp is situated in the eastern part of the coastal plain in southeastern Virginia and northeastern North Carolina (Fig. 1). It is developed on a broad plain of low relief. The Suffolk Scarp, a sharply delineated Pleistocene shoreline, defines the western boundary of the Swamp. On the east it laps up against the Fentress Rise, a subtle north-south topographic high consisting of interglacial marine and barrier sediments (Oaks and Coch 1963, 1973). Northward it extends along topographic lows to within 11 kilometers of the James River and Chesapeake Bay, and on the south it reaches to within 22 kilometers of Albemarle Sound. One of the most interesting features is Lake Drummond, a large, shallow body of water located just north of the center of the Swamp.

Early investigation of the Swamp suggested that its surface was convex and that the highest elevations occur in the neighborhood of Lake Drummond (e.g., Lewis and Cocke 1929). More recent work has suggested that this is incorrect, and that the peat surface slopes gently eastward. The highest elevations appear to lie along the Suffolk Scarp (7.5–8.0 meters above mean sea level), and the lowest, along the Fentress Rise (3.0–4.4 m). Peat thickness is quite variable, reflecting the undulating nature of the underlying surface. The maximum peat thicknesses appear to be approximately 3.5 to 4 meters.

The preswamp surficial sediments of the region are virtually all interglacial in age and marine or lagoonal in origin. The coastal plain in the vicinity of the Dismal Swamp was thought to be characterized by four gently seaward-sloping marine terrace plains separated by three eastward-facing marine shorelines, or scarps (e.g., Wentworth 1930; cf. Oaks and Coch 1963). The Suffolk Scarp, which defines the

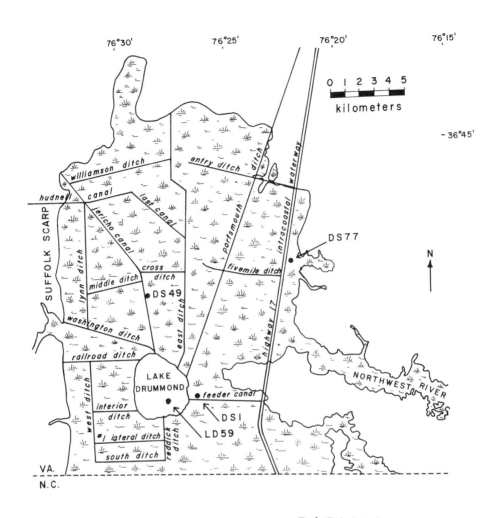

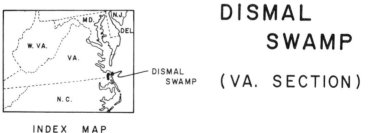

DISMAL
SWAMP

(VA. SECTION)

INDEX MAP

Fig. 1. Dismal Swamp area. From Whitehead 1973 (fig. 1), reproduced by permission of Duke University Press. Copyright 1972 by the Ecological Society of America.

western boundary of the Swamp, separates the Wicomico Terrace from the Dismal Swamp Terrace, the general surface on which the Swamp is developed. The next lower scarp, the Princess Anne, occurs east of the Swamp. Formerly the Pleistocene history of the region was interpreted simply. It was thought that each of these associated terraces and scarps dated from different interglacial marine transgressions. As we shall see later, this interpretation needs revision.

The forests of the Dismal Swamp are rather variable. The differences in structure and species composition reflect the thickness of the peat, length of the hydroperiod, and successional stage. It is clear that there are many secondary communities within the Swamp (the various "light swamp" complexes discussed by Kearney in 1901 and Whitehead in 1972), most generated by fire or other human-influenced disturbances.

Some early paleontological studies of the peat by Lewis and Cocke (1929) and Cocke et al. (1934) provided information on the history of the northern half of the Swamp. Their work suggested that peat deposition did not begin synchronously and uniformly throughout the area but was initiated in topographic lows on the preswamp surface. There were indications of brackish conditions initially and of a possible reinvasion of salt water later in the Swamp's history. The evidence suggested a vegetational progression from an open freshwater marsh to a typical swamp forest.

The implications of this work are intriguing. First, it suggests that deposition was initiated in a brackish lagoon, thus implying that sea level was high. Secondly, a second marine transgression is implied. Since the most recent transgressions were interglacial and perhaps mid-Wisconsin, considerable antiquity would be suggested for the Swamp. As this conclusion does not appear to be supported by the fossil pollen data from their studies, confusion existed. Thus the present work was undertaken.

PALEOECOLOGICAL STUDIES OF THE DISMAL SWAMP

Attempts to elucidate the geological history of the Virginia Coastal Plain and the environmental history of the Dismal Swamp were initiated jointly in the early 1960s. The geomorphic and stratigraphic studies were carried out by Richard Foster Flint, John Sanders, Nicholas Coch, and the junior author, all then at Yale University, and studies of the Dismal Swamp peat were initiated by myself with the aid of a number of students at Williams College.

Field studies were carried out in the Dismal Swamp during the summers of 1961 and 1962. During this period more than 130 cores were taken in the Virginia section of the Dismal Swamp, including many borings taken in Lake Drummond. Cores were spaced at intervals along the many canals throughout the Swamp (Fig. 1) and at intervals between the canals. The boring transects between canals often necessitated backpacking coring equipment for considerable distances into densely vegetated sections of the Swamp. At each coring station our primary objective was to locate the position of the contact between organic sediments of the Swamp and the underlying inorganic interglacial deposits. Samples were usually taken from this interface. From this network of cores and 187 borings made by the junior author it was possible to construct a map depicting the topography of the underlying surface (Fig. 3) and to locate the deepest peat sections from which complete cores could be taken. Figure 1 indicates the four locations from which the principal cores were taken (DS1, DS49, DS77, LD59).

The geological investigations indicated the nature of the surface on which the Dismal Swamp formed. That surface is rather flat and consists of a complex series of interglacial lagoonal and shallow marine deposits. Immediately beneath the peat are lagoonal deposits of the Sand Bridge Formation.

The pre–Dismal Swamp history of this portion of the coastal plain was once thought to be simple, with one marine transgression responsible for the cutting of the Suffolk Scarp and shaping of the Dismal Swamp terrace. It was generally assumed that this transgression took place during the last, or Sangamon, interglacial. The detailed work of Oaks, Coch, and others has demonstrated that the Pleistocene history of this region was, in fact, quite complex, and that as many as five transgressions may have taken place during the last interglacial (Oaks and Coch 1963, 1973).

At any rate, it is apparent that the surface on which the Swamp eventually formed dates from the Sangamon interglacial; hence the Dismal Swamp must be less than 80,000 years old.

The many cores that we have taken within the Swamp have indicated that there is subtle topography developed on the surface of the Sand Bridge Formation beneath the peat. It is clear that this topography is a subdued dendritic drainage pattern (Fig. 3) developed by stream action at a time when sea level was considerably lower than during either the present or last interglacial. It is assumed that this erosion took place during the last, or Wisconsin, glacial period. The most extensive Wisconsin glaciations culminated between 20,000 and 16,000 C [14] years ago, so it is logical to assume that the pattern developed during this time period and, accordingly, that the Dismal Swamp is younger.

As one might expect, the deepest and most complete peat sections are found in drainage lows on this preswamp surface. Our studies indicate that swamp sediments first began to accumulate along these stream courses on the eastern half of the Dismal Swamp Terrace and gradually extended both upstream (toward the Suffolk Scarp) and laterally onto the drainage divides. A combination of pollen evidence and radiocarbon dates shows that swamp formation was intitiated in the late-glacial, about 12,000 to 11,000 C^{14} years ago.

If we examine the nature of the peat in any of the deep sections, it is apparent that the Swamp was very different in character during that early period. It was not only greatly restricted in area (confined to drainage lows on the eastern half of the present Dismal Swamp), but it was apparently an open freshwater marsh characterized by many aquatic herbs. This is suggested by the fact that the sediments are fine-grained organic clays and that there are many pollen grains from deep-water aquatics. As we move up any one core, we first encounter these fine-grained sediments, then slightly more fibrous ones, and, eventually, forest peat. Simultaneously the pollen flora of aquatic plants shifts to those characteristic of shallow water and eventually to those found on muddy shores or on peaty surfaces. Thus the development of a forested swamp took much time and progressed through a series of marshy phases.

At this point it would be instructive to examine a generalized pollen diagram of the Swamp (Fig. 2). This diagram is based on the four major diagrams published by Whitehead (1972) and averages the trends from each. Only the dominant pollen types are included in the generalized diagram. Note first that the vertical scale is not depth, but time. The time scale is based on the radiocarbon dates which are available. Note secondly that the diagram may be differentiated into a number of pollen zones: (1) pine-spruce; (2) beech-hemlock-birch; (3) oak-hickory; and (4) cypress-gum. In some cases subzones may be delineated within a major pollen zone. This is particularly true of the oak-hickory assemblage zone within which an obvious change in the types of aquatic plants takes place. The lower portion of the zone (and the lower portion of the entire profile) has many grains of aquatics found in deeper water, such as water milfoil, mermaid weed, water lily, spatterdock, bladderwort, and pondweeds. The upper half of the zone is characterized by pollen of emergent aquatics such as pipewort, arrowleaf, and goldenclub, plus pollen of plants common on peaty or wet shores.

Let us now examine each of the major pollen assemblage zones and

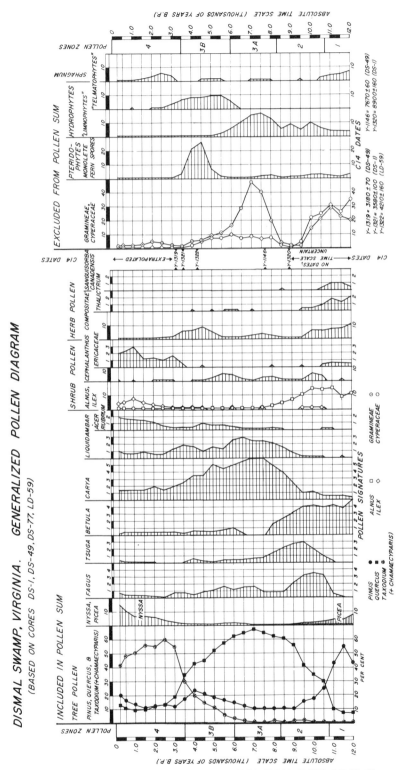

Fig. 2. Generalized pollen diagram. Based on cores DS1, DS49, DS77, LD59. Note that vertical scale is time, not depth. From Whitehead 1965 *a* (fig. 5), reproduced by permission of Princeton University Press.

see if we can arrive at vegetational (and climatic) reconstructions for them.

Pine-Spruce Assemblage

The lowest (and hence oldest) pollen assemblage zone found in the cores is indicated as Zone 1 in Figure 2. It is the pine-spruce zone. Pine and spruce pollen are dominant, along with birch, alder, a variety of herbs, deeper water aquatics, and pollen of a number of plants now found much farther to the north (in addition to spruce, there is fir, burnet, and several northern species of club moss). A study of the pine pollen has indicated that most of the grains are small, which suggests the presence of jack pine (possibly also red pine), a northern species (Whitehead 1964).

Intuitively it would appear that this pollen assemblage was produced by a vegetation type quite different from that currently occupying the coastal plain of Virginia. Few temperate elements are represented. Instead, the assemblage is dominated by many plants now found far to the north in spruce-fir forests. This would certainly suggest significantly colder conditions. A search of the literature on modern pollen rain (data derived from studies of modern pollen rain in many of the major vegetational types in North America) provided no perfect matches for this fossil pollen assemblage, although the best fit is with pollen spectra from areas of jack pine forest in Manitoba (Lichti-Federovich and Ritchie 1965). This certainly supports the contention that conditions were considerably colder in coastal Virginia at the time the pine-spruce assemblage was deposited. However, the vegetation in the Dismal Swamp region at that time was identical in structure and species composition to the area of jack pine forest in Manitoba.

It is interesting that there are some excellent matches for the pine-spruce assemblage in a number of pollen diagrams from fossil sites reasonably close to the Dismal Swamp. Comparable fossil assemblages can be found in (1) peat horizons located considerably below present sea level in the mouth of Chesapeake Bay (Harrison et al. 1965); (2) profiles from several shallow ponds in the Shenandoah Valley of Virginia (Craig 1970); (3) profiles from a number of Carolina "bays" in southeastern North Carolina (Frey 1951, 1953, 1955; Whitehead 1965a, 1967); and (4) profiles from a Carolina bay in northeastern North Carolina (Whitehead 1973). The relevant fossil assemblages generally date from the early late-glacial (12,000 to 10,000 C[14] years ago) or from the full-glacial.

Thus the pine-spruce assemblage from the Dismal Swamp profiles appears to have been deposited in the late-glacial at a time when the vegetation of southeastern Virginia was distinctly boreal in character and the climate was colder. The character of the sediment (fine-grained organic clays), the pollen of aquatics (and remains of algae), and the locations of the deep sections all suggest that the developing Swamp was confined to drainage lows (stream channels) in the eastern half of the present Dismal Swamp and that it was an open freshwater marsh rather than a true swamp at that time.

Beech-Hemlock-Birch Assemblage

Pollen Zone 2, the beech-hemlock-birch assemblage, occurs immediately above the pine-spruce zone in all of the profiles from the Swamp itself. This assemblage (Fig. 2) is characterized by decreasing percentages of pine and other boreal taxa, increasing percentages of oak, and coordinated maxima for beech, hemlock, and birch. Grains of sugar maple and white pine are also found in this zone. Deeper water aquatics are still common. As many of the taxa found in this zone now occur together as components of the "northern hardwoods" forest in the Northeast and at intermediate elevations in the mountains in the Southeast (see Braun 1950), it might be reasonable to assume that the vegetation was similar to the modern northern hardwoods forest. However, perfect matches among modern pollen rain samples taken from the northern hardwoods forest have not been found. Thus caution is necessary in reconstructing the vegetation that produced this assemblage.

Examination of pollen diagrams available from fossil sites proximate to the Dismal Swamp reveals many fossil assemblages that are quite similar. This is true of the diagrams from all four regions mentioned above. Thus forests characteristic of the northern hardwoods type were apparently well developed in much of the southeastern United States at some time in the past. The available radiocarbon dates suggest that this was in the late-glacial and early postglacial. In the case of the Dismal Swamp this zone was deposited between 10,600 and 8200 C^{14} years ago. As the sediments at this time were still fine grained and as pollen of many aquatics (and remains of algae) were still present, it is reasonable to assume that the developing Swamp was still an open freshwater marsh during this time interval. The data further indicate that it was still restricted to stream courses in the eastern half of the present Dismal Swamp, although it was clearly expanding inland and laterally onto the interfluves.

Oak-Hickory Assemblage

The next youngest pollen assemblage zone, the oak-hickory zone (Zone 3, Fig. 2), is quite variable. In general, it is characterized by a distinct dominance of oak and hickory pollen along with a variety of other temperate hardwoods such as sweet gum, red maple, elm, and ash. It can generally be differentiated into subzones, although the subzones tend to differ somewhat from core to core. In at least one core there is a distinct maximum of sweet gum pollen at the base of the oak-hickory zone which permitted the designation of a *sweet gum subzone*. This is not apparent in the other cores. The most characteristic change within the zone involves the pollen of aquatic and semiaquatic plants. Pollen of grasses and aquatics of deeper water dominate the lower half of zone (thus a *"grass-limnophyte" subzone*), while the upper half of the zone is dominated by pollen of emergent aquatics (particularly goldenclub), composites, and fern spores (*goldenclub-composite-fern subzone*). Pollen of plants of peaty and wet soils are also common in this latter subzone.

The presence of pollen of many trees now found in the "upland" region surrounding the Swamp suggests that by 8200 C[14] years ago the regional forests and climate had become reasonably similar to the present. An exact vegetational reconstruction is difficult, as, once again, there are no precise matches among modern pollen spectra, at least so far as can be determined. Relatively little work on pollen rain has been carried out in eastern deciduous forests. As for the previous pollen assemblage zones, there are reasonably good fossil matches in the diagrams from both Virginia and North Carolina. Radiocarbon dates indicate that this assemblage was deposited between 8200 and 3500 years ago.

The progression from fine-grained to peaty sediment types within the zone and the distinct change in the aquatic and semiaquatic community suggest that significant changes were taking place within the Swamp. Although the organic sediment continued to build up, it is apparent that the relationship of the water table to the peat surface underwent a profound change. The water table apparently came to stand lower with respect to the peat surface, and/or there was standing water on the surface for a shorter period of time each year. Thus open marsh began to transform into forested swamp at least locally. The appearance of *Sphagnum* spores, and pollen of cypress, cedar, and black gum, is indicative of this change. This might suggest either that the rate of peat development began to exceed the rate of rise of the water table, or perhaps both.

The continued accumulation of organic sediment resulted in a landward extension of the Swamp toward the Suffolk Scarp and laterally onto the drainage divides. This situation is depicted in Figures 3 and 4.

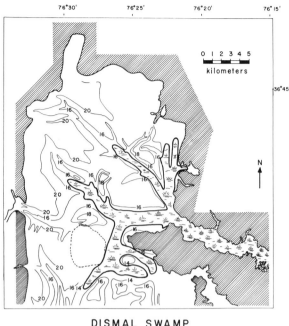

DISMAL SWAMP
(ca. 8300 B.P.)

Fig. 3. Reconstruction of Dismal Swamp, 8300 radiocarbon years before present. Contour interval, 2 feet. From Whitehead 1973 (fig. 7), reproduced by permission of Duke University Press. Copyright 1972 by the Ecological Society of America.

Cypress-Gum Assemblage

The cypress-gum assemblage (Zone 4) is distinctive; it is characterized by the pollen of many plants now found within the Dismal Swamp, including abundant cypress, cedar, gum, red maple, sweet bay, and a great variety of swamp shrubs and herbs. Spores of *Sphagnum* are abundant, and the sediment is a coarse, often woody peat. This assemblage spans the time interval from 3500 years ago to the present.

This pollen assemblage is further characterized by significant changes within each section (often reciprocal changes in gum and cypress). This suggests that once the peat developed sufficiently to result in an extensive forested swamp mantling the entire surface of the Dismal Swamp (Fig. 5), there was a variety of local changes in forest composition. The changes differed from area to area. These changes may have been a function of changes in water level, fires, windfalls, human activities, etc. Such local variations in forest composition are quite evident in the Swamp today.

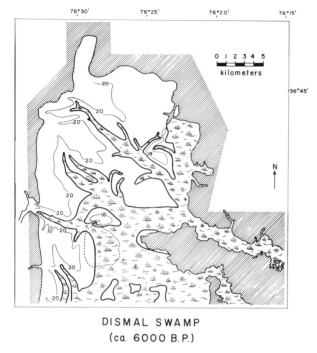

DISMAL SWAMP
(ca. 6000 B.P.)

Fig. 4. Reconstruction of Dismal Swamp, 6000 radiocarbon years before present. From Whitehead 1973 (fig. 8), reproduced by permission of Duke University Press. Copyright 1972 by the Ecological Society of America.

THE DEVELOPMENT OF THE DISMAL SWAMP: A SYNTHESIS

From all of the geological and paleontological evidence it is apparent that the Dismal Swamp is a relatively young feature. Swamp formation first began along stream courses in the present area of the Dismal Swamp between 12,000 and 11,000 C^{14} years ago. At that time, immediately after the last major advance of ice, the climate was considerably colder than at present, and vegetation was boreal in character. The entire region was forested by a complex apparently dominated by jack pines, spruces, and other northern species. Open marshes characterized many of the water courses, particularly on the eastern edge of the present Dismal Swamp.

By 10,600 C^{14} years ago, the climate had ameliorated sufficiently so that the boreal forest had been replaced by a variety of more temperate deciduous species, many of which are now found together in northern hardwoods forests. The developing Swamp itself was still confined largely to stream courses in its present eastern portion but was gradually extending itself inland and laterally onto the interfluves. It was still an open freshwater marsh.

By 8200 C^{14} years ago the character of the vegetation had changed again as oaks, hickories, and other deciduous species now common in the Southeast had replaced the northern hardwoods species. The Swamp was still confined to water courses and was marshy in character but was continually progressing inland toward the Suffolk Scarp (Fig. 3).

By 6000 years ago not only had the Swamp progressed considerably farther inland and laterally onto drainage divides (Fig. 4), but it had also changed in character dramatically. The sediments on the surface were now decidedly peaty in character and the hydroperiod was significantly shorter (i.e., the water table dropped beneath the peat surface for at least a short portion of the year). The regional forests were still oak-hickory in nature, but typical southern swamp species had begun to appear within the Swamp.

Peat development had progressed sufficiently to cover virtually the entire present Dismal Swamp by 3500 C^{14} years ago (Fig. 5). This resulted in the inundation of all of the topographic highs on the terrace surface which, in turn, resulted in the elimination of oak-hickory forests and their replacement by cypress-gum swamp. Subsequent peats are all typical forest peats, fibrous and often woody in character and containing *Sphagnum* spores.

It is apparent that the forests within the Swamp were spatially and temporally variable from this point to the present. Many percentage changes are evident for cypress, gum, and a variety of swamp shrubs within each profile. As mentioned previously, the changes are not entirely comparable from one profile to the next. This is not especially surprising, as the present Swamp is a mosaic of communities controlled by peat depth, water table fluctuations, fires, logging, windfalls, canal building, etc.

Although the forest within the Swamp changed gradually from oak-hickory to cypress-gum around 3500 C^{14} years ago, evidence from other areas on the coastal plain indicates that the upland forests around the Swamp remained largely oak-hickory, although pine apparently increased.

In summary, the outline and chronology of vegetational and developmental events can be reconstructed from palynological and geological studies. Nevertheless, important questions remain. For example, why did the Swamp begin to form? What controlled its development? What maintains its equilibrium today?

To answer the first question, we can look at the general environmental changes that were taking place at the time that organic sediments of the Swamp first began to form (12,000 to 11,000 years ago).

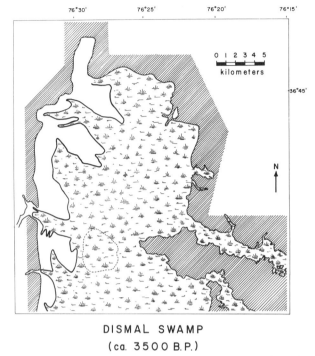

DISMAL SWAMP
(ca. 3500 B.P.)

Fig. 5. Reconstruction of Dismal Swamp, 3500 radiocarbon years before present. From Whitehead 1973 (fig. 9). reproduced by permission of Duke University Press. Copyright 1972 by the Ecological Society of America.

Two major environmental changes are evident during this time period. (1) Pollen evidence from all over North America indicates that there was a sharp amelioration of climate beginning about 11,000 years ago (Ogden 1967). (2) Contemporaneous with the climate change there was an increase in the rate at which sea level was rising due to glacial melting, to an average of about 15 meters per 1000 years (Emery and Garrison 1967). The climatic change was in the direction of a warming of climate, which might facilitate the initiation of the Swamp, but it would appear that available moisture would be more important. There is little evidence that there was a significant change in the precipitational regime. Thus it would seem that a major factor stimulating the development of the Dismal Swamp may have been the pattern of sea level rise in the late-glacial. The rise of sea level may have caused a marked rise in the regional water table, especially on a low-lying surface such as that beneath the Dismal Swamp. This might cause ponding for some distance inland and permit the formation of freshwater marshes.

There is additional reason to suggest that the development of the Swamp has been controlled by sea level. We noted previously that there is a distinct change in the character of the peat shortly after 6000 years ago. The peat is more fibrous, emergent aquatics and plants of boggy soils are present, there is also some evidence of a stump layer in the peat at that level, and there is some evidence of pollen decomposition. All of this suggests that the relative positions of the peat surface and the water table must have undergone a change. As there is little evidence of a change in the rate of sediment accumulation, it is logical to assume that there must have been a slowing in the rate of rise of the water table instead. The problem, then, is to determine what may have brought this about. Again, two factors appear possible: (1) a general warming and/or drying of climate (there is pollen evidence for this from the Midwest and the Northeast); and (2) a change in the rate of sea level rise.

There is little convincing pollen evidence for a postglacial dry period in the Southeast. Therefore, it seems possible that the rate of rise of sea level may be involved. There is abundant evidence from the Atlantic coast that the rate of rise of postglacial sea level slowed at about that time to about 3.5 meters per year; sea level reached its present level about 3000 C^{14} years ago in coastal Virginia (Redfield 1967, Emery and Garrison 1967, Newman and Rusnak 1965).

Thus it would appear that major events in the history of the Dismal Swamp may have been influenced strongly by postglacial changes in sea level, while the major vegetational changes in the region were influenced by postglacial changes in climate. There is one interesting exception to the latter, however. It could be argued that the shift from oak-hickory to swamp forest was a function of climatic warming (and an increase in precipitation). However, an examination of peat depths and rates of peat accumulation shows very clearly that at the beginning of swamp forests the peat had built up sufficiently to mantle the whole surface of the Swamp east of the Suffolk Scarp. This would obviously result in an elimination of oak forest, and, as peat thickness increased at any one place, swamp forest species would take over. Thus, at least indirectly, sea level changes may have been responsible for this major vegetational change within the Swamp about 2500 C^{14} years ago.

The Origin of Lake Drummond

As mentioned previously, there is a large, shallow lake centrally positioned in the Virginia section of the Dismal Swamp. The origin of this feature remains enigmatic, and there are many myths associated with it. It has been argued (1) that the lake might be the last vestige of an open-water phase of the Swamp (much like the remaining open portion of a centripetally developing bog); (2) that it might represent a

Carolina bay (thus formed by whatever geological forces were responsible for forming Carolina bays); (3) that it might be a recent feature, perhaps a function of a deep peat burn at a time when water level was low, or (4) that it might represent a solution-collapse feature.

We can easily eliminate the first hypothesis. We know that the Swamp did not develop centripetally; furthermore, pollen in sediments within the lake indicates that it is a young feature, originating no more than 4000 C^{14} years ago. The second theory is also untenable, as the lake and its shoreline have none of the characteristics of a true Carolina bay. Furthermore, we now know that such features formed during glacial maxima (Thom 1967, 1970, and pers. comm.). Lake Drummond formed instead during the middle of the post-glacial. The third theory cannot be excluded, although there is no direct evidence of deep peat burn at that point in the Swamp's history. However, such burns are not uncommon in swamps of the Southeast and often result in the formation of shallow ponds. It is also well known that peat-ringed lakes in the Southeast can enlarge by lateral erosion of peat (Frey 1954). The presence of many cypress trees growing at some distance from the existing shore of the lake and the presence of stumps on the lake bottom indicate that the size of Lake Drummond has changed and that the lake level, and hence the water table, have fluctuated considerably through time. The last theory cannot be excluded, but data on solution of the underlying Pleistocene and Tertiary sediments are lacking.

EARLY MAN IN THE DISMAL SWAMP

Although it is well known that modern man has gained abundant, often destructive access to the Dismal Swamp, it is interesting to note that prehistoric man ventured there as well. Pollen studies of core DS1 from just east of Lake Drummond (Fig. 1) revealed the presence of maize pollen at a level that can be dated at about 3000 years old. As pollen of maize is extremely large, it is unlikely to have been transported an appreciable distance. Furthermore, from the same level there is pollen evidence of a localized clearing in the Swamp (Whitehead 1965b). It can thus be suggested that local Indian populations may have cultivated corn, perhaps in small clearings caused by fire.

MODERN MAN AND THE DISMAL SWAMP

It is obvious that modern civilization has had tremendous impact on the Dismal Swamp. This is indicated by the shrinkage in surface area, the loss of the characteristic trees, and increased frequency of fires. Palynological studies indicate yet another important impact. One of the coring stations (DS77, Fig. 1) is located just east of the Intra-coastal Waterway (Dismal Swamp Canal). The pollen diagram from this core is obviously truncated at the top, as virtually the entire cypress-gum zone is missing. Furthermore, there is distinct evidence of oxidation of pollen in the surface layers. This suggests that considerable thickness of peat (perhaps as much as a meter or more), has been lost from this region. Shaler (1890) indicated that the building of the Intra-coastal Waterway resulted in a blockage of the normal pattern of water flow within the Swamp. This was due both to the presence of a deep canal and also to the spoil from the excavation, which was placed adjacent to the canal. Thus the water which normally percolated through the peat surface from west to east was prevented from reaching the region east of the waterway. This change in water budget apparently resulted in the loss of peat by oxidation.

It is important to emphasize that the survival of many of the characteristic species and vegetational associations of the Swamp is dependent on the maintenance of a considerable thickness of peat. It must also be noted that some 3000 years were required for the peat now lost by oxidation to accumulate (in contrast, the loss rate was greater than 1 m/125 years). In the presence of a normal pattern of water flow, new peat would probably accumulate, but our evidence indicates that the rate is extraordinarily slow, about 0.05 cm per year.

It is true that we have evidence of many localized changes and successional sequences within the Swamp during the last several thousand years. This indicates that the Swamp was in a state of dynamic equilibrium and that successional processes could reconstitute areas that were disturbed in some way. Thus a modicum of capacity for repair was inherent in the swamp ecosystem. If we look at the rates at which these changes took place, we must think in terms of many centuries. Thus vegetational repair was also a very slow process in the absence of disturbances generated by modern civilization.

In short, the Dismal Swamp is in a tenuous state of equilibrium and is presently threatened to an unprecedented degree. The Swamp as we know it is a very young feature, having become fully developed only some 3000 years ago. Its survival depends on the maintenance of a considerable thickness of peat, and that in turn depends on the preservation of a normal water budget and unobstructed patterns of water flow. Yet the dynamics of the peat surface are being threatened continuously by ditching, fires, tree farming, and a variety of other land uses. If we wish to save even a small fraction of the once magnificent wilderness, it will require recognition of the many factors that have permitted the Swamp to develop and of the variety of forces that have maintained it over the last several thousand years. The Swamp obviously has the capacity for some degree of self-repair, but with the disappearance of the species that were once dominant and with dramatically altered water budgets, this may well become impossible in the near future.

The Dismal Swamp is clearly an invaluable aesthetic and biological resource. As such it should be preserved. However, can we alter the course of contemporary society in time to effect the changes necessary to insure preservation? And if we can, will it be done?

SUMMARY

Analysis of pollen in cores indicates that the Dismal Swamp in southeastern Virginia is a rather young feature. It began as extensive freshwater marshes along streams, the result of a rising water table, perhaps caused by the postglacial rise of sea level. As the water table rose, marsh development proceeded inland. By 6000 C^{14} years B.P. (before present) fine-grained peat mantled about half of the present Dismal Swamp. From 6000 to 3500 C^{14} years B.P. peat accumulation continued at an appreciably lower rate that corresponds both to the Hypsithermal interval and to a distinct decrease in the rate of rise of sea level. By 3500 C^{14} years B.P. peat had mantled virtually all of the interfluves and "islands" within the Swamp.

The pollen diagrams suggest a gradual change from boreal spruce-pine forests during the full-glacial, to somewhat less boreal pine-spruce forests during the early late-glacial, to hardwood forests containing many species characteristic of the present "northern hardwood" forests during the latter portion of the late-glacial, to hardwood-dominated forests containing species now found in southeastern Virginia during the early postglacial. This general sequence suggests a unidirectional climatic amelioration from conditions comparable to those in northern New England at present, during the full-glacial, to a climate comparable to Virginia at present by 8000 C^{14} years B.P. The climate may have been warmer and drier during the Hypsithermal, but the observed changes also might have resulted from a decrease in the rate of sea level rise. The cypress-gum forests that have characterized the Dismal Swamp for the past 3500 years have been variable both spatially and temporally. These variations doubtless reflect local differences in water table, peat depth, fires, wind throws, and a variety of human disturbances.

The origin of Lake Drummond remains an enigma. It is a young feature of the Swamp, apparently originating about 4000 C^{14} years ago. Although the origin is unknown, it is clearly not the last vestige of an earlier open-water phase of the Swamp.

REFERENCES CITED

Braun, E. Lucy. 1950. *Deciduous forests of eastern North America.* McGraw Hill, N.Y. 596 pp. (available from Hafner as 1972 reprint)

Cocke, E. C., I. F. Lewis, and Ruth Patrick. 1934. A further study of Dismal Swamp peat. *Amer. J. Bot.* 21:374–395.

Craig, A. J. 1970. Vegetational history of the Shenandoah Valley, Virginia. *Geol. Soc. Amer., Spec. Pap.* 123:283–296.

Emery, K. O., and L. E. Garrison. 1967. Sea levels 7000 and 20,000 years ago. *Science* 157:684–687.

Frey, D. G. 1951. Pollen succession in the sediments of Singletary Lake, North Carolina. *Ecology* 32:518–533.

———.1953. Regional aspects of the late-glacial and postglacial pollen succession of southeastern North Carolina. *Ecol. Monographs* 23:289–313.

———. 1954. Evidence for recent enlargement of the "bay" lakes of North Carolina. *Ecology* 35:78–88.

———. 1955. A time revision of the Pleistocene pollen chronology of southeastern North Carolina. *Ecology* 36:762–763.

Harrison, W., R. J. Malloy, G. A. Rusnak, and J. Terasmae. 1965. Possible late Pleistocene uplift, Chesapeake Bay entrance. *J. Geol.* 73:201–229.

Kearney, T. H. 1901. Report on a botanical survey of the Dismal Swamp region. *Contrib. U.S. Natl. Herbarium* 5:321–585.

Lewis, I. F., and E. C. Cocke. 1929. Pollen analysis of Dismal Swamp peat. *J. Elisha Mitchell Sci. Soc.* 45:37–58.

Lichti-Federovich, S., and J. C. Ritchie. 1965. Contemporary pollen spectra in central Canada. II. The forest grassland transition in Manitoba. *Pollen et Spores* 7:63–87.

Newman, W. S., and G. A. Rusnak. 1965. Holocene submergence of the eastern shore of Virginia. *Science* 148:1464–1466.

Oaks, R. Q., Jr., and N. K. Coch. 1963. Pleistocene sea levels, southeastern Virginia. *Science* 140:979–983.

———. 1973. Post-Miocene stratigraphy and morphology, southeastern Virginia. *Va. Div. Mineral Resources, Bull.* 82. 135 pp.

Ogden, J. G. 1967. Radiocarbon and pollen evidence for a sudden change in climate in the Great Lakes region approximately 10,000 years ago. Pp. 117–127 *in* E. J. Cushing and H. E. Wright, Jr. (eds). *Quaternary paleoecology.* Yale Univ. Press, New Haven.

Redfield, A. C. 1967. Postglacial change in sea level in the western North Atlantic Ocean. *Science* 157:687–691.

Shaler, N. S. 1890. General account of the fresh-water morasses of the United States, with a description of the Dismal Swamp district of Virginia and North Carolina. *U.S. Geol. Survey, Ann. Rpt.* 10:255–339.

Thom, B. G. 1967. Coastal and fluvial landforms: Horry and Marion counties, South Carolina. *Coastal Studies Series* no. 19. Louisiana State Univ. Press, Baton Rouge. 75 pp.

———. 1970. Carolina bays in Horry and Marion counties, South Carolina. *Geol. Soc. Amer., Bull.* 81:783–814.

Wentworth, C. K. 1930. Sand and gravel resources of the coastal plain of Virginia. *Va. Geol. Survey, Bull.* 32. 146 pp.

Whitehead, D. R. 1964. Fossil pine pollen and full glacial vegetation in southeastern North Carolina. *Ecology* 45:767–776.

———. 1965a. Palynology and Pleistocene phytogeography of unglaciated eastern North America. Pp. 417–432 *in* H. E. Wright, Jr., and D. J. Frey (eds). *The Quaternary of the United States.* Princeton Univ. Press, Princeton, N.J.

———. 1965b. Prehistoric maize in southeastern Virginia. *Science* 150:881–883.

———. 1967. Studies of full-glacial vegetation and climate in southeastern United States. Pp. 237–248 *in* E. J. Cushing and H. E. Wright, Jr. (eds). *Quaternary Paleoecology.* Yale Univ. Press, New Haven.

———. 1972. Developmental and environmental history of the Dismal Swamp. *Ecol. Monographs* 42:301–315.

———. 1973. Late-Wisconsin vegetational changes in unglaciated North America. *Quaternary Res.* 3:621–631.

EVIDENCE OF ABORIGINAL UTILIZATION OF THE BOLA IN THE DISMAL SWAMP AREA

Edward Bottoms and Floyd Painter

INTRODUCTION

The Dismal Swamp area of the Virginia–North Carolina Coastal Plain is one of the most important archaeologically along the Atlantic seaboard.[1] Artifacts recovered from hundreds of campsites, quarry areas, and village sites demonstrate that aboriginal cultural groups inhabited the area from the close of the Pleistocene epoch through the period of European exploration and colonization.

Within the aggregate artifact assemblage from the area are the manifestations of four cultural periods that represent a continuum of human inhabitation. Each period was characterized by predominant patterns of subsistence and settlement, a distinctive artifact inventory, and a singular style of demographic grouping. The life-style during each period (Paleo-Indian, Archaic, Woodland, and Historic) developed in response to local ecological conditions and was influenced to some extent by technological and sociological elements diffused from other geographic and cultural areas. A cultural and ecological chronology for the Dismal Swamp area is provided in Table 1 (data derived from Griffin 1967, Hranicky 1973, McCary 1963, Oaks and Coch 1973, Whitehead 1965, 1972).

The most intensive occupation of the area occurred during the Archaic period, circa 9000–3500 B.P. (before present). Archaic habitation sites are numerous and, with few exceptions, are located on the higher elevations adjacent to extant or former water courses and marshes. The sites are concentrated on the Fentress Rise in Chesa-

---

[1] For the purpose of this study the Dismal Swamp "area" is defined as the total of 2373 square miles occupied by the Virginia cities of Suffolk (incorporating former Nansemond County), Chesapeake, Portsmouth, Norfolk, and Virginia Beach and the North Carolina counties of Camden, Currituck, Gates, Pasquotank, and Perquimmans. Included is the Dismal Swamp itself, which, by a 1973 U.S. Department of the Interior delineation, covers 328 square miles (Hill 1973).

Table 1. Cultural and environmental chronology of the Dismal Swamp area

Years B.P.	Cultural periods, subsistence methods, artifact inventories	Environmental conditons
400	*Historic:* Acculturation to western life.	
1000	*Woodland:* Subsistence primarily upon agriculture, secondarily upon hunting and fishing. Development of village life and tribal affiliations. Bow and arrow and	Cypress and gum predominant. Swamp develops into present
2000	clay pottery developed. *Artifacts:* Clay potsherds, stone and clay tobacco pipes, stone arrowpoints, chisels and pestles,	state, to be reduced in size by drainage during
3000	shell and copper beads, stone, shell, and copper pendants.	past two centuries
4000	*Archaic:* Increase in population. Subsistence based on seasonal semi-	Lowered water table. Swamp continues to
5000	sedentary hunting, fishing, and foraging for natural vegetal resources. Primary use of locally occurring lithic materials in the manufacture of implements. Begin-	move inland. Hard-woods replace cypress and gum. Aquatic plants abundant along muddy
6000	nings of village life and clay pottery manufacture. *Artifacts:* Proliferation of stemmed and notched projectile point	shores. Climate similar to present.
7000	styles, specialized polished tools (axes, chisels, gouges), steatite bowls, flaked knives and scrapers, stone mortars used in processing vegetal foods, stone ornaments	Continued inland extention of fresh-water reed marsh with aquatic plants.
8000	(gorgets and pendants), steatite sinkers, atlatl with bannerstone weights used in hunting mammals, bolas employed for dispatching	Hardwoods along interfluves. Ponding of water. Cli-mate similar to present.
9000	waterfowl. *Paleo-Indian:* Occupation by small groups of nomadic people whose subsistence	Inland extension of marshes. Standing water in low areas.
10,000	involved the hunting of mammalian forms possibly including now-extinct herbivorous megafauna. Campsites were	Beech, hemlock, birch.
11,000	small and occupied for short periods. *Artifacts:* Fluted projectile points of the Clovis type, specialized and sometimes	Climate cooler than at present. Marsh flora along freshwater streams.
12,000	multipurpose cutting and scraping tools.	Boreal pine-spruce along interfluves

peake, Virginia, Pungo Ridge in Virginia Beach, and Land-of-Promise
Ridge, which extends southward from Chesapeake, Virginia, into
Camden and Currituck counties, North Carolina. The greatest con-
centration of Archaic habitation localities is found on the Suffolk
Scarp in Suffolk, Virginia, and Gates County, North Carolina, on the
western periphery of the Swamp (McCary 1963).

Subsistence during the Archaic was based upon a concept of "primary forest efficiency" (Caldwell 1958, pp. 6–18) and involved
"complete harmonious parasitism upon the varied offering of the
woodlands [with] seasonal shifts in subsistence base" (Jennings 1968,
p. 112). In the Dismal Swamp area the economic pattern encompassed
hunting, fishing, shell fishing, and foraging, with the result that the
total environment was exploited for naturally occurring food resources.
Artifacts of the Archaic period reflect a technology devoted to the production of implements to be utilized in such environmental exploitation.

Hunting was the most productive subsistence activity, for it could
be conducted on a year-round basis with predictably satisfactory results. It involved the pursuit of both mammals and birds.

Mammals were abundant and therefore the primary prey. They
were hunted with spears and darts having short shafts tipped with
stone points, which are found in a myriad of styles and sizes on all local
habitation sites. Atlatls, or "spear-throwers" to which counterweights
called "bannerstones" were sometimes attached, were frequently used
as aids in propelling the projectiles toward the animal quarry (Bottoms 1965, Hibben 1965, Dickson 1967, McCary 1968, McAvoy 1970,
Hranicky 1973).

Extensive freshwater marshes, present in the Swamp area between
7000 and 4000 B.P., would have provided excellent habitat conditions
for many species of waterfowl (Mary Keith Garrett, pers. comm.;
Whitehead 1972). Because of the combined factors of soil acidity,
erosion, and two centuries of cultivation, osteological material has not
been preserved on aboriginal sites in the Dismal Swamp area. However, we have concluded that the bola was employed here during the
Archaic period for the hunting of waterfowl (Bottoms and Painter
1972).

THE BOLA

Also known as the compound sling (Nelson 1899, p. 134), the bola is a
weapon consisting of two or more weights attached to cords of equal
length. The cords are joined together in a knot, thus allowing the

weights to hang separately. When employed (in hunting or war), the knotted end of the bola cords is held in the user's hands, the weights are whirled over the head, and the entire device is loosed toward the intended quarry. During their flight the weights spread and gyrate; if one strikes the prey, the others, because their paths of momentum have been disturbed, enwrap the animal and render it immobile.

The bola has been used in many parts of the world and is, apparently, of ancient origin. Stones thought to be bola weights have been found on Chellean living floors in Olduvai Gorge in Tanzania, East Africa. Their age is an estimated 400,000 years (Leakey and Sisson 1961).

During Pre-Columbian times the bola was used by South American groups in hunting rheas, guanacos, and pumas in open country. During the Conquest era the Incas of Peru used bolas made of three stones attached to llama tendons for combating invading Spanish Cavalry. The weapons were effective, not only in entangling the legs of the horses, but in disabling the riders as well. In some instances the horsemen were freed only after members of the infantry came forward and cut the tough immobilizing bola cords (Hemming 1970, p. 195).

The bola continues to be a favored weapon among the Charrua, Querandi, and Tehuelche of Patagonia and the Argentine Pampas, and of the Uru for hunting ducks in the marshes along the southern margin of Lake Titicaca in Bolivia and Peru. According to Darwin ([1840] 1972:37–38, 96–97), it was used by gauchos for catching "ostriches" (rheas) on the pampas. It is still used there by cattlemen.

Contemporary utilization of the bola in the Northern Hemisphere has been observed only among the Eskimos of Siberia and Alaska. Nelson (1899, p. 134) reported its use "for catching birds by the people of the coast from Unalaklit to Kotzebue Sound, the islands of Bering Strait, St. Lawrence Island, and the adjacent Siberian coast." James A. Ford observed Eskimos of the Point Barrow, Alaska, area using the device in hunting ducks (Ford and Webb 1956). Graphic descriptions of the practical use of the bola are given by these authors, but Nelson's (1899, pp. 134–135) is considered more meaningful:

When in search of game the bolas is worn wound around the hunter's head like a fillet, with the balls resting on the brow. When a flock of ducks, geese, or other wild fowl pass overhead, at an altitude not exceeding 40 or 50 yards, the hunter by a quick motion untwists the sling. Holding the united ends of the cords in his right hand, he seizes the balls with the left and draws the cords so tight that they lie parallel to each other; then, as the birds come within throwing distance, he swings the balls around his head once or twice and casts them, aiming a little in front of the flock. When the balls leave the hand they are close together, the cords trail behind, and they travel so swiftly that it is difficult to follow their flight with the eye. As they begin to lose their impetus they acquire a gyrating motion, and spread apart until at their highest point they stand out to the full extent of the cords in a circle four or five feet in diameter; they seem to hang thus for a moment, then, if nothing has been encountered, turn and drop to the earth. While in the air the cords do not appear to interfere with each other . . . if a bird is struck it is enwrapped by the cords and its wings so hampered that it falls helpless. . . . They [the bolas] are used mostly on low points over which waterfowl fly at certain hours of the day.

Archaeological evidence indicates that the bola was used at an early date in the continental United States. In a "section" of Manzano Cave, New Mexico, which yielded both cultural material and the remains of the late Pleistocene forms *Camelops* and *Nothrotherium*, four grooved stone balls were excavated. Three of the balls, all of limestone and nearly equal in size and weight, "were found together and apparently represent a set. . . . Each of the three has a well-defined groove encircling it . . . these balls have been identified as bola balls" (Hibben 1941, pp. 35–36, and Plate 14, no. 2).

Bola weights have been discovered on archaeological sites throughout the United States. Usually their true function has gone unrecognized. In many archaeological reports the weights have been identified only as "plummets" because of their close resemblance to modern iron plumb bobs. They are most often found singly, having been removed from their original contexts by erosion and cultivation. The junior author recalls seeing thousands of elongated bola weights that had been recovered from the dry beds of Buena Vista Lake and Tulare Lake, located in Kern and Kings counties, California, respectively. What now remains of Buena Vista Lake is a waterfowl haven of tule bulrushes and shallow waterways.

Occasionally bola stones have been discovered in situ during excavations. At the Ohioview site in Beaver County, Pennsylvania, "three hematite bola stones, in a line six inches apart . . . were found in association with early Woodland pottery" (Citron 1967). A cache of at least twelve "plummets" was discovered in a mound in Brevard County, Florida. They had apparently been originally attached to cords joined in a knot (Hodge 1910, p. 268). Perino (1961) reported "plummets" found in burials in the Illinois River Valley. At the Hathaway Site in Passadumkeag, Maine, stones interpreted as bola weights were found with Archaic burials (Snow 1969).

Poverty Point, a square-mile late-Archaic site on Bayou Macon near Epps, Louisiana, has produced a substantial number of bola weights made of hematite and magnetite. Farmers there reported plowing up "nests" of six to eight "plumb bobs." Ford and Webb (1956), the principal investigators of the site, examined a total of 406 bola weights of several types. Ford (1955) related that the bola was a "common weapon" of the Poverty Point people, who used it for hunting birds and small game.

THE BOLA IN THE DISMAL SWAMP AREA

Hundreds of bola weights have been encountered on Archaic sites in the Dismal Swamp area. Many Indian relic collectors and curio-seekers here, like their counterparts in other parts of the country, have mistakenly classified them as gamestones, netsinkers, charmstones, and even as "medicine men's" stones. Such classifications, which are unfortunately enduring ones, are not surprising, for the weights have been recovered from localities adjacent to heavily forested tracts where the use of bolas would now be impractical.

Utilization of the bola in hunting would, however, have been successful during the Archaic period. Analysis of pollen samples from approximately 80 coring stations in the Virginia portion of the Swamp has revealed that between 8200 and 3500 B.P. the present Swamp was covered with expanses of open water and marsh supporting aquatic plants, grasses, and sedges. Oak, hickory, and sweet gum grew only on the elevations above the Swamp's general surface, and dominance by cypress and gum developed after 3500 B.P. (Whitehead 1965, 1972).

Although bola weights are found throughout the area, they are conspicuously absent from sites along saline watercourses. Instead, they are restricted to the higher elevations above the Dismal Swamp and above local freshwater marshes. We estimate that nearly 75 percent of the weights from this area have been recovered from numerous Archaic sites on the Suffolk Scarp, on the western periphery of the Swamp in Suffolk, Virginia, and Gates County, North Carolina. We have also noted concentrations of bola stones near the Washington Ditch, Moss Swamp and Cypress Swamp, and Hamburg Ditch, where the Swamp's major inlets dissect the Suffolk Scarp. During the period 8200 to 3500 B.P. these inlets emptied into localized freshwater marshes that would have provided suitable habitat for waterfowl.

We have carefully examined 290 bola weights from the area under study. These constitute only a small portion of the total found here. We are aware that others (unavailable to us) are in the collection of the Museum of the American Indian (Heye Foundation), New York City, and in widely scattered private collections.

Five basic styles of bola weights, which we have divided into eleven substyles, are represented in collections from the area. These are classified in Table 2 and illustrated by Figures 1-12.

Ungrooved ovoid bola weights (Fig. 1) are the most common in the area, outnumbering the total of all other styles found thus far. We note, incidentally, that many farmers who have recovered them from fields used the stones as nest eggs in hen houses.

The dimpled ovoid substyle (Fig. 6) is represented by only two specimens, both from a single site near Great Bridge in the City of Chesapeake. Ford and Webb (1956), who reported that such "dimpled egg" weights occurred on sites in Argentina, related that the "dimples" served as seats for knots securing the weights in rawhide pouches.

All of the other substyles illustrated are found occasionally on sites in the area. We suspect that some of the small, naturally shaped stones frequently encountered on Archaic sites may also have been used as bola weights. Three of the weight styles—ovoid, rectanguloid, and ungrooved amphipunctate—are apparently peculiar to the Dismal Swamp area. To our knowledge, they have not been reported elsewhere in the United States. The grooved spherical substyle has been reported from New York (Ritchie 1965), and the grooved ovoid from Georgia (Fairbanks 1952), New York (Ritchie 1965), and the lower Mississippi Valley (Ford and Quimby 1945).

The grooves completely encircling some of the weights provided for the attachment to bola cords, which presumably were made of rawhide or sinew. Ungrooved weights were, we believe, encased in rawhide pouches connected to the cords of the device.

Table 2. Shape classification of bola weights from the Dismal Swamp area

Basic style	Substyles
1. Ovoid	(a) Ungrooved (Fig. 1)
	(b) Grooved (Fig. 2)
	(c) Dimpled (Fig. 6)
2. Rectangular	(a) (Fig. 3)
3. Spherical	(a) Ungrooved (Fig. 4)
	(b) Grooved (Fig. 5)
4. Amphipunctate	(a) Ungrooved (Fig. 7)
	(b) Grooved (Figs. 8 and 9)
5. Knoblike	(a) Square base (Fig. 10)
	(b) Pointed base (Fig. 11)
	(c) Rounded base (Fig. 12)

With two exceptions noted below, all weights we have examined were made of lithic materials available in local gravel deposits. Lithic and numerical data are provided in Table 3.

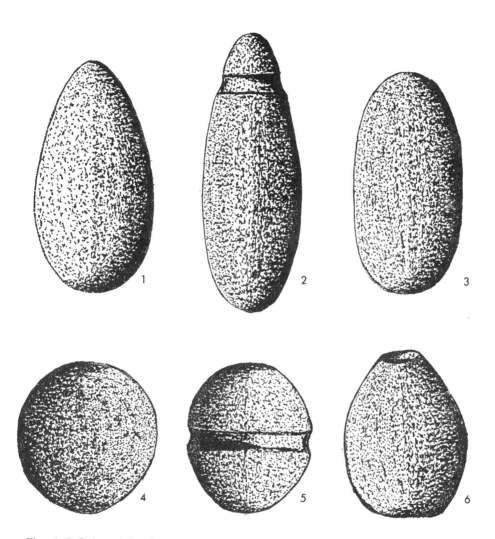

Figs. 1–6. Bola weights from the Dismal Swamp area (actual size). 1, ungrooved ovoid; 2, grooved ovoid; 3, rectanguloid; 4, ungrooved spherical; 5, grooved spherical; 6, dimpled ovoid.

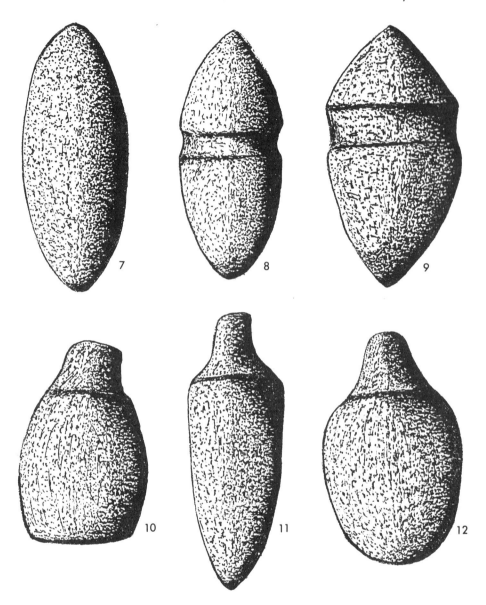

Figs. 7–12 Bola weights from the Dismal Swamp area. 7, ungrooved amphipunctate; 8 and 9 grooved amphipunctate; 10, knoblike with square base; 11, knoblike with pointed base; 12, knoblike with rounded base.

Table 3. Mineralogical composition of bola weights from the Dismal Swamp area

Lithic materials	Numbers of bola weights
Quartzite	232
Granite	15
Quartz	15
Mica Schist	13
"Siltstone"	13
Magnetite	2

The presence of two bola weights of magnetite (iron ore), both found on a single site in Chesapeake, is most enigmatic in that the material does not occur near the Dismal Swamp. Although iron ore is a component of the Silurian Clinton formation in Lee and Wise counties, Virginia (Butts 1940, pp. 237–245), the closest source known to have been utilized by aboriginal people is at Leslie, Missouri (Holmes 1919, pp. 266–276).

Twenty-five randomly selected bola stones of varying styles and lithic composition averaged 180.4 grams (5.8 oz) in weight, with a range of 124.5 to 280 grams (4 to 9 oz). Although we have not yet experimented with reconstructed bolas, it seems reasonable that those used locally may have consisted of three to five weights attached to cords approximately one meter in length.

Bola weights were manufactured by the "pecking" (battering) process. This utilized a hammerstone of hardness equal to or greater than that of the stone being shaped. The bola stone was struck repeatedly to remove unwanted material, then smoothed by abrasion with other smooth stones or perhaps animal skins containing dampened sand. In *The voyage of the* Beagle, Charles Darwin ([1840] 1972:61) noted that the manufacture of bola stones by the battering technique was one of the "chief indoor occupations" of the native men of the Rio Colorado, Argentina.

Whether the bola was developed independently in the Dismal Swamp area or introduced by another culture cannot be determined with certainty. We strongly suspect, however, that the latter may have been the case, for the implement saw widespread use in the eastern, southern, and western United States during the Archaic period. Most likely it would have been introduced from New England, for other Archaic traits characteristic of that section (ulus, or polished-slate knives, and smoothed concavo-convex gouges) have also been found near the Swamp. As mentioned previously, some weight styles are evidently peculiar to this area.

The replacement of marshes and waterways in the Dismal Swamp by peat deposits and cypress-gum forests after 3500 B.P. reduced the waterfowl habitat and rendered further utilization of the bola impractical. Peat deposition and forest development coincided with the end of the Archaic period, and the arrow became the principal hunting weapon (see Table 1).

CONCLUSIONS

The bola was utilized principally for the hunting of waterfowl during the Archaic period in the Dismal Swamp, when extensive marsh habitats should have supported a large and diversified waterfowl population. Moreover, since the bola is demonstrably effective as a hunting device only in open country, its abundant presence here is thought to support the (preceding) geological and palynological evidence that during the Archaic period the now densely forested Swamp consisted of marshlands and open-water areas among smaller stands of timber at the higher elevations.

SUMMARY

That the bola is optimally suited for the hunting of waterfowl has been demonstrated by contemporary reports of its use among South American aboriginal groups and the Alaskan Eskimo. Our archaeological findings indicate that the bola was employed in hunting throughout the Dismal Swamp area during the Archaic cultural period, circa 9000-3500 B.P.

It is concluded that the bola was utilized principally for hunting waterfowl during the Archaic period in the Dismal Swamp. Since the bola is effective only in open country, its presence here also supplements the extensive geological and palynological evidence that during the Archaic period this now densely forested swamp consisted of marshlands and open-water areas among smaller stands of timber at the higher elevations.

REFERENCES CITED

Bottoms, E. 1965. The James Byrd bannerstone. *Chesopiean* 3:20.

Bottoms, E., and F. Painter. 1972. Bola weights from the Dismal Swamp region of Virginia and North Carolina. *Chesopiean* 10:19–30.

Butts, C. 1940. Geology of the Appalachian Valley in Virginia, Part 1. *Va. Geol. Survey, Bull.* 52. 568 pp.

Caldwell, J. R. 1958. Trend and tradition in the prehistory of the eastern United States. *Amer. Anthropol. Assoc., Mem.* 88. 137 pp.

Citron, H. 1967. Some recent discoveries at the Ohioview archaeological site in Beaver County, Pennsylvania. *Chesopiean* 5:4–7.

Darwin, Charles. 1972 reprint. *The voyage of the* Beagle. Bantam Books, New York. 439 pp. [First published in 1840.]

Dickson, D. R. 1967. Some notes on the atlatl. *Arkansas Amateur* 6:5–9.

Fairbanks, H. 1952. Creek and Pre-Creek. Pp. 285–300 *in* J. B. Griffin (ed). *Archaeology of the eastern United States.* Univ. of Chicago Press.

Ford, A. 1955. The puzzle of Poverty Point. *Natural History* 68:466–472.

Ford, A., and G. I. Quimby, Jr. 1945. The Tchefuncte culture: an early occupation of the lower Mississippi Valley. *Soc. Amer. Archaeol., Mem.* 2. 113 pp.

Ford, A., and C. H. Webb. 1956. Poverty Point: a late archaic site in Louisiana. *Amer. Mus. Nat. Hist., Anthropol. Pap.* 46:1–142.

Griffin, J. B. 1967. Eastern North American prehistory: a summary. *Science* 156:175–191.

Hemming, J. 1970. *The conquest of the Incas.* Harcourt Brace Jovanovich, New York. 641 pp.

Hibben, F. C. 1941. Evidences of early occupation in Sandia Cave, New Mexico, and other sites in the Sandia–Manzano region. *Smithsonian Misc. Collection* 99. 44 pp.

———. 1965. America's oldest hunting weapon. *Field and Stream* (July): 48–50, 108–109.

Hill, D. 1973. Dismal Swamp size defined by U.S. study. *Norfolk Virginian-Pilot* (29 July).

Hodge, F. W. (ed). 1910. Handbook of American Indians north of Mexico. *Bur. Amer. Ethnol. Bull.* 30, pt. 2. 1221 pp.

Holmes, W. H. 1919. Handbook of aboriginal American antiquities, pt. 1: The lithic industries. *Bur. Amer. Ethnol., Bull.* 60. 380 pp.

Hranicky, W. J. 1973. Survey of the prehistory of Virginia. *Chesopiean* 11:76–94.

Jennings, J. D. 1968. *Prehistory of North America.* McGraw-Hill, New York. 376 pp.

Leakey, L. S. B., and R. F. Sisson. 1961. Exploring 1,750,000 years into man's past. *Natl. Geog. Mag.* 120:561–589.

McAvoy, J. M. 1970. The S. L. Jordan bannerstone. *Chesopiean* 8:81–84.

McCary, B. C. 1963. The archaeology of the western area of the Dismal Swamp in Virginia. *Quart. Bull. Archeol. Soc. Va.* 17:40–48.

———. 1968. Bannerstones of the Dismal Swamp area in Virginia and North Carolina. *Quart. Bull. Archeol. Soc. Va.* 22:118–155.

Nelson, W. E. 1899. The Eskimo about Bering Strait. *Bur. Amer. Ethnol., Ann.* 18:19–518.

Oaks, R. Q., Jr., and N. K. Coch. 1973. Post-Miocene stratigraphy and morphology, southeastern Virginia. *Va. Div. Mineral Resources, Bull.* 82. 135 pp.

Perino, G. 1961. Tentative classification of plummets in the lower Illinois River Valley. *Central States Archaeol. J.* 8:43–56.

Ritchie, W. A. 1965. *The archaeology of New York State.* Natural History Press, Garden City, N.Y. 355 pp.

Snow, D. R. 1969. *A summary of excavations at the Hathaway Site in Passadumkeag, Maine, 1912, 1947, 1968.* Dept. Anthropology, Univ. Maine. 106 pp.

Whitehead, D. R. 1965. Palynology and Pleistocene phytogeography of unglaciated eastern North America. Pp. 417–432 *in* H. E. Wright, Jr., and D. G. Frey (eds). *The Quaternary of the United States.* Princeton Univ. Press, Princeton, N.J.

_____. 1972. Developmental and environmental history of the Dismal Swamp. *Ecol. Monographs* 42:301–315.

MAN AND THE SWAMP:
THE HISTORICAL DIMENSION

Peter C. Stewart

Humanity's historic use of the Dismal Swamp has included both physical and mental aspects. Like most human endeavors, material progress blended with romantic appreciation. A wide variety of folk, including wealthy Virginia planter-surveyors, several agricultural reformers, scores of lumbermen, an unknown number of escaped slaves and free blacks, teachers, natural scientists in nearly every specialty, guerilla fighters, poets, artists, a black composer, adventurous New England ladies, a multitude of sportsmen, health fadists, and journalists, have used the Swamp itself or the theme of its existence. This paper examines the record of man's past relationship with the Swamp.

But before we explore the historical dimension, a word about prehistoric people. Archaeologists have unearthed ancient relics both within the Swamp and along the edges. These discoveries have bolstered the theory that prehistoric people used the area as a vast hunting and fishing range abounding in waterfowl and other sources of food. Extensive prehistoric use of the area now known as the Dismal Swamp was possible because, at one or several times in the remote past, the area contained a higher water level which eliminated or prevented timber growth and allowed a larger concentration of grasslands. The findings of corn pollen buried in peat not far from Lake Drummond by palynologist Donald Whitehead (1965) tend to confirm the notion that ancient man farmed in the Swamp, but raise questions about the pervasiveness of the aquatic environment.

By the time whites first arrived the area had acquired its swamplike character, and most of the Indians lived in peripheral settlements. The Nansemond Indians settled along the Suffolk Escarpment, and the present community of Chuckatuck is the site of one of their main towns. The remnants of this and related tribes of the Powhatan Confederation as well as at least one independent group have been found throughout lowland Virginia and North Carolina.

Their hatchets and other utensils indicate the presence of a forest-oriented people (Traver 1963, McCary 1963, 1972, Bottoms and Painter 1972, Painter pers. comm.; also see preceding paper, this volume).

For over a century after the English occupied Virginia there was little expressed interest either in the Swamp or in making use of it. Settlers were certainly aware of its existence and surely attempts were made to explore it, but for most of the seventeenth century Virginia's governors directed official survey parties to the west, paticularly toward the Roanoke River and beyond. Though civilization nibbled at the edges of the Swamp, great sections of it remained uncharted and unknown. In 1665 a governor from North Carolina, William Drummond, hunting along the fringes, somehow became lost, wandered into the heart of the Dismal Swamp, and came upon a large lake that now bears his name. A figure of some importance, Drummond died as a result of picking the wrong side in Bacon's Rebellion, 1675–76 (McKnight 1959). No known development ever occurred as a result of his earlier discovery. Virginians and Carolinians directed their attention to farming, exploration, and land speculation elsewhere. So little attention was paid to the Swamp that few even bothered to claim title to the core of the Swamp until nearly halfway through the eighteenth century—unusual behavior for the title- and property-conscious people of English extraction, who normally spent huge amounts of time making surveys, drawing boundary lines, transferring titles, making wills, and suing each other over land ownership. In 1655 William Wright patented 2250 acres of what might well qualify as part of the modern Dismal Swamp, but claims or entries to the central portion of the Swamp either in North Carolina or Virginia were rare at this early date (Berkeley and Berkeley 1976).

Finally a controversy between Virginia and North Carolina forced the governors of each colony in 1728 to assign a commission to draw a dividing line. Headed by William Byrd II, the survey crew had relatively easy going except when it encountered the Dismal Swamp. The men eagerly tackled the task as they desired to be the first ever to cross the morass. Byrd did not walk along the boundary, but he and the other commissioners went around the edge of the Swamp and waited for the surveyors and their helpers on the other side. On the way, according to his accounts (he actually produced two, one later called a "Secret History of the Line"), Byrd fired shots to keep contact with the survey party. After losing contact and waiting for several days, the commissioners realized that the crew must have consumed their provisions and had to depend on whatever game they ran across. The haggard men finally appeared, however, to report that the place was practically impossible to pass through; had it not been the dry season, the passage could not have been made (Boyd 1929, Wright and Tinling 1958).

Byrd came away from his partial encounter with the distinct impression that the place was bleak. His crew saw no mammals or birds. Even the turkey buzzard avoided the place. In the leader's eyes the Swamp, or "horrible dessert," was a blot on His Majesty's Kingdom. But being a substantial Virginia planter, he believed something could be done with the Dismal Swamp and suggested the formation of a company of British and American investors which would drain portions and produce, among other commodities, hemp—1 pound of which would be given to the government annually (Byrd, 1789). The sources, unfortunately, are mute on what the king or his representatives were supposed to do with a pound of hemp.

Byrd was quite specific in his proposal for a work force. Like most Virginia planters, he favored the system of slavery. He suggested that ten blacks be bought to start the plantation. The purchase of both men and women would, when they were paired, allow better work performance and provide children who could eventually replace their parents (Byrd 1789, 1837).

His suggestions were not acted on immediately, but several decades later George Washington and several prominent Virginia land speculators organized the Dismal Swamp Land Company, otherwise known as the "Adventurers for Draining the Dismal Swamp." William and Thomas Nelson, Thomas (Dr. John) Walker, Col. Fielding Lewis, and the other investors already had money in land development firms such as the Virginia Company, which possessed rights to several hundred-thousand acres in the Ohio Valley. The fact that the Virginia Company predated the Dismal Swamp organization by fifteen years indicates the relative interest in the two ventures. Speculators like Washington were just beginning to exploit the Swamp, then the last remaining large undeveloped tract in Tidewater Virginia, a decade and a half after they sought the privilege of developing what is now western Pennsylvania. In 1763, following the war with France that secured the disputed Ohio valley territory, Washington, one of the "Adventurers" and leader of Virginia's troops during the war, explored the core of the Dismal Swamp and waded through an occasional morass in search of drainable land (See Fitzpatrick 1925, pp. 188–194; 1931, pp. 410–411; Jackson 1976, pp. 319–326, for Washington's impressions of the Swamp). Although Washington concluded that farming was a real possibility on certain kinds of reclaimed soil, nearly another decade passed before the company began to farm the land. Finally, in the late 1770s, despite damage inflicted during the Revolution, a plantation located roughly six miles southeast of Suffolk began to yield rice and corn. Rice, the principal crop, amounted to 10,000 pounds in the best years. The volume of production indicates that, although 12 prominent and well-endowed Virginia planters held the stock, the plantation itself, operating on the edge of the Swamp, should be considered a rather modest business. Some of the rice made its way to the Caribbean, but the collapse of the British West Indies trade, plus a general economic downturn and some internal problems, brought the experiment to an end. The Revolution also intruded into the affairs of the company. One manager left to join the army and failed to return. In 1779 a redcoat incursion, which also decimated Suffolk, destroyed plantation supplies and caused the loss of several slaves. The management complained that neighbors kept some of the slaves who wandered off. For a short time during the War of 1812 the management resumed farming in the belief that wartime market conditions in Norfolk warranted such production, but the entire business was finally given up and the land leased to outside interests (Reid 1948, Berkeley and Berkeley 1976).

The Land Company also dabbled in other activities not normally associated with Swamp life. It constructed a gristmill between Suffolk and Lake Drummond. The company named the mill, and a new canal built to the lake, "Jericho." Having run into serious problems with proper water levels and inadequate equipment, the organization lost interest in the project. Later in the 1830s during the nationwide silk boom, the company grew mulberry trees on its property to support silkworms (Anonymous 1783, Reid 1948).

When first organized, the Land Company built canals, particularly one known as Washington's Ditch, named for its presumed surveyor, to Lake Drummond to promote drainage and primarily to transport lumber. The lands below Norfolk, stretching into North Carolina and including the Dismal Swamp as a major part, contained a great diversity of trees as the source of potential lumber products. In the Swamp itself the cypress and Atlantic white cedar (juniper) offered the most immediate remuneration. Long before the company was organized, the local settlers supplied Norfolk markets with shingles, staves, planking, naval stores, etc. The work was done by farmers who put their dull times to use in "shingle getting" or a similar sideline. In his account of surveying the boundary line, William Byrd noted that the commercial center of Norfolk had "a pretty deal of lumber from the Borderers on the Dismal, who make bold with the King's land thereabouts, without the least ceremony. They not only maintain their stocks upon it, but get Boards, Shingles and other lumber out of it in great abundance" (Wright and

Tingling 1958). Just how freely the residents made use of the king's property can be imagined, as from 1730 to 1772 the volume of shingles exported from Norfolk, mostly to the British islands in the Caribbean, leaped from about 500,000 to 8 million (Great Britain, Naval Office Returns, 1730–1772). At the latter date the Land Company began to employ slave labor in gathering juniper shingles (Reid 1948, p. 22).

According to production records in the years before the Civil War, the Land Company itself was producing only 6 or 7 million shingles annually. The shingle business was not a monopoly of the company. Records of the Dismal Swamp Canal, over which most of the nineteenth century shingle production was transported, reveal that by about 1850 annual hauls of shingles ranged between 35 and 47 million of one type alone (Anonymous 1858). The number poached from company lands or produced by other lumbermen who held titles or leases to the Dismal Swamp is unknown. Although several persons conducted extensive lumbering activities on property holdings amounting in some cases to a few thousand acres, the New Lebanon Company, composed of a group of investors in North Carolina, claimed nearly 50,000 acres in the Tar Heel State. These holdings, located just south of the state line, are about the same size as those of the Land Company in Virginia. But even the two of them together at no time controlled a majority of the Dismal Swamp. Furthermore, the company once owned by 12 Virginia planters was now owned by a host of descendants.

Considerable quantities of timber for ship construction also passed along the canal together with substantial numbers of studs for ship and house construction. Since the Land Company records show only a small interest in this kind of lumbering, one can presume that the entire forest area in upper North Carolina and lower Virginia yielded these products.

As early as 1836 shortages became apparent in the supply of prime juniper, source of the best-quality shingles, probably aggravated by a remarkable amount of shingle poaching on company lands. The company task workers were forced to move continuously to new locations with a more bountiful supply and hence cut into more and more new wood. Huge fires, resulting from the elimination of ground cover, burned slowly through the hardened peat. Those who visited the Swamp after the Civil War noticed new stands of juniper growing in areas obviously cut over some time before. Perhaps to slow down the process, or possibly because of a change in demand, the company shifted in the 1850s to cypress for shingles and quickly their number surpassed that of juniper. By 1861 cypress-shingle production was above 6 million and juniper just over 1 million (Reid 1948, pp. 98, 102, 134). During the Civil War the lack of markets forced a temporary halt to production, giving a little time for natural replenishment. Once work resumed, the problem of shortages returned. A company that, during the second quarter of the nineteenth century, paid its owners one of the best dividends of any corporation in the United States found itself unable to continue. Changes in taste and new developments doomed the cypress shingle for roofing (Reid 1948, pp. 140–150). John Roper, a northern postwar businessman, began to use machines to produce shingles from swamplands adjacent to those owned by the Land Company. Local residents marveled at the speed of the machine; one steamboat captain who frequently passed the sawmill remarked in awe, "A shingle a clip" (B[ishop] 1882). The company could benefit little from this machine which depleted natural resources all the more rapidly and in 1871 leased its holding to John Roper who, however, agreed not to unleash his infernal shingle machine on the property. He was also restrained from cutting all but the largest trees, and he agreed to continue working his own land simultaneously (Reid 1948, pp. 157–158). As the century progressed, general lumbering replaced shingle production, and in the early twentieth century A. L. Camp obtained title to the old Land Company's property. Logging operations using railroads and other modern equipment continued in several locations throughout the Swamp until quite recently.

During the nineteenth and early twentieth centuries the timber interests were dominant, but the idea that the Swamp was reclaimable as agricultural land persisted. Farmers occupied the high ground at the edges and drained what lowlands they could, until the swamplands were reduced to perhaps a third of their original precolonial area. Only the core remains.

Much of this reduction came about in the eighteenth century because merchants and farmers of the time preferred to deal with tobacco or wheat rather than shingles. A full load of shingles and staves yielded too little profit. Also, antilumber attitudes may have been engendered in these businessmen by an idealizing of the planter way of life. In eighteenth-century Virginia there were serious attempts to revive the old crop economy and political system based upon slavery.

It grieved lower Hampton Roads farmers that their land was unsuitable for crops such as tobacco and wheat. Much land surrounding the Dismal Swamp, called "pine barrens," was so poor that it yielded only 8 bushels of corn per acre. One Norfolk County farmer, moaning about the twin evils of poor farm practices and deference to shingle making, in a letter to an agricultural journal reported that in his neighborhood "the old men are novices and our young men the hopeless victims of lumber getting" (Foreman 1834). Such people hoped the Swamp could be reclaimed and brought into proper cultivation.

The most well-known advocate of this view in the nineteenth century was Edmund Ruffin (Taylor 1961, pp. 317–318), later and better known as the gentleman who fired the first shot that commenced the Civil War and who, upon seeing the outcome of the war, noted his "unmitigated hatred to Yankee rule" and committed suicide. Constantly seeking ways to restore Virginia's agricultural prominence, Ruffin (1852) read scientific treatises and concluded that ample applications of marl, already available in the area, on Virginia's exhausted soil would markedly increase yields. Given the production figures, the goal was laudable.

But Ruffin did not stop with trying to revitalize worn-out lands. In 1837 he took up the cause of reclaiming the Dismal Swamp, and after an excursion into the area he thought that the peatlands, which he said differed from those in Europe, could be converted to hemp farms. The idea, of course, revived William Byrd's (1789) suggestion made over a hundred years earlier. Ruffin, in fact, included Byrd's full proposal (Byrd 1837) in the farm journal he edited in Petersburg.

In Ruffin's view farmers regarded the Swamp as a threat. It served as a hideaway for escaped slaves and allowed slaves hired out to work as shingle hewers to make extra money with which they might purchase their own freedom. In this respect, though Ruffin did not develop this idea, the Swamp was very similar to a large city, which swallowed up fugitives and also allowed opportunities to blacks not found within an agricultural setting. Richard Wade (1964) theorizes that slavery declined in urban areas because city blacks could find ways of minimizing the impact of the institution on their lives and often freed themselves completely from its shackles. Blacks in the Swamp did the same. Nansemond and Norfolk counties, in which the Dismal Swamp is located, contained very high percentages of free blacks in the population compared to the Virginia counties with traditional agriculture. The solution, of course, was to let only small commercial centers exist and to eliminate the Swamp. Ruffin even used scare tactics, implying that the Swamp and related forest environment were to be feared. At one point the agricultural editor cautioned the residents of the counties south of Hampton Roads to restore agriculture, or the howling of wolves would soon be heard on the outskirts of Norfolk (Ruffin 1837, p. 524).

In lower Virginia an agricultural revival took place featuring the development of vegetable and melon growing, particularly in Norfolk

County, which, in the 1850s, led all counties in the state in truck production. Introduced by New Jersey migrants in the 1830s, vegetable growing expanded tremendously in the decades just before the Civil War. The value of such production surged from $50,000 in 1849 to $292,000 in 1860. Peas, beans, and melons grew mostly on the light, sandy soil in Norfolk County, though the Nansemond River was also known for its exported watermelons as early as the 1830s. In addition to these vegetables and melons, Irish and sweet potatoes also were grown. A large sweet potato belt stretched from the Eastern Shore, through Princess Anne and Norfolk counties, and Nansemond, interrupted by the Chesapeake Bay and the Dismal Swamp. Corn and even wheat production increased during this era of agricultural reform. Growth in grain and potatoes was due in part to agricultural improvements but also as a result of general farmer prosperity throughout the United States at this time. Truck farming, which continued its remarkable rate of expansion after the Civil War, existed primarily because of the nature of the soil underneath the "piney woods," but also because steamboat lines began to offer daily service to northern cities in the early 1850s (Stewart, 1967, pp. 38–46).

With such opportunities the drive to reclaim the swamplands accelerated. Many wondered if such agriculture could flourish if the Swamp were reclaimed. Having such a conversion in mind, former general Ben Butler, "the man in the South called Beast," returned to Norfolk, where he had commanded the Union occupation during the war, with the idea that a large ship canal could be built through the Swamp with a half mile on each side taken up with truck crops (Schwartz 1972). Butler received such an unpleasant welcome from the local citizens that he dropped the whole idea (B[ishop] 1882), but truck farming continued.

In the early twentieth century, botanist Thomas Kearney in a survey of the area noted that the Dismal's black gum land with the addition of lime yielded 80 bushels of corn per acre, and even after years of cultivation with no fertilization produced at least half that amount. Potatoes were then grown on heavy, rich soils on the eastern border of the Swamp with two crops of 80 barrels annually. Garden vegetables, including celery, were also important items produced in reclaimed swamplands. Kearney, however, warned prospective farmers that much of the Swamp, particularly the juniper or white cedar lands, was not suitable for cultivation while other heavier soils were too rich for truck crops (Kearney 1901). Yet the notion of reclaiming the Dismal Swamp continued well into the twentieth century. Just after Teddy Roosevelt called for measures to conserve natural resources, both he and agricultural scientists in his administration were calling for reclamation of the nation's swamplands (see Hart and Ferleger 1941, p. 103).

While the concern for agriculture waned, other uses for the Swamp were discussed. As recently as the late 1950s a North Carolina newspaper reported the promotional idea of a large waterway serving all kinds of industries and making the Dismal Swamp into a "Ruhr Valley" (Brown 1967).

The thought that a canal should be built through the Swamp, like so many other projects, had its origin in the mind of William Byrd, who proposed such a waterway after his expedition (1789). A few years before the Revolution, surveys were conducted for a canal between Virginia and North Carolina. Merchants and farmers in both states had an obvious need for such a connection, but so did the timber interests.

Letters between a North Carolina Continental Congressman, Hugh Williamson, and George Washington clearly reveal that members of the New Lebanon Company were responsible for reviving the idea of a canal after the Revolution. Washington thought the undertaking might prove too burdensome, at least for land companies that were primarily interested in securing lumber products (Fitzpatrick 1938, pp. 377–381, 391), but there was obviously a shared concern between timber interests and other groups concerned with improved transportation. The Dismal Swamp Land Company had already built small canals north and west of Lake Drummond to carry out lumber, and although the Land Company and the Canal Company were separate entities, the former for a few years owned small amounts of stock in the latter (Reid 1948, p. 31).

The new canal, which ran about three miles east of Lake Drummond, permitted the development of a new shingle grounds in a relatively unscathed portion of the Swamp. With the assistance of the governor, Patrick Henry, who appointed delegates to cooperate with North Carolina in the project, and Thomas Jefferson, who wrote, "It is the only speculation in my life I have decidedly wished to be engaged in" (Boyd 1953), the Canal Company received its Virginia charter in 1787. Economic reverses in the late 1780s slowed stock sales and prevented any actual digging for six years. Another dozen years passed before the canal was opened for small rafts. Additional improvements allowed the passage of the first small decked boat, carrying bacon and brandy to Norfolk in 1814 (Brown 1967, p. 47). A year later some Bedford County men rafted a barrel of flour all the way down the Roanoke River and came through the sound and up the Canal. Norfolk's merchants now realized that the tobacco and cotton of the Roanoke Valley might come to them via the new canal (Anonymous 1815). Such a volume of business had not been predicted and required a major reconstruction of the Dismal Swamp Canal, including the building of several locks and a feeder ditch to Lake Drummond to provide a steady and adequate level of water (the original canal would run out of water during certain seasons of the year). When the Dismal Swamp Canal, with the federal government now a part owner, opened in 1829, such a volume of commerce floated toward Norfolk that a special company organized to run three steamers hauling several barges (Emmerson 1949, pp. 88, 122, 133, 148). The future of the canal and the economy of Norfolk seemed secure.

The merchants of Petersburg, Virginia, responded with a railroad to the Roanoke River, diverting tobacco and cotton to their city. The coastal communities reciprocated by building the Portsmouth and Roanoke Railroad, which sliced through a portion of the Swamp on its way to Suffolk and then to the river. Thus deprived of distant markets, the Dismal Swamp Canal reverted to serving a small clientele around the sounds of upper North Carolina and the wetlands below Norfolk. Corn and lumber products comprised almost the total trade of the waterway in those years (Stewart 1973).

The lack of canal maintenance and partial destruction during the Civil War, the construction of a railroad between Norfolk and Elizabeth City, North Carolina, plus competition by a rival freight canal nearby that was shorter and wider (the A. and C.) slowly strangled the company. In the late nineteenth century more reconstruction took place, resulting in fewer locks; but though some increase in commerce resulted, the hoped-for renaissance failed to materialize. The federal government finally took over the operation in 1929 (Brown 1967, pp. 87–131).

In its best times the canal served as more than simply an artery for commerce. Along its banks, for example, Isaiah Rogerson built the infamous Half Way House, which stood over the boundary between the two states and served those who desired a quick marriage, a quiet duel, or wished to indulge in other forms of social and antisocial behavior. Another hostelry already operated below the boundary line near the canal, and just after the Civil War, when these two establishments had ceased to function, still another hotel was built on the other side of Lake Drummond with access from the Suffolk side, but it also enjoyed only a brief career (Pugh and Williams 1964).

If the Dismal Swamp served as a negative symbol in the mind of people like Edmund Ruffin, the Dismal Swamp Canal with its Half Way House offered proof that "progress" could be achieved even in the Dismal Swamp. Thomas Williamson symbolized the victory in his drawing that portrayed the stern-wheeled and shallow-drafted steamer *Lady of the Lake* loaded with passengers making its way past the Half Way House. Williamson's work became so popular that it appeared on various authorized paper currencies during the era. Starting with the Virginia Bank of Exchange, which was chartered in 1837 with its headquarters in Norfolk, the lithograph spread to other states like New Jersey and Delaware. The scene usually appeared in a circle along with similar representatives of progress like railroads or mills (Muscalus 1965). Hence, even bankers used the symbol of the Dismal Swamp.

Every generation divides its collective personality. Romantic and realistic sides exist simultaneously. While many people in the nineteenth century viewed the Swamp as a place to conquer, others stressed its mystical qualities. During the decade in which Williamson drew the famous canal scene, the *Knickerbocker* magazine produced an engraving showing an eerie-looking Lake Drummond surrounded by moss-draped trees (Chapman 1839). Like the bustling scene along the canal, the engraving of the lake seemingly unscathed by human activities was popular. Still a third engraving depicts George Washington, pencil in hand, standing on a slight rise beside his gear-laden horse (Freston 1973). The background features a Lake Drummond almost identical with that in the *Knickerbocker*. If the latter symbolizes romance and mystery, and the Williamson drawing man's progress over nature, then the third artist's conception blends man and the Swamp in a historical setting.

The number of artists, poets, novelists, and even musicians who worked with the theme of the Dismal Swamp is legion. The most famous literary figure to deal with the Dismal Swamp was Thomas Moore, the curly-haired Irish poet who stayed in Norfolk in 1803. Whether he actually visited Lake Drummond is uncertain, but hearing tales about a demented soul who wandered into the Swamp in the belief his wife was there, Moore wrote the ballad "The lake of the Dismal Swamp" (Moore 1846, Gains 1954).

> "They made her a grave, too cold and damp
>   For a soul so warm and true;
>
> And she's gone to the Lake of the Dismal Swamp,
>   Where, all night long, by a fire-fly lamp,
>   She paddles her white canoe.
>
> And her fire-fly lamp I soon shall see,
>   And her paddle I soon shall hear;

Long and loving our life shall be,
And I'll hide the maid in a cypress tree,
   When the footstep of death is near."

Away to the Dismal Swamp he speeds—
   His path was rugged and sore,
Through tangled juniper, beds of reeds,
Through many a fen, where the serpent feeds,
   And man never trod before.

And near him the she-wolf stirr'd the brake,
   And the copper-snake breathed in his ear,
Till he starting cried, from his dreams awake,
   "Oh! when shall I see the dusky Lake,
   And the white canoe of my dear?"

He saw the Lake, and a meteor bright
   Quick over its surface play'd—
"Welcome," he said, "my dear one's light!"
And the dim shore echoed, for many a night,
   The name of the death-cold maid.

Till he follow'd a boat of birchen bark,
   Which carried him off from shore;
Far, far he follows the meteor spark,
The wind was high and the clouds were dark,
   And the boat return'd no more.

But oft, from the Indian hunter's camp,
   This lover and maid so true
Are seen at the hour of midnight damp
To cross the Lake by a fire-fly lamp,
   And paddle their white canoe!

Like many poets of this period, Moore was fascinated by forests, Indians, and mysteries; all three themes appear in the poem. Another poet, Howard Caldwell, composed (1855) a piece very much like Moore's with similar-sounding phrases. According to Robert Morrison (1947, pp. 44–46), the only expert on Dismal Swamp literature, even Edgar Allan Poe was probably thinking of Lake Drummond and Moore's impressions when he wrote a poem called "The lake." Henry Wadsworth Longfellow, while returning from Germany in 1842 (1908), produced a series of antislavery poems, one being "The slave in the Dismal Swamp."

In dark fens of the Dismal Swamp
 The hunted Negro lay;
He saw the fire of the midnight camp,
And heard at times a horse's tramp
 And a blood hound's distant bay.

Where will-o-the-wisps and glow-worms shine,
 In bulrush and in brake;
Where waving mosses shroud the pine,
And the cedar grows, the poisonous vine
 Is spotted like the snake;

Where hardly a human foot could pass,
 Or a human heart would dare,
On the quaking turf of the green morass
He crouched in the rank and tangled grass,
 Like a wild beast in his lair.

A poor old slave; infirm and lame;
 Great scars deformed his face;
On his forehead he bore the brand of shame,
And the rags, that hid his mangled frame,
 Were the livery of disgrace.

All things above were bright and fair,
 All things were glad and free;
Lithe squirrels darted here and there,
And wild birds filled the echoing air
 With songs of Liberty!

On him alone was the doom of pain,
 From the morning of his birth;
On him alone the curse of Cain
Fell, like a flail on the garnered grain,
 And struck him to the earth!

Longfellow may have been influenced in the cause of abolitionism by Dickens's *American notes,* which he had just read, and by Benjamin Lundy, a Quaker abolitionist, whose works Longfellow had read some years before. But Longfellow probably got the idea of slaves escaping into the Swamp from newspaper and periodical accounts of the flight of runaways into the Dismal (Morrison 1947).

Another romantic, Harriet Beecher Stowe, used the Dismal Swamp for one of her antislavery novels (1856). A lengthy piece of fiction which Mrs. Stowe wrote on her way to England to secure a copyright for it,

Dred; a tale of the Great Dismal Swamp, never attained the popularity of her more famous *Uncle Tom's cabin* (Wilson 1941), but it contains similar basic elements: (1) all kinds of southern stereotypes; (2) a good narrative culminating in the escape of some slaves; and (3) extended conversations that served to criticize slavery—morally, socially, and economically.

The Swamp actually plays no role until nearly midway through when Mrs. Stowe introduces Dred, a fugitive slave, living in its recesses. There are some reasonably accurate descriptions of the Swamp which the writer must have gained from reading travelers' accounts. Mrs. Stowe was certainly familiar with an event in nearby Southampton County in 1831 known as the Nat Turner Rebellion, for she attached an appendix that included Turner's supposed confessions. Dred in reality was the name of one of Nat's co-conspirators; in the story Dred is the unknown son of Denmark Vesey, a free black executed for plotting insurrection in Charleston in 1822. Through the novel Dred spouts Biblical-like phrases threatening whites with the wrath of a just God. Finally Dred gathers in the Swamp a little band who make their final escape. After the unfortunate Dred's death they make their way to the Dismal Swamp Canal, take a shingle boat to Norfolk, and thence escape to freedom (Stowe, 1856).

Dred is doubtless the best novel about the Swamp. John Hamilton Howard produced *In the shadow of the pines* in 1906, which dealt with Deep Creek and the Swamp during the Civil War. On the whole the book is, according to one critic, very shallow in its setting, for the writer doubles the real size of the Swamp during the period in question and contends that none had yet returned from a trip into its heart (Morrison 1947, pp. 78–79). Howard at least knew something about the products of the Swamp, for one of his central characters owned a shingle business.

John Boyle O'Reilly, another poet, shows a rather odd blend of romance and realism concerning the Swamp. While visiting the Swamp in 1888, O'Reilly dashed off a note to the *Boston Herald* in which he pointed out that the Dismal Swamp was potentially the "greatest sanitarium on the American Continent." This poet accepted the widely held belief that the Swamp prevented malaria and that its water contained a special antiseptic quality (Stewart 1902, p. 261). At the time he was writing, some folks believed that no one ever died in the Dismal Swamp—an excellent advertising point for a potential health resort. Man's impression of the Swamp had obviously changed since William Byrd described the infectious air and urged the elimination of the Swamp to improve health in the surrounding countryside: "It [the Swamp] makes them [the nearby inhabitants] liable to agues, pleurises and many other distempers that kill an abundance of people and make the rest look no better than ghosts" (Boyd 1929, p. 84).

Strangely enough, despite its better qualities, including excellent fishing, which O'Reilly praised, the poet moaned that "the story of Dismal Swamp is a tragedy of nature and a disgrace to civilization" and that it was "a desolate land crying for attention and reclamation, (Stewart 1902, p. 261). The desire to conquer the Swamp was so great that even a poet who recognized and experienced its pleasures called for its demise.

As the accompanying bibliographic materials at the end of this volume suggest, all kinds of people have written about a variety of topics connected with the Dismal Swamp. Nearly all have wondered what the Swamp and its people were like, how the Swamp developed, and, most importantly, what would be the fate of the Dismal Swamp.

The last question is the one that now occupies our attention. Proposals to drain the Swamp seem to be in abeyance; lumber operations no longer threaten the core around Lake Drummond. As a symbol of remoteness and inaccessibility the Swamp must remain if only to serve as a foil, much the same as in the nineteenth century, to material progress. Humanity needs a place that symbolizes romance and remoteness.

REFERENCES CITED

Anon. 1783. Letter to Samuel Gist, 7 November 1783, *in* Robert Gilmore Petition. *Loyalist Claims.* Great Britain. Public Record Office. Survey Report 2394.

Anon. 1815. Enterprize of the interior. *Norfolk American Beacon* (14 Dec.).

Anon. 1858. Trade of the Dismal Swamp Canal. *Hunt's Merchants' Mag.* 29: 247.

Berkeley, E., and Dorothy Berkeley. 1976. Man and the Great Dismal. *Va. J. Sci.* 27: 141–171.

B[ishop], W. H. 1882. To the Great Dismal Swamp. *Nation* (New York) 35 (14 Dec.):502–504.

Bottoms, E., and F. Painter. 1972. Bola weights from the Dismal Swamp region of Virginia and North Carolina. *Chesopiean* 10:19–30.

Boyd, W. K. (ed). 1929. *William Byrd's histories of the dividing line betwixt Virginia and North Carolina.* N.C. Hist. Comm., Raleigh. 341 pp.

Boyd, J. P. (ed). 1953. *The papers of Thomas Jefferson,* v. 7 (2 Mar. 1784–25 Feb. 1785). Princeton Univ. Press, Princeton, N.J. 652 pp.

Brown, A. C. 1967. *The Dismal Swamp Canal*. Norfolk Co. Hist. Soc. Chesapeake, Va. 143 pp.

Byrd, W. 1789. A description of the Dismal Swamp, in Virginia; with proposals for and observations on the advantages of draining it. *Columbian Mag.* (Philadelphia) 3(Apr.): 230–234. [Written by William Byrd but not published until after the death of his son, Col. Byrd].

_____. 1837. Proposal to drain the Dismal Swamp, with introduction by Edmund Ruffin. *Petersburg* (Va.) *Farmers' Register* 4: 521–524.

Caldwell, H. 1855. *Oliatta and other poems*. J. S. Redfield, New York. 200 pp.

Chapman, J. G. 1839. The lake of the Dismal Swamp. *Knickerbocker* 13 (May): 367 (an engraving).

Emmerson, J. C., Jr. (comp). 1949. *The steam-boat comes to Norfolk Harbor, and the log of the first ten years; 1815–1825.* . . . Lithoprint by Edwards Bros., Ann Arbor, Mich. 455 pp.

Fitzpatrick, J. C. (ed). 1925. *The diaries of George Washington, 1748–1799*, v. 1. Houghton Mifflin, Co., Boston. 455 pp.

_____. (ed). 1931. *The writings of George Washington 1745–1799*, v. 2, 1757–1769. U.S. Govt. Print. Off., Washington. 582 pp.

_____. (ed). 1938. *The writings of George Washington 1745–1799*, v. 27, 1783–1784. U.S. Govt. Print. Off., Washington. 557 pp.

Foreman, A. S. 1834. Farming in Norfolk County. *Petersburg* (Va.) *Farmers' Register* 2: 247, 248.

Freston, T. E. (ed). 1973. *Contact* 8(1). Dismal Swamp issue. Union Camp Corp., Wayne, N.J. 24 pp. (cover scene).

Gains, W. H. 1954. The minstrel sang of a dusky lake. *Va. Cavalcade* 4(Winter): 30–31.

Great Britain. Naval Office Returns. 1730–1772. Lower James River District. (Univ. Virginia microfilm.)

Hart, A. B., and H. R. Ferleger (eds). 1941. *Theodore Roosevelt Cyclopedia*. Roosevelt Mem. Assoc., New York. 674 pp.

Howard, J. H. 1906. *In the shadow of the pines*. Eaton and Mains, New York. 249 pp.

Jackson, D. (ed). 1976. *The diaries of George Washington*, v. 1., Univ. Press Va., Charlottesville. 373 pp.

Kearney, T. H. 1901. Report on a botanical survey of the Dismal Swamp region. *Contrib. U.S. Natl. Herb.* 5: 321–550.

Longfellow, H. W. 1908. *The complete poetical works of Henry Wadsworth Longfellow*. Houghton Mifflin Co., Boston. 689 pp.

McCary, B. 1963. The archeology of the western area of the Dismal Swamp in Virginia. *Quart. Bull. Archeol. Soc. Va.* 17:40–48.

_____. 1972. A concentration in Va. of the Perkiomen broad spearpoint. *Quart. Bull. Archeol. Soc. Va.* 26:145–149.

McKnight, F. 1959. The Great Dismal Swamp. Pp. 181–190 *in* R. Whichard (ed). *The history of Tidewater Virginia*, v. 2. Lewis Historical Publ. Co., New York.

Moore, T. 1846. *Poetical works of Thomas Moore*. D. Appleton and Co., New York. 747 pp.

Morrison, R. H. 1947. The literature and legends of the Great Dismal Swamp.
    Master's Thesis Univ. North Carolina (Chapel Hill). 107 pp.

Muscalus, J. A. 1965. *The Dismal Canal and Lake Drummond Hotel on paper money,
    1838–1865.* Historical Paper Money Res. Inst., Bridgeport, Pa. 8 pp.

Pugh, J. F., and F. T. Williams, 1964. *The hotel of the Great Dismal Swamp and
    contemporary events thereabouts.* Old Trap, N.C. 174 pp.

Reid, R. 1948. History of the Dismal Swamp Land Company of Virginia.
    Master's Thesis Duke Univ. 167 pp.

Ruffin, E. 1837. Observations made during an excursion to the Dismal
    Swamp. *Petersburg* (Va.) *Farmers' Register* 4 (1 Jan.):513–521.

———. 1852. *Essay on calcareous manures,* 5th ed. J. W. Randolph, Richmond.
    493 pp.

Schwartz, K. 1972. Ben Butler and the occupation of Norfolk, 1862–1865:
    a reappraisal. Master's Thesis Old Dominion Univ. 136 pp.

Stewart, W. H. 1902. *History of Norfolk County, Virginia, and representative citizens.*
    Biographical Publ. Co., Chicago. 1042 pp.

Stewart, P. C. 1967. The commercial history of Hampton Roads, Virginia,
    1815–1860. Ph.D. Diss. Univ. Virginia. 345 pp.

———. 1973. Railroads and urban rivalries in antebellum eastern Virginia.
    Va. Mag. Hist. Biog. 81(Jan.):3–22.

Stowe, Harriet B. 1856. *Dred; a tale of the Great Dismal Swamp.* v. 1, 242 pp. v.
    2, 391 pp. Sampson Low, Son & Co., London. (1972 reprint is available
    from ASM Press, New York).

Taylor, W. 1961. *Cavalier and yankee.* G. Braziller, New York. 384 pp.

Traver, J. 1963. Paleo artifacts from northeastern North Carolina. *Quart. Bull.
    Archeol. Soc. Va.* 18: 35–36.

Wade, R. 1964. *Slavery in the cities: the south, 1820–1860.* Oxford Univ. Press.
    340 pp.

Whitehead, D. R. 1965. Prehistoric maize in southeastern Virginia. *Science*
    150:881–883.

Wilson, F. 1941. *Crusader in crinoline: the life of Harriet Beecher Stowe.* Lippincott,
    Philadelphia. 706 pp.

Wright, L. B., and M. Tinling (eds). 1958. *William Byrd of Virginia: the London
    diary (1717–1721) and other writings.* Oxford Univ. Press, New York. 647
    pp. (1972 reprint available by Arno Press, New York.)

PUBLIC USE POLICY OF THE NATIONAL WILDLIFE REFUGE SYSTEM

James W. Pulliam, Jr.

The National Wildlife Refuge System contains 34 million acres. This nationwide network of wildlife lands began with the establishment of the Pelican Island National Wildlife Refuge in 1903. This tiny island refuge was subsequently followed by additional acreage scattered throughout the country. The System began to grow rapidly during the devastating drought of the mid-1930s when the entire continental waterfowl population was threatened. This drought focused attention on the need to preserve rapidly disappearing waterfowl breeding habitat, and a major land acquisition program was started.

National Wildlife Refuges play an important part in the conservation story of the United States. This far-flung collection of lands and waters has been selected for its value to America's wildlife populations, particularly migratory birds and endangered species. Although refuges protect many types of wildlife, they play an especially important role in the management of the international migratory waterfowl resource. Three-fourths of all refuges were established originally for these birds.

In addition to 384 National Wildlife Refuges, there are numerous waterfowl production areas. These small pothole marshes in the North Central prairie states (the Dakotas, Minnesota, Montana, and Nebraska) produce large numbers of ducks annually. Since 1962, emphasis has been placed on the acquisition of these areas to prevent their destruction by drainage and conversion to nonwildlife uses. Over a million acres of these small but valuable wetlands have been purchased and leased.

Some 50 refuges were established chiefly for migratory birds other than waterfowl. On them are found nesting colonies of pelicans, herons, ibises, egrets, spoonbills, and a large array of sea birds.

A number of refuges are well known for providing habitat for endangered species. Perhaps the most famous of them all, the Aransas National Wildlife Refuge in Texas, is the principal winter home of the endangered whooping crane.

The refuges are popular as places to find large numbers of many kinds of wildlife. These not only harbor birds and mammals, but also provide for plants, insects, amphibians, and reptiles. Many refuges have scenic and historical values that are preserved along with wildlife.

As the National Wildlife Refuge System grew, so did public interest. This certainly is not unique to the National Wildlife Refuges. Everyone is aware of the steady increase in the number of users of national parks, the national forests, other public lands, and lands managed by state and private interests. There are more people, and these people have more leisure time. More and more people are taking advantage of the recreational opportunities offered by the public lands and waters of this country.

The Refuge System includes lands in every state of the nation except West Virginia. It embraces wildlife habitat and recreational opportunity of every description. Because of its relatively narrow purpose—the preservation and enhancement of wildlife and its habitat—the System also has its share of conflict.

In spite of a basic purpose which would seem to preclude many of the more common kinds of recreation, the Refuge System nevertheless includes lands and waters theoretically suitable for almost every kind of outdoor activity.

It would serve no useful purpose to recite all the various kinds of conflicts of demand and interest that affect the Refuge System, but suffice it to say, the Refuge System experiences conflicts between purpose and interest as diverse as whooping cranes and oil exploration, hunters and antihunters, the water skier and the fisherman, the noisy snowmobiler and the solitude seeker, developer, preservationist, etc.

Basically the problem facing the U.S. Fish and Wildlife Service, as well as other federal land management agencies, is the conflict between demand for recreational opportunity and the ability of the resource to accommodate that use. This is further conditioned by the funds and manpower available for the management of public use. People come to the refuges, for example, because they like what they find there. Problems often ensue, however, when the hordes of people finally compromise the quality of the experience to the point where the basic values which attracted the visitors in the first place no longer exist. In 1973, 5 National Wildlife Refuges had visitation exceeding one million visitors, and 17 refuges had visitation in excess of 250,000. It became increasingly apparent that the Fish and Wildlife Service had to do something about these hordes of people.

As I stated earlier, the basic responsibility of the Bureau is the management of its land to preserve and enhance their intrinsic values, to insure that these values are not diluted or eroded, and to manage them to yield the greatest possible return in terms of wildlife (waterfowl production, endangered species preserved and protected, rare and unique habitats preserved).

In 1962 the Recreational Use of Conservation Areas Act was passed by the United States Congress. This legislation authorizes recreational use of National Wildlife Refuges, but at the same time clearly states that public use on National Wildlife Refuges is secondary to the primary responsibility for protection and perpetuation of wildlife resources.

The greatest contribution of National Wildlife Refuges is to foster those public uses associated directly with fish and wildlife and its habitat. To achieve this objective, consideration is first given to those appropriate public uses directly associated with public enjoyment by the observation, utilization, interpretation, and understanding of fish and wildlife populations, habitats, and conservation values.

In mid-1972 the public use program underwent careful review in Washington and a new public use policy was developed. As a result of our analysis, we determined that we should make a strong effort to begin the de-emphasis of non-wildlife-related public uses of refuges. These uses are exemplified by swimming, recreational boating, camping, the use of off-road vehicles, picnicking, and similar activities which do not have a direct relationship to the wildlife and wildland values for which these lands were created and are managed.

As a matter of policy these are the basic guidelines relating to non-wildlife-oriented uses:

1. These activities will be de-emphasized with the long-term goal being their virtual elimination. This recognizes that many such uses are traditional and have a long and successful history. It is not intended that any of these uses will be discontinued immediately; indeed, in many cases phaseout will have to be gradual and may involve many years in the process.

2. Plans now being developed for existing areas or for areas to be acquired must not include programs or facilities providing for non-wildlife-oriented recreation unless they are part of and essential to a wildlife-oriented experience.

3. Phaseout or discontinuation must be in accordance with well-considered plans or procedures. Substitution of the true wildlife/wildlands-related recreation for nonprogram recreation is the preferred approach.

4. The Service does endorse the advancement of program-related recreation. These activities must be funded and supported adequately, however. Existing programs are being reviewed and the adequacy of their funding is determined before new efforts are begun. Our immediate objective is to be sure that today's programs are conducted properly before we take steps to begin new ones.

We recognize that wildlife refuge lands are primarily for wildlife; therefore, public use activities conducted on these lands must be diectly derived from and directly related to the wildlife value represented by these lands. Specifically, in the order of their value as we see them, we regard these kinds of uses as being:

1. Scientific investigation (research)
2. Environmental education
3. Interpretation
4. General wildlife-oriented activities such as birdwatching, fishing, hunting, etc.

While these are the priorities in general, it must be understood that these uses need not, indeed cannot, always be conducted on all lands nor are all lands suited to all these programs.

The Service is taking definite, positive steps to emphasize those uses that are directly related to the wildlife and wildland values. Incidentally, the Service is taking the same stand on other kinds of uses, for example, grazing or timber harvests when those uses are not directly in support of identifiable wildlife or habitat-management aims.

As I stated earlier, the long-term objective of the Service is the virtual elimination of all non-program-related uses of its lands. This is not a move to lock up lands but to assure their preservation and retention of their increasing values.

The public uses that will be encouraged will be program related, that is, directly related to the basic purposes for which the lands were established, but only on these terms:

1. The use must be consistent with the basic purpose for which the area was established.

2. The use must not represent a conflict with the basic objective of the area (for example, birdwatching is consistent with the purposes of the Aransas Refuge, but ill-timed or improperly controlled visits by birdwatchers might present a conflict with the welfare of whooping cranes, for which Aransas is critical).

3. Funds must be available to support properly the permitted public uses (that is, the funding of public use activities must not be at the expense of wildlife management needs).

4. Permitted public uses are controlled as necessary to prevent visitors from creating problems of inconsistency, conflict, or funding; capacities and use limits must be established during planning and those limits recognized and honored.

As I stated earlier, the number-one-priority public use of refuges will be scientific investigations, which of course includes research.

The Service encourages and supports wildlife-oriented research on units of the National Wildlife Refuge System. Service funds, labor and/or material when available, may be committed when there is a high-priority need for significant management-oriented information, but generally the Service does not provide funds for research projects conducted by non-Service personnel. Refuge lands, water, and facilities may be made available for research by non-Service entities when not in conflict with the other refuge system outputs or responsibilities of greater value or priority and a mutual benefit may be obtained.

Especially encouraged on National Wildlife Refuges are management-oriented research projects or studies that will lead toward solving management problems on individual refuges or the system as a whole. All research must have clearly defined objectives and justification.

All research or study proposals that are to be conducted on National Wildlife Refuge units must be approved by the refuge manager. This insures that, at the resource level, due consideration is given the biological, social, and economic aspects and that potential conflicts with other Service programs are recognized and resolved.

I would now like to turn your attention to the environmental education and interpretation portion of the Service's recreational program.

The Service envisions two types of education programs with essentially similar goals, but with differences of technique and audience. For discussion purposes, these programs will be referred to as separate and distinct from each other despite similar objectives and philosophical overlap.

We define environmental education as school (or educationally related groups), grades kindergarten through 12th grade, teacher- or leader-conducted, and scientific studies and environmentally associated activities for adults, which may or may not utilize Service lands but which employ the discovery-involvement approach to teaching. Emphasis is on the teaching technique or approach to problem-solving or fact-finding. Young people are naturally process-oriented, seeking out activities which they can physically manipulate, where they can practice a skill, or where their interaction can influence an outcome. The more senses we use, the more we are willing to get our feet wet and our hands dirty, the better we will remember; the more we are presented with problems, the more we are likely to think about solutions. Environmental education, as we propose it, should be a style or technique of teaching, conducted by professionals, in which students participate in environmental learning situations where they are actively involved in problem-solving situations.

The environmental education program is a joint responsibility of both the Service and the teacher or school system.

A primary role of the Service in environmental education is to provide the land base, the "outdoor classroom" or "environmental study area." Facilities for environmental study areas need only include access and parking, drinking water, toilets, and some sort of shelter for use when needed. The functions of Service personnel include the selection of appropriate environmental study sites; assistance in the development of study guides with suggested activities to aid teachers in using the area; coordinating the use of the study area; conducting teacher workshops or serving as a consultant to the teacher. Service personnel would seldom have the training, expertise, or time to do the actual teaching. Teaching is a job best suited to the professional teacher. However, only a small percentage of teachers are oriented toward our concept of environmental education. Thus, teachers and, more importantly, the educational systems in which they operate, will often need to be oriented toward, and sold on, our concept of environmental education. Service personnel will frequently go through community education channels to stimulate this interest. Colleges are also encouraged to give courses in environmental education techniques for teachers; and in-service workshops should be encouraged to expose teachers to the types of programs we are advocating.

Interpretive education programs are usually conducted by Service personnel and are directed to the casual visitor or general public (which may or may not include students or other groups).

A variety of techniques may be used for interpretation, including signs, leaflets, exhibits, lectures, demonstrations, tours, slides or films. Interpretive programs are less formal than school-associated environmental education programs. They may be informative, provocative and impart environmental understanding, but they often lack the organization, involvement, and discipline of teacher-conducted environmental education programs. Participation is usually optional.

Interpretive programs have been conducted by the Service for some time. Environmental education programs are relatively new, but experimentation has shown them to be highly successful. This is not to say that there has been no demand for Service lands and personnel by school classes and other groups. On the contrary, demand and use has often been more than we can handle. There are numerous requests for movies, bus tours, or lectures on "conservation" etc. Occasionally a subject is selected that fits into the curriculum, but more often the request is for "anything" and may serve merely as a break from the routine or a form of entertainment. This type of program is probably of some value to students. Nevertheless, we feel that our lands and personnel can best be utilized through environmental education and interpretive programs.

REMOTE SENSING APPLICATIONS TO THE DISMAL SWAMP

Virginia Carter

INTRODUCTION

Inland wetlands in the United States are coming into sharp focus in a new era of public concern for the environment. State and local governments—for example, Connecticut, Rhode Island, Wisconsin, and Delaware—are mandated by legislation to inventory and regulate uses in inland wetlands. On the federal level, wetland inventory and classification on an overall national basis is a controversial and challenging problem. Preservation and protection of unique wetlands are often a federal task. Wider recognition and better understanding of wetland values have been followed by public concern. Expansion of agriculture, residential housing, and industry may destroy vast acreages of valuable natural habitat, potential water supplies, and recreational and scenic areas. The extent to which wetlands can be considered a multiple-use resource remains to be established.

Most of the needs and requirements for informed and effective wetland management on the local, state, or national level can be placed in two general categories:

1. Basic research to establish criteria for decision making. This need is pointed up by the scarcity of current data clarifying the hydrologic relationships of inland wetlands—recharge, discharge, flood storage, and water quality. Only a few local or regional wetland hydrology studies have been made, such as those on the prairie potholes (Eisenlohr et al. 1972) and on wetlands in the northeast (Hall et al. 1972, Larson 1973). Additional research is also needed on relative wetland values (Gupta 1972).

2. Near real-time information systems to provide wetland managers with information for inventory, classification, and monitoring of wetlands, and for water resource management decisions. Remotely sensed (RS) data can be a powerful tool to meet management and inventory needs. Many parameters of interest to the resource manager, such as species composition, soil moisture, surface water, and adjacent land use, can be easily measured by aerial photography or by Earth Re-

sources Technology Satellite (ERTS, or LANDSAT) imagery. Repetitive ERTS imagery or aerial photography can be used to monitor changes resulting from alternative patterns of land or water management.

The advantages of applying remote sensing techniques to the inventory, delineation, and classification of wetlands are:

1. Reduction of costs and manpower requirements for extensive ground surveys

2. More rapid completion of inventory or mapping

3. More efficient monitoring and detection of change

4. Collection of multipurpose data useful to future projects, including those not under consideration when data collection was planned

The difficulties in using remote sensing include:

1. Scheduling simultaneous ground data collection during remote sensing missions

2. Lack of efficient storage and retrieval methods for the large quantities of data generated by remote sensors such as the ERTS Multispectral Scanner (MSS) or low-altitude cameras

3. Adverse atmospheric conditions precluding the successful gathering of RS data.

Interpretation of RS data is based on the special characteristics of surface features, such as water, vegetation, and soil. Texture, geographic location, and topographic features aid the interpretive process. Collection of field data is usually required, although in the case of satellite data, aircraft overflights can supply information to minimize the amount of data needed. Seasonal collection of RS data is often useful. In investigations of wooded swamps such as the Dismal Swamp the presence of water or wet soil, diagnostic of these areas, may be obscured by vegetation during the growing season. Discrimination between deciduous and evergreen trees is easier during the winter, but total species composition may be better interpreted by comparison of summer and winter data.

The recent Dismal Swamp Study (P.L. 92–478) provides a demonstration of the application of RS data to a multidisciplinary study investigating the multiple-use potential and management needs of a large inland wetland. This paper is a summary of remote sensing applications to the study and of possible future applications to management and further research in the Swamp.

DISMAL SWAMP STUDY

In 1972 Congress authorized the Department of the Interior to conduct
a comprehensive study of the Dismal Swamp and the Dismal Swamp
Canal. The study was needed to determine the desirability and feasibility of protecting and preserving the ecological, scenic, recreational,
historical, and other resource values of the Swamp and Canal and to
consider the alternatives for preservation. Consideration was also given
to potential alternative uses of the water and related land resources for
residential, commercial, industrial, agricultural, and transportation
services. Eight federal agencies participated in the investigation, including the U.S. Geological Survey (USGS), which was responsible
for water dynamics and mineralogical data.

THE DISMAL SWAMP

The Dismal Swamp comprises approximately 850 square kilometers
(210,000 acres) of viable wooded swamp or forested bog straddling the
Virginia–North Carolina border (Fig. 1).

AVAILABLE REMOTE SENSING DATA

Four kinds of RS data are presently available for the Dismal Swamp.
Table 1 is a listing of National Aeronautics and Space Administration
(NASA) photography—both high- and low-altitude—taken with a
variety of films and filters. The high-altitude color infrared (IR) photography taken in December 1972 was particularly useful for this study
because only eight photographs, at a scale of 1:130,000, are needed
to show the entire Dismal Swamp and major drainage. Table 2 is a
listing of USGS photography, black and white (B/W) panchromatic,
taken for mapping purposes. The most recently available quad-
centered photography (1973) was used for this study. B/W orthophoto quadrangles, currently in various stages of preparation by the
USGS, will provide up-to-date maps of the entire Swamp at a scale
of 1:24,000. An orthophoto mosaic at a scale of 1:100,000 has also
been prepared by USGS. Table 3 is a listing of ERTS MSS imagery
available in four spectral bands in B/W 70 mm or 9.5-inch format
(other formats also possible) as of April 1974. Color composites of this
imagery are available for only two dates (10 October 1972 and 13
February 1973). Computer Compatible Tapes are available for some
of the ERTS images. In addition there have been a number of low-

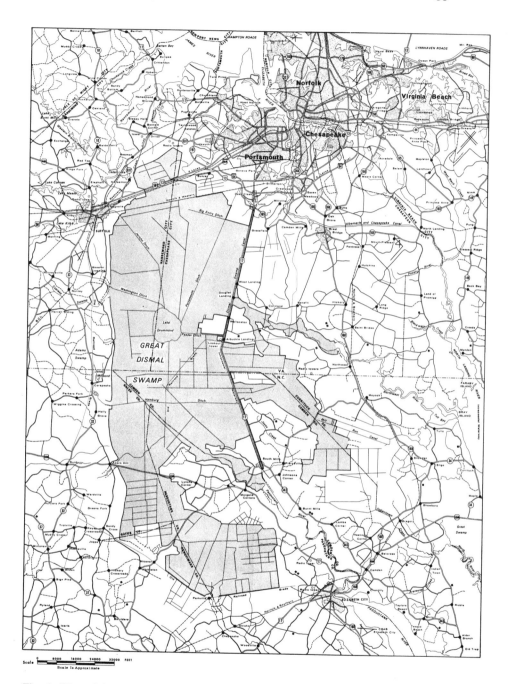

Fig. 1. Dismal Swamp Study area, Virginia–North Carolina, P.L. 92–478. Compiled in the Division of Engineering from surveys by USGS, Boston, Mass., June 1973.

Table 1. NASA photography of the Dismal Swamp

NASA–MSC (RB57 Aircraft) Flight Altitude: 18.29 km (ca. 60,000 feet)
Mission 144 (Central Atlantic Coastal Area) Date: 23 September 1970

Roll No.	19	20	21	22	23	24	25	26	27
Sensor	RC-8/4R	RC-8/4L	Zeiss	Hass. 1	Hass. 2	Hass. 3	Hass. 4	Hass. 5	Hass. 6
Film	2445	3443	2443	2402	2402	2424	SO-278	SO-278	SO-117
Filter	2E	12	D	25A	25A	89B	HF3	2E	15+30B

Frame Nos. 7431–7438, 7400–7405, 7370–7373
RC-8 photograph scale: 1:120,000

NASA–AMES (U2 Aircraft) Flight Altitude: 19.82 km (ca. 65,000 feet) Date: 2 December 1972
Flight No.: 720208 South Expanded CARETS

Accession No.	00839	00840	00841	00842	00843
Sensor Type	Vinten	Vinten	Vinten	Vinten	RC-10
Film Type	Plus X, 2402	Plus X, 2402	Infrared Aerographic, 2424	Aerochrome Infrared, 2443	Aerochrome Infrared, 2443
Spectral Band	475–575nm	580–680nm	690–760nm	510–900nm	510–900nm

Frame Nos. (RC-10) 6445–6457, 6475–6482, 6490–6495
RC-10 photograph scale: 1:130,000

Table 1. (cont.)

Flight No.: 73–185 South Expanded CARETS   Date: 1 November 1973

Accession No.	01531
Sensor Type	RC-10
Film Type	Aerochrome Infrared 2443
Spectral Band	510–900nm
Frame Nos. (RC-10)	5598–5600, 5610–5612
RC-10 photograph scale: 1:130,000	

NASA–Wallops

Mission No. W209 (Flight 2) Flight Altitude: 0.90 km (ca. 3000 feet) Date: 18 May 1973

Roll No.	W2090202	W2090201
Sensor	T–11	T–11
Film	2443	SO–397
Filter	12AV + CCIOM	CAV
Frame Nos.	0121–0191	0120–0190

Mission No. W210 (Flight 1) Flight Altitude: 3.05 km (ca. 10,000 feet) Date: 21 May 1973

Roll No.	W2100101		W2100102
Sensor	I²s		T–11
Film	2424	2424	2424	SO–397
Filter	47B	57A	25	88A 12AV + CCIOM
Frame Nos.	0090–0125		

Table 1. (cont.)

Mission No. W240 (Flight 1) Flight Altitude: 3.20 km (ca. 10,500 feet) Date: 31 October 1973

Roll No.	W2400101		W2400102		W2100102	
Sensor	I²s	I²s			T-11	
Film	2424	2405	2405	2424	SO-397	
Filter	89B	25A	57	88A	CAV	
Frame Nos.	0032–0050,	0101–0114				

Table 2. U.S. Geological Survey photography for Dismal Swamp area: B/W Panchromatic

Project no.	Date	Scale
TG	1952	1:28,400
TU	1953	1:28,400
VAPM	1963	1:24,000
VAPY	1963	1:24,000
VBYJ	1968	1:24,000
VCIY	1970	1:24,000
VCRA	1971	1:36,000
VCVX	1972	1:24,000
VDEY*	1973	1:76,000

*High-altitude quad-centered orthophotos.

Table 3. Earth Resources Technology Satellite (ERTS, or LANDSAT) images available for the Dismal Swamp, satellite altitude 900 km

Image no.	Date	Comments
1079–15142	10 Oct. 1972	Some clouds at south end
1133–15150	3 Dec. 1972	Band 4 missing
1187–15145	26 Jan. 1973	High haze
1205–15150	13 Feb. 1973	Cloud-free, snow
1313–15150	1 June 1973	Heavy cloud cover at north end of Dismal Swamp
1349–15143	7 July 1973	Scattered clouds
1385–15140	12 Aug. 1973	Almost cloud-free. Only bands 5 and 6
1403–15134	30 Aug. 1973	Almost cloud-free
1421–15132	17 Sept. 1973	N. end of Swamp, cloud cover
1439–15125	5 Oct. 1973	Excellent
1475–15122	10 Nov. 1973	Good, clouds offshore
1583–15100	26 Feb. 1974	Excellent
1619–15092	3 Apr. 1974	Scattered clouds
1637–15005	21 Apr. 1974	Excellent

NOTE. Approximate center coordinate: N31-45/W80-44.

altitude color photographs taken by several investigators from small aircraft during the course of study.

NASA photography and ERTS data are available to the public through the EROS Data Center. Sample order forms (including current prices) are available directly from:

> USGS EROS Data Center
> Karl E. Mundt Federal Building
> Pecora Way
> Sioux Falls, SD 57198
> Phone: Commercial 605-594-6511

USGS photography may be ordered from the EROS Data Center if available, or from:

> Chief: National Cartographic Information Center
> USGS National Center
> 12201 Sunrise Valley Drive
> Reston, VA 22092

ERTS data and color IR photography (NASA Flight 720208) used for the Dismal Swamp Study were supplied by The American University (NASA Contract NAS5-21752; UN006).

CHOICE OF STUDY AREA

Choice of study area by the Bureau of Sport Fisheries and Wildlife (Fish and Wildlife Service) was assisted by the use of both color IR and B/W photographs and required approximately three man-weeks. The NASA high-altitude color IR photographs from December 1972 were combined into a mosaic by the Bureau to give a complete picture of the entire Dismal Swamp and adjoining drainage. ERTS imagery provided the big picture as the entire Dismal Swamp and its geographic setting can be seen on one ERTS frame. Figure 2 is an enlargement of a part of an ERTS MSS image (No. 1205-15150-7) taken in February 1973. This imagery was used to verify the boundaries of the selected study area. Comparison of this image with the map of the area (Fig. 1) illustrates the utility of ERTS data in the determination of wetland boundaries. Delineation of the study area from the ERTS image would have reduced the time required to select the study area from three weeks to less than three man-days, including field checking. Many of the roads, canals, and vegetative associations can be clearly identified on a 1:250,000 scale enlargement of the ERTS image. Moreover, ERTS imagery could be used to construct a reliable map of similar large wetland areas without the need for extensive or repetitive field work and low-altitude aircraft coverage.

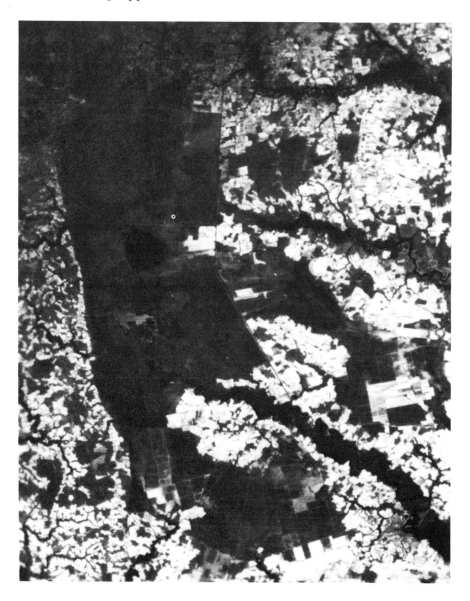

Fig. 2. Enlarged ERTS MSS 7 (2/13/73) winter image showing the Dismal Swamp and associated drainage systems. NNE approx. vertical.

USE OF REMOTE SENSING DATA FOR FIELD INSPECTION

Both the color IR (December 1972 scale 1:130,000) and the recent B/W (scale 1:78,000) photographs in the 9.5 inch format are extremely useful for field work within the Dismal Swamp. The lake, drainage ditches, canal, and roads can be clearly identified so that locating representative sites for ground studies is accomplished rapidly and economically. The 8 color IR or 16 B/W photographs are easier to use for reference in the field than the 7.5 minute topographic maps (scale 1:24,000, approximately 15 in number) of the area, plus they are more up-to-date. All major vegetative associations or plant communities are recognizable in the photographs. Researchers working in specific areas can examine surrounding vegetation and adjacent drainage patterns to predict vegetational trends. Land-use changes near the north and east edges of the Dismal Swamp, where road building and clear-cutting are taking place, were noted between the December 1972 color IR photographs and the March 1973 B/W photographs.

HYDROLOGIC STUDIES

Hydrologic studies have considered water conditions and movement within the Dismal Swamp, as well as flow into and out of the Swamp by surface and subsurface routes. These studies were carried out by the Virginia District of the USGS (Lichtler and Walker 1974 and this volume). Remote sensing data contributed to these studies in several ways, and future studies could utilize more fully some of the attributes described in the following.

1. Both ERTS imagery and aircraft photography show surface drainage patterns in and adjacent to the Swamp. Figure 2 shows the major routes of surface drainage clearly, as streamflow enters the Swamp from the Suffolk Scarp to the west and leaves to the south, east, and north. Once surface drainage channels are located, detailed ground-based studies of discharge and water quality can be done as needed.

2. Surface-water distribution and drainage patterns within the Dismal Swamp can be observed from photography or imagery taken during the winter, when deciduous trees are leafless. The areal extent of standing water can be correlated with water level measurements at Lake Drummond. Thematic extractions from ERTS data distinguish standing water beneath trees from the relatively dry areas.

3. Winter aerial photography was used to help select areas for preliminary groundwater investigations. Vegetative composition and soil
moisture were shown, which are useful in the selection of representative sites for drilling test wells in future hydrologic studies.

4. High- and low-altitude aerial photography and ERTS imagery
were used for vegetation analysis or mapping. The various vegetation
communities are associated with differences in water regime and soils.

THEME EXTRACTION

It is possible to produce maps of themes such as vegetation, water, or
snow from small-scale imagery. Producing these thematic maps by
automated methods rather than conventional mapping methods by
hand would save time and money. ERTS imagery is produced by
NASA from MSS digital information stored on Computer Compatible
Tapes. The imagery is important in understanding the Dismal Swamp
as an ecological unit and in identifying areas where more precise information would be desirable. The USGS is developing an Autographic
Theme Extraction System (ATES) to apply photographic and digital
processing to images, in order to obtain specific theme isolations that
retain the geometry and resolution of the original image. These extractions, or spectral images, are based on distinctive film densities, or
combinations of densities, and are presently being done on an experimental basis with ERTS-1 and SKYLAB images (Smith 1973). The
isolated thematic data are stored in the form of a photographic trans-
parency resembling a high-contrast B/W negative. Two or more of
the properly processed "negatives" can be combined into a photographic composite to eliminate unwanted or spurious data.

ERTS-1 images from 11 October 1972 (No. 1079–15142–5, 7), and
13 February 1973 (No. 1205–15150–5, 7), have been used as the base
for a series of wetlands extractions in the Dismal Swamp (Carter and
Smith 1973). Figure 3 is an enlargement of part of an MSS-7 positive
(10/10/72) of the Dismal Swamp on the North Carolina–Virginia
border south of Norfolk, Virginia. Part of Currituck Sound and
Great Swamp in North Carolina can be seen to the east. A bend in the
Chowan River including part of the Chowan Swamp appears in the
southwest corner. Figure 4 is an extraction showing the wettest area
of the Dismal Swamp, dense white cedar, and the urban communities
of Norfolk and Suffolk (black). Figure 5 shows the drier deciduous or
low flat evergreen areas within the Swamp where snow can accumulate
(white).

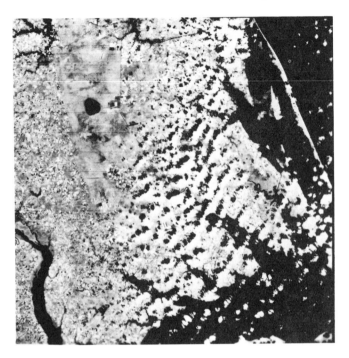

Fig. 3. ERTS MSS-7 (10/10/72) fall image showing the Dismal Swamp. Currituck Sound is on the right and the Chowan River appears in the southeast corner. NNE approx. vertical.

ERTS imagery can be enlarged to approximately 1:125,000 without loss of resolution, but the ERTS digital data can be used to map at scales as large as 1:20,000, each resolution element being approximately 4500 m^2 (1.1 acres). Theme extractions are also possible using ERTS digital data. A preliminary analysis of ERTS digital data from the Dismal Swamp, 13 February 1973, was made using General Electric's IMAGE-100, an interactive multispectral analysis system. The major vegetative associations in the Swamp can be mapped and their areas measured using the ERTS digital data. Canals, roads, standing water, and special interest areas can be clearly identified on photographs made of the interactive color display screen. Theme extractions of standing water, the *Ilex*–pond pine association, pure stands of Atlantic white cedar, and dry deciduous woods appear to be quite accurate. A series of such theme extractions, made over a period of years, can be used to detect changes in the Swamp.

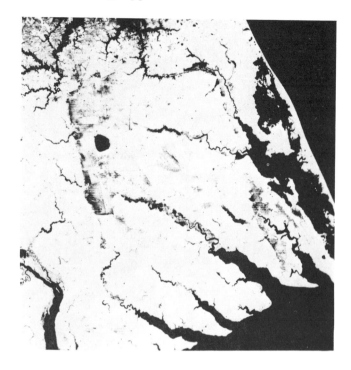

Fig. 4. Theme extraction showing wettest areas of Swamp, dense white cedar, and urban communities of Norfolk and Suffolk, Va. NNE approx. vertical.

VEGETATION MAPPING

Use of color IR photography for vegetation mapping of wetlands has increased in recent years (Anderson and Wobber 1973, Seher and Tueller 1973). Plant communities with distinct or unique tonal signatures may be differentiated and mapped to a scale commensurate with the scale of the photography. Where sufficiently large plant communities exist, as in the Dismal Swamp, mapping of vegetation types can be done from ERTS imagery or digital data.

The flora of the Dismal Swamp is a diverse mixture of northern and southern species. Many plants primarily associated with the swamplands of the Deep South reach their northernmost extent here, and in the Pocomoke River Swamp on the eastern shore of Maryland. The Pocomoke River Swamp differs, however, from the Dismal Swamp in being under tidal influence, with an average tidal range of less than 1 meter (3 ft.) (Beaven and Oosting 1939). Distribution of vegetation in the Dismal Swamp is controlled by moisture, soil, and

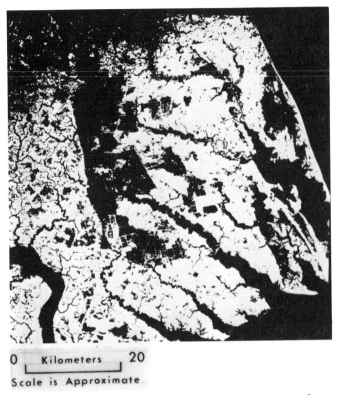

Fig. 5. Theme extraction showing drier deciduous or low, flat evergreen areas where snow accumulates. NNE approx. vertical.

light conditions. However, fire, drainage, and timber cutting have played a dominant role in establishing the present vegetative composition (Dean 1969). Virtually all of the Swamp has been logged at least once and is now covered with second-growth plant associations. The present diversity makes vegetational mapping more difficult and increases the amount of field checking needed.

Forest-cover mapping for the Dismal Swamp Study has been done by the U.S. Forest Service using the USGS B/W orthophotographs rectified to an existing topographic map base at a scale of 1:24,000. High-altitude color IR photography was used to assist and verify the B/W interpretation. Levy (pers. comm. 1973) and Meanley (1972, pp. 27–40; 1973) have indicated that several discrete plant communities exist in the Swamp. Both aerial photography and ERTS imagery provide a useful basis for identifying these plant communities as well as for discriminating between deciduous and evergreen species. A more rapid and accurate delineation of plant communities is possible using aerial photography with selected ground sampling than using conventional ground mapping methods alone.

Figure 6 is a B/W copy of a color IR photograph of part of the Dismal Swamp showing a number of the important plant communities. The hydric, or deepwater, swamp (*A*) is characterized by cypress (*Taxodium distichum*), black gum (*Nyssa sylvatica*), water gum (*Nyssa aquatica*) and red maple (*Acer rubrum*) growing in as much as 60 centimeters (2 ft.) of water during the wetter part of the year. Dense, monospecific stands of Atlantic white cedar (*Chamaecyparis thyoides*) (*B*) occupy areas of deep peat with little or no standing surface water. Large stands of loblolly pine (*Pinus taeda*) (*C*) occur north and south of Lake Drummond. An *Ilex*–pond pine (*Ilex glabra–Pinus serotina*) association may be differentiated from the pine by its light tone (*D*). This is a vast, low, and relatively open community with scattered trees and is an example of an evergreen shrub-bog community (Meanley 1972, pp. 27–40; 1973). The semihydric, or mixed, swamp hardwood forest (*E*) grows in wet areas without standing surface water. Black gum, sweet gum (*Liquidambar styraciflua*), red maple, water oak (*Quercus nigra*), red bay (*Persea borbonia*), swamp magnolia (*Magnolia virginiana*), and yellow poplar (*Liriodendron tulipifera*) dominate this forest type, and the evergreen understory distinguishes it from the denser hydric forest. The mesic, or hammock, forest (*F*) found in drier parts of the Swamp contains oaks (*Quercus spp.*), beech (*Fagus grandifolia*), yellow poplar, red maple, loblolly pine, and holly (*Ilex opaca*).

Areas disturbed by cutting or fire can also be identified on the photography. Revegetating clear-cut areas contain evergreen shrubs and vines mixed with red maple and pine (*P. serotina* or *P. taeda*) (*G*). Recent burns result in a variety of vegetative associations, including a heavy concentration of cane (*Arundinaria sp.*), honeysuckle, and shrubs in dry areas, and bulrushes (*Scirpus spp.*), grasses, evergreen vines, and shrubs in wetter areas (*H*). The evergreen briar (*Smilax laurifolia*) grows up into the trees to heights of approximately 15 meters (50 ft.). Where large concentrations exist, the signature on color IR photograph is identical to that of pine.

LOCATION OF SPECIAL INTEREST AREAS

One useful and important outcome of the study is the identification of unusual and distinct ecological communities whose existence contributes to the diversity of the Swamp (U.S., Dept. of the Interior, BSFW, 1974). Two of these special interest areas were located in the Swamp using the color IR photographs (see Fig. 6). The first is a small marsh area (*I*) in which the water table is just below the ground surface. It contains grass and aquatic emergents such as cattails (*Typha spp.*),

Fig. 6. Black-and-white reproduction of NASA U-2 color IR photograph of the Dismal Swamp. (*A*) hydric, or deepwater, swamp, (*B*) Atlantic white cedar, (*C*) pine, (*D*) *Ilex*–pond pine association. (*E*) semihydric swamp, (*F*) mesic forest, (*G*) revegetating clear-cut area, (*H*) revegetating burn, (*I*) marsh, (*J*) mesic "islands." NNE approx. vertical.

arrowheads (*Sagittaria spp.*), goldenclub (*Orontium aquaticum*), and sedges (*Carex spp.*). A large part of the Dismal Swamp was covered by this type of plant community some 8000–4000 years ago. Both the grass-"limnophyte" and *Orontium*-composite-fern subzones defined by Whitehead (1972) are present. Historic records (Reid 1952) suggest that this marsh was originally 122 hectares (300 acres) in extent and was used by George Washington to grow rice. Today only about 24 hectares (< 60 acres) remain. The rest is covered by a dense mature stand of gum and cypress.

The second special interest area (*J*) is a series of low ridges that cross the southern part of the Dismal Swamp in an east-west direction. These small mesic "islands" are mostly underlain by sand and sandy loam with either a 5-centimeter (2-in.) cover of roots and leaf litter or a shallow layer of peat. Large beech, oak, loblolly pine, sourwood (*Oxydendrum arboreum*), sweet gum, and yellow poplar form a sparse growth with many wind-thrown trees evident. Holly, cane, and young hardwoods are the principal understory species. This area possibly represents the highest ground originally present in the sloping hill-side (Oaks and Coch 1973) on which the Swamp was formed.

FUTURE APPLICATIONS

Monitoring and Change Detection

Comparison of old (1953) and recent (1973) USGS photographs would serve to indicate the rate of change in the Dismal Swamp during the past 20 years. Although 20 years is not a long period of time relative to the Swamp's existence, useful information on revegetation in old burns or clear-cut areas is readily available. Changes in the north and south ends of the Dismal Swamp and in secondary areas along the Pasquotank and Northwest rivers due to man's drainage and construction activities can be measured. For the future, the aquisition of other high-altitude color IR photography would facilitate updating of vegetational maps and measurement of burned or clear-cut areas.

The monitoring potential of a satellite system such as ERTS is excellent for supplying data on effects of water management practices within the Dismal Swamp Wildlife Refuge and in the Swamp as a whole. Stressed vegetation and open-water areas could be quickly detected on a repetitive basis. It is not feasible to monitor the vast acreages affected by water management by conventional methods.

Hydrologic Studies

As a result of the hydrological study, it has been theorized (Lichtler and Walker 1974) that the movement of groundwater into the Dismal Swamp from the shallow Norfolk aquifer was a factor in formation of the Swamp and contributes to its present condition. The temperature of groundwater fluctuates little throughout the year and remains near the mean annual air temperature. Surface water temperature fluctuates widely during the year tending to be warmer in summer than groundwater and colder in winter. For this reason, thermal imagery of the Dismal Swamp, taken from low altitude during the winter, could yield important information on areas of groundwater outflow. Also the location and areal extent of surface water determined by thermal imagery could be correlated with concurrent water levels in Lake Drummond to develop a relationship between stage and water surface area. The relationship between water levels in Lake Drummond and areal extent of surface water in the Dismal Swamp can also be established using ERTS imagery. Expansion of this relationship to include estimates of surface inflow and outflow made from ground measurements at selected points would give information usable in a hydrologic model of the Dismal Swamp.

Automated Theme Extraction

As mentioned previously, the automatic extraction of themes, such as water or vegetative cover, from satellite imagery or digital data would provide timely information to resource managers in a useful format. Systems like ATES and IMAGE-100 are presently being developed to provide this theme extraction capability. For the Dismal Swamp the extraction of forest-cover types, extent of surface water, areas of stressed vegetation, and burned, clear-cut, or regenerating areas could be of considerable value in development and implementation of management plans.

SUMMARY

The study of the Dismal Swamp utilized ERTS imagery, and color IR and B/W photography in (1) overall study area selection, (2) location of intensive study areas, (3) hydrologic studies, (4) vegetation mapping and (5) field studies, including identification of special interest areas. Because of the large size of the entire Dismal Swamp and inaccessibility of many interior parts, remote sensing provided a powerful tool to meet study needs. Use of RS data minimized the extent of the ground survey needed and allowed for more rapid completion of certain special interest areas that would not have been noticed by conventional methods.

Possible future applications of remote sensing to the Dismal Swamp include (1) making a detailed hydrologic study utilizing ERTS data or thermal imagery, (2) monitoring the effects of water level management with repetitive satellite data, (3) detecting vegetative changes with additional high-altitude color IR photography or ERTS data and (4) making detailed ecological studies using low-altitude aircraft coverage of selected sites. Thematic extraction of surface water area, plant communities, and burned or clear-cut areas from satellite data in a repetitive basis could provide timely and useful information for resource management.

REFERENCES CITED

Anderson, R. R., and F. J. Wobber. 1973. Wetlands mapping in New Jersey. *Photogramm. Eng.* 39:353–358.

Beaven, G. F., and H. J. Oosting. 1939. Pocomoke Swamp: a study of a cypress swamp on the Eastern Shore of Maryland. *Bull. Torrey Bot. Club* 66:367–389.

Carter, Virginia, and D. G. Smith. 1973. Utilization of remotely-sensed data in the management of inland wetlands. Pp. 144–158 *in* A. Anson (ed). Management and utilization of remote sensing data. *Am. Soc. of Photogramm, Symp. Proc.*

Dean, G. W. 1969. Forests and forestry in the Dismal Swamp. *Va. J. Sci.* 20:166–173.

Eisenlohr, W. S., Jr., and others [*sic*]. 1972. Hydrologic investigations of prairie potholes in North Dakota, 1959–68. *U.S. Geol. Survey, Prof. Pap.* 585-A. 102 pp.

Gupta, T. R. 1972. Economic criteria for decisions on preservation and use of inland wetlands in Massachusetts. *J. Northeastern Agric. Econ. Council* 1:201–210.

Hall, F. R., R. J. Rutherford, and G. L. Byers. 1972. The influence of the New England wetland on water quantity and quality. *New Hampshire Univ. Water Resources Res. Center, Res. Rpt.* 4. 51 pp.

Larson, J. S. 1973. A guide to important characteristics and values of freshwater wetlands in the Northeast. *Univ. Mass. Water Resources Res. Center Pub.* 31. 35 pp.

Lichtler, W. F., and P. N. Walker. 1974. Hydrology of the Dismal Swamp, Virginia–North Carolina. U.S. Geol. Survey, Richmond, Va. 50 pp.

Meanley, B. 1972. *Swamps, river bottoms and canebrakes.* Barre Publishers, Barre, Mass. 142 pp.

———. 1973. *The Great Dismal Swamp.* Audubon Nat. Soc. Cent. Atlantic States, Washington, D.C. 48 pp.

Oaks, R. Q., Jr., and N. K. Coch. 1973. Post-Miocene stratigraphy and morphology, southeastern Virginia. *Va. Div. Mineral Resources, Bull.* 82. 135 pp.

Reid, J. H. 1952. Report on Dismal Swamp. Camp Manufacturing Co., Franklin, Va. 19 pp.

Seher, J. S., and P. T. Tueller. 1973. Color aerial photos for marshland. *Photogramm. Eng.* 39:489–499.

Smith, D. G. 1973. Autographic theme extraction system. Paper delivered to UN Regional Cartographic Conf. for Asia and the Far East, Tokyo, Japan, Oct. 15–27, 1973.

U.S. Dept. of the Interior, Bur. of Sport Fisheries and Wildlife, Northeast Region. Rpt. of the Dismal Swamp National Wildlife Refuge, Suffolk, Va. Pursuant to P.L. 92–478. 1974. Developmental history and ecology of the Dismal Swamp with recommendations for public ownership and management. 49 pp.

Whitehead, D. R. 1972. Developmental and environmental history of the Dismal Swamp. *Ecol. Monographs* 42:301–315.

[Editor's note: also see Virginia Carter, Mary Keith Garrett, Lurie Shima, and Patricia Gammon, 1977. The Great Dismal Swamp: management of a hydrologic resource with the aid of remote sensing. *Amer. Water Resources Assn. Bull.* 13:1–12.]

FOREST DYNAMICS IN
THE DISMAL SWAMP OF VIRGINIA

Gerald F. Levy and Susan W. Walker

INTRODUCTION

The Dismal Swamp of North Carolina and Virginia is one of the largest remaining swamp forests within the southeastern coastal plain. The first extensive floristic study of this Swamp was by Kearney (1901). Whitehead (1972) includes a general description of the plant communities in his comprehensive examination of the development of the Swamp. Meanley (1968) and Waters et al. (1974) have published species lists, and Dean (1969) discussed the forest communities in general terms. Musselman et al. (1977) have published a complete flora.

Most descriptions of the vegetation of the Dismal Swamp are basically floristic listings with divisions between communities based on qualitative assessments. Many of the descriptions have not included scientific names of species, and confusion exists as to the exact meaning of some common names.

Kearney (1901) distinguished between two hydrophilic forest formations: the Dark Swamp, a heavy, deciduous virgin forest, and the Light Swamp, which consisted of almost pure stands of Atlantic white cedar (*Chamaecyparis thyoides*) that resulted from the disturbance of the virgin formation.

Meanley (1968) recognized several community types within the Swamp, including cypress–tupelo gum (*Taxodium disticum–Nyssa aquatica*); swamp black gum (*N. sylvatica*); mixed swamp, composed of red maple (*Acer rubrum*), swamp black gum, and tupelo gum; pocosin, or evergreen shrub bog; Atlantic white cedar; switch cane; and the upland border community composed of oaks (*Quercus* spp.), ash (*Fraxinus* spp.), elm (*Ulmus americana*), and lobolly pine (*Pinus taeda*). However, Dean (1969) combined several of Meanley's community types. His classification included gum swamps composed of maple, bays, cypress, and gums along natural drainage, and a pine zone composed of lobolly and pond pine (*Pinus serotina*) along the banks of ditches and canals where they could survive fires. Other communities proposed

by Dean were "lights," composed of reeds and water grass, and white
cedar stands on acidic peat overlying a sandy subsoil.

The region in which the Dismal Swamp lies exhibits a great diversity of plant communities, ranging from coastal marshland to swamps
and upland forests. These communities have probably resulted primarily from the response of vegetation to edaphic and physiographic
variations, as the regional climate is relatively uniform (Wells 1942).
The origin of the edaphic and physiographic features of the southeastern coastal plain has been attributed to the erosion of older terraces, producing an uneven relief composed of ridges and poorly
drained, low-lying flatter areas. Swamps lie in the low areas in which
soil is saturated or covered by standing water one or more months
during the growing season (Penfound 1952). Penfound proposed that
depth and duration of standing water have been the major controlling
factors of swamp succession. The origin and nature of the mucky peat
substratum that occurred over about 70 percent of our study area are
discussed by Oaks and Whitehead, and the prevailing climatic and
hydrological conditions by Lichtler and Walker in this volume. Additional general information on the edaphic factors has been given
by Henry (1970) and the U.S. Department of Agriculture (1974), on
the waters by Ramsey et al. (1970), and the climate by the U.S. Department of Commerce (1970).

The Dismal Swamp has been greatly disturbed by numerous fires
and about 200 years of logging. In addition, the extensive construction
of drainage ditches has accelerated changes in moisture relations that
normally are brought about only after centuries of aggradation of inorganic and organic materials. Most plant communities occurring in
the Dismal Swamp today consist of second- or third-growth forest and
dense brushlands that represent a variety of seral stages.

Our major purpose has been to initiate quantitative phytosociological investigations which, unlike the previously conducted qualitative studies, lend themselves to more precise analysis and provide a
basis for making detailed reappraisals in future years. In addition, we
have utilized these results to provide insight into the Dismal Swamp's
vegetational dynamics and successional trends, and some of their controlling environmental factors. This study has concentrated on closed
forest communities.

METHODS

Most of the study area was restricted to sites in the City of Suffolk previously owned by the Union Camp Corporation, Franklin, Virginia.

This area, recently deeded by The Nature Conservancy to the Department of the Interior, constitutes the Dismal Swamp National Wildlife Refuge. Approximate locations of the 14 forest stands sampled are shown in Figure 1.

Field work was conducted June 1971 through April 1972. The areas sampled ranged from moist sites with peaty soils to drier ones with mineral soils. Potential sampling sites were located on aerial photographs and later confirmed in the field. A sampling of 14 stands revealed no significantly different species combinations; hence an adequate representation of forest diversity was assumed to have been included.

Each stand was sampled using five random points on each of five parallel lines located 13–25 paces apart. Defining two paces as 5 feet, the area sampled was approximately 1.6 acres. A modified circular quadrat-Bitterlich method, similar to that of Lindsey et al. (1958), was developed by Levy and Walker (1971) for sampling each point. Trees, i.e., individuals greater than four inches diameter at breast height (dbh), were counted and identified by species within a radius of 18.5 feet to determine density and frequency. The Bitterlich method (Grosenbaugh 1952) was used at each point to determine dominance. Saplings, i.e., individuals between 1 and 4 inches dbh, were identified and tallied if they occurred within a radius of 7.5 feet from the center point. Three smaller circles, 1 foot in diameter, were located 7.5 feet from the center point for seedling and shrub identification and tallies. Seedlings and shrubs above 4.5 feet in height were included in size class I and those under 4.5 feet in size class II.

Field moisture was measured in situ at 1- and 12-inch depths with a Buoyoucos Moisture Meter from November 1971 through April 1972, at two stations in each of six stands selected to represent all community types sampled. Fluctuations in the water table above or below the soil surface were noted. General observations and features indicative of stand history were also noted at each stand.

Soil samples were collected at a different random point on each line at depths to 2 feet. The samples were analyzed for pH, water retention capacity (WRC), and texture. The pH was measured with a Beckman pH meter on field-moist samples diluted 1:2.5 with distilled water. Textural analysis for sand, silt, and clay fractions was conducted according to the hydrometer method of Bouyoucos (1936). Nutrient determinations for calcium, magnesium, phosphorous, potassium, and salt concentrations were made by the Virginia Truck Experiment Station, Virginia Beach.

Field data were converted to the phytosociological statistics, density, frequency, and dominance, which were transposed to importance values (IV) and relative importance values (RIV) for each tree

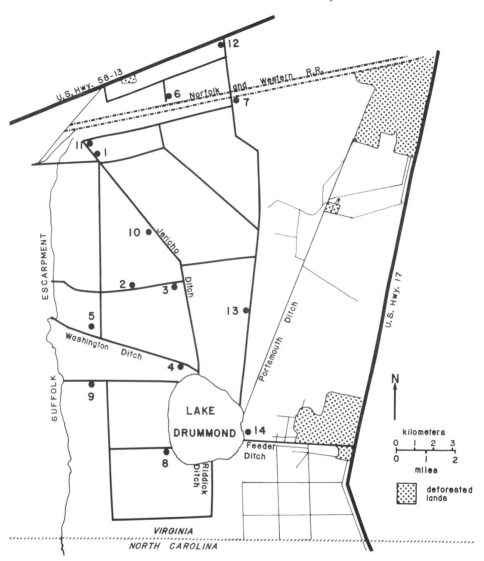

Fig. 1. Location of stands included in this study within the Dismal Swamp of
Virginia.

species in each stand. RIV was calculated by dividing IV values by 3,
thus placing them on a 0–100 scale rather than the standard 0–300
scale. Sapling importance values (IV_s) and relative values (RIV_s)
were based upon density and frequency data. Only relative frequency
was determined for seedlings.

Ordination of stands followed the Wisconsin Method (Bray and
Curtis 1957), in which calculated dissimilarity values between stands
are used to define axes. These values were derived from the index of
dissimilarity, $100 - 2W/(a + b)$, which is discussed in detail by Mueller-

Dombois and Ellenberg (1974, pp. 276–297). In some instances the term *similarity* may be used, which is simply the reciprocal of dissimilarity. Separate ordinations were constructed for tree composition, based on RIV, and for sapling composition, based on RIV$_s$ (Levy 1970). Three axes were extracted and three-dimensional models developed. These techniques were facilitated by the Old Dominion University IBM 1130 computer and the College of William and Mary IBM 360–50 computer.

Stands may occur close to one another on an ordination due to their sharing a common dissimilarity to the axis end points, and not because they are actually similar. To counteract this possibility, two-dimensional models were developed, resulting in interrelated clusters (Figs. 2 and 3) in which stands were arranged on the basis of the index of dissimilarity (Mueller-Dombois and Ellenberg 1974). By using dissimilarity values the two stands most like any other selected stand were identified. Also, the two most like each of these stands were identified, and the process repeated until all relationships were established. Stands were then arranged so that interstand distances were scaled by dissimilarity values; hence, the more alike two stands are, the closer they occur in the model. A dissimilarity value of 40 or less generally delimited the tree clusters and of 45 or less delimited the sapling clusters. These levels were chosen arbitrarily as cutoff points after many trials revealed that lesser dissimilarity values greatly reduced the number of phytosociological relationships, while higher values produced so many relationships that no meaningful separation could occur. The geometric configurations of the models are the result of subjective treatment to produce a clear representation of the relationships among the clusters.

Analysis of dominant species was conducted for each cluster and for stands not incorporated into a cluster. The dominant species were defined as those having the highest and second highest RIV and RIV$_s$ values in each of the 14 stands.

Taxonomic nomenclature including common names follows Radford et al. (1968). Ashes (*Fraxinus* spp.) were not identified to species, but included water ash (*F. caroliniana*), red ash (*F. pennsylvanica*), and white ash (*F. americana*). Varieties of black gum (*Nyssa sylvatica* Marsh) were not distinguished. Pond pine (*Pinus serotina* Michaux) and loblolly pine (*P. taeda* L.) were not distinguished in the field and all individuals of these species were designated loblolly pine.

RESULTS

The 14 stands were initially classified according to the two main substrate types, peat and mineral soils. Eight stands occurred on peat substrates and six on mineral soils, although one of the latter also contained some peat. The phytosociological characteristics of principal species within the stands grouped by substrate are summarized in Table 1. The soil characteristics for each stand are given in Table 2. Average soil moisture is reported only for the 1-inch depth since the readings from 12 inches were always 100 percent.

Stands on Peat

Table 1 shows that red maple (*Acer rubrum*) was the principal dominant in five of the eight stands occurring on peat soils (nos. 2–4, 8 and 14). Exceptions were one stand dominated by black gum and ash (9), one by black gum and red maple (10), and one by Atlantic white cedar (13). The principal sapling species were red maple in two stands, red bay (*Persea borbonia*) in three, both of these species in one stand, black gum in one, and holly (*Ilex opaca*) in one.

The peat was intermixed with sandy loam in four stands, loamy sand in two, sand in one, and sandy clay loam in one. Mean values for soil moisture were consistently very high, the lowest being 90.9 per cent saturation. The substrata in three stands had mean WRC greater than 700 per cent, while the lowest was 336 per cent. Portions of two stands were inundated during the winter and early spring of 1971 and 1972. A shallow ditch in another stand was dry during the summer but was filled with water by winter.

Stand 8 was characterized by scattered islands of trees producing shaded areas with sparse ground cover. These islands were separated by almost impenetrable treeless areas. The situation at stand 4 was similar to that at 8, but with smaller and less dense treeless areas.

Low brushland covered the east side of stand 13, which may have been cut over recently. Microtopography in many stands was extremely irregular, with many hummocks and depressions caused by windfalls.

Stand on Mineral Soils

In general, the stands on mineral soils exhibited a greater diversity of tree and sapling species than those on peat. Red maple was the principal dominant in two stands but with lower RIV values than on peat. Red maple and sweet gum (*Liquidambar styraciflua*) dominated

Table 1. Phytosociological characteristics of principal trees and saplings on peat and mineral soils

Stands on peat soils

Stand no.	Trees	RIV (%)	No. of tree species present	Saplings	RIV$_s$(%)	No. of sapling species present
2	Red maple	64.9	4	Red bay	56.3	4
	Black gum	25.5		Holly	18.3	
3	Red maple	61.4	5	Red bay	79.8	3
	Black gum	32.4		Red maple	10.1	
				Sweet bay	10.1	
4	Red maple	52.9	6	Red maple	83.8	2
	Ash	27.0		Black gum	16.2	
8	Red maple	36.5	6	Red bay	38.0	5
	Red bay	28.4		Pawpaw	34.4	
9	Black gum	23.3	9	Red maple	33.1	6
	Ash	22.6		Ash	17.2	
				Black gum	15.6	
10	Black gum	44.4	5	Red maple	50.0	2
	Red maple	43.9		Red bay	50.0	
13	Atlantic white cedar	58.2	7	Black gum	60.4	3
				Sweet bay	23.8	
	Red maple	15.1		Red maple	15.7	
14	Red maple	32.0	7	Holly	81.9	3
	Holly	26.2		Pawpaw	10.9	
				American elm	7.3	

Stands on mineral soils

Stand no.	Trees	RIV (%)	No. of tree species present	Saplings	RIV$_s$(%)	No. of sapling species present
1	Red maple	16.8	19	Holly	24.1	11
	Sweet gum	16.6		Sweet gum	15.5	
				Sourwood	14.2	
5	Red maple	22.6	15	Red maple	41.4	9
	Black gum	14.7		Ash	19.3	
6	Sweet gum	38.6	4	Sweet gum	75.5	5
	Loblolly pine	33.2		Red maple	9.8	
7	Loblolly pine	44.0	4	Red maple	45.1	3
	Red maple	25.2		Sweet gum	32.6	
				Black gum	22.6	
11	Black gum	21.0	10	Holly	24.4	9
	Sweet gum	15.9		Black gum	22.8	
	Red maple	15.5		Sweet bay	13.2	
12	Red maple	42.9	7	Red maple	56.4	4
	Sweet gum	39.3		Sweet gum	23.0	

Table 2. Soil characteristics of stands

Stand no.	Texture of mineral components	Mean WRC (%)*	Mean soil pH	Mean soil moisture (%)†
Stands on peat soils				
2	Sand	719	4.5	—
3	Loamy sand	712	4.6	99.6
				98.8
4	Sandy loam	336	5.2	—
8	Sandy loam	414	3.7	99.8
				100.0
9	Sandy clay loam	501	4.8	100.0
				98.5
10	Sandy loam	406	3.6	—
13	Loamy sand	734	3.8	100.0
				90.9
14	Sandy loam	547	3.9	—
Stands on mineral soils				
1	Sandy loam	83	4.3	100.0
				100.0
5	Clay loam	108	5.3	—
6	Sandy loam	157	4.5	—
7	Sandy loam	298	4.2	89.4
				96.5
11	Sandy loam	141	4.1	—
12	Sandy loam	198	4.1	—

*Water retaining capacity (%) = $\dfrac{\text{Saturated wt.} \times 100}{\text{Oven-dry wt.}}$; hence, values exceed 100% using this standard method.

† Two stations were maintained in each of 6 representative stands.

one stand, and sweet gum, loblolly pine, or black gum one each. Red maple, holly, sweet gum, and black gum had almost equal importance in two of the six stands. Each of these four species clearly dominated one stand while in the sixth ash and maple had equal importance.

Sandy loam was found on all sites but one, which had clay loam. The pH range was less extreme for mineral soils (4.1–5.3) than for peat (3.5–5.2). Stand 7 had the lowest mean soil moisture (Table 2). Portions of three stands were inundated throughout the winter and early spring 1971–72. On the other hand, in the summer stand 11 was quite dry, as was the ditch adjacent to it. This was the only major ditch found completely dry during the study.

Stand 12 had soil and vegetational characteristics of stands on both peat and mineral soils. A small portion was on peat with a mean WRC of 571 per cent, but most of the area had mineral soils with a mean of only 167 per cent. The highest and lowest values were included in calculating a mean WRC of 198 for this stand (Table 2). Microtopographic changes were quite noticeable, especially where charred old cypress stumps and knees occurred along the east side of the sample area. Partially healed fire scars and multiple-trunk trees were also evident.

Analyzing the principal dominants in stand 12 using a t-test showed a heterogeneous distribution of red maple at the 90 per cent level and of sweet gum at 98 per cent. Testing with the McGinnies Index (McGinnies 1934) showed that sweet gum was randomly distributed (D/d = 1.44) while red maple was aggregated. That such aggregated distributions are often due to fire is widely known.

Cluster Analysis

Although the stands were initially classified according to substrate type and moisture conditions, it was evident from the diversity of principal dominants that further categorization of stands was possible. Figure 2 is a cluster analysis diagram based on tree composition, and Figure 3 on sapling composition. Each of these cluster analysis diagrams indicates four distinct groupings, with three isolated stands in the tree model (nos. 8, 13, and 14) and two in the sapling model (6 and 14). Generally speaking, stands having dissimilarity values less than 45 units were treated as sufficiently alike to belong in the same cluster. However, stand 4 was somewhat arbitrarily included in tree cluster A (Fig. 2) as a borderline case, although showing relatively greater dissimilarity to stands 2 and 3 (59 units).

Mean RIV for each cluster and the isolated stands of trees were calculated using only the principal dominants (Table 3). Overall, cluster A had the highest mean value for red maple (55.8%) and black gum (27.1%), cluster B for ash (15.3%), and cluster D for sweet gum (28.7%) and loblolly pine (26.9%). Isolated stands were characterized by high mean RIV for one species occurring almost singularly within that stand, e.g., red bay in stand 8, Atlantic white cedar in 13, and holly in 14.

Mean RIV, for the clusters and isolated stands of saplings (Table 4) were distinguished by having the highest mean values for one or more of the most important species included. As a result, cluster A' had the highest mean for red bay (57.9%), cluster B' for ash (24.7%), cluster C' for black gum and sweet bay (*Magnolia virginiana*) (28.3% and 17.4%,

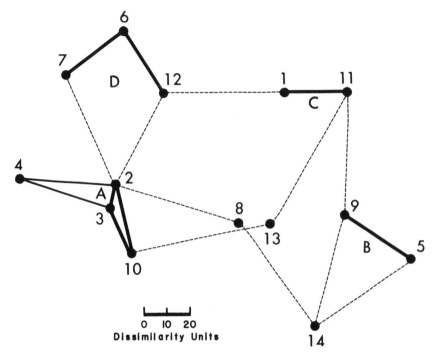

Fig. 2. Cluster analysis diagram based on similarity in tree composition. Solid lines indicate stands included within a cluster, while dashed lines indicate similarity values less than the minimum used in defining clusters. Stands most similar to each other are connected by thick, solid lines; lesser relationships are indicated by narrow lines.

Table 3. Mean relative importance values (%) by clusters for the most important tree species and their percent presence in all stands

Species	Tree cluster							Presence (%)
	A	B	C	D	8	13	14	
Red maple	55.8	19.7	16.2	30.9	36.5	15.1	32.0	100.0
Atlantic white cedar	1.2	0.0	0.0	0.0	0.0	58.2	0.0	21.4
Ash	6.8	15.3	0.0	0.0	0.0	0.0	0.0	28.5
Holly	0.0	0.0	11.2	0.0	12.8	0.0	26.2	28.5
Sweet gum	0.9	10.5	16.2	28.7	0.0	0.0	2.3	64.2
Black gum	27.1	19.0	15.3	11.2	2.5	12.7	10.8	100.0
Red bay	0.0	0.0	0.0	0.0	28.4	1.3	0.0	14.2
Loblolly pine	0.0	0.3	1.3	26.9	0.0	0.3	0.0	42.8

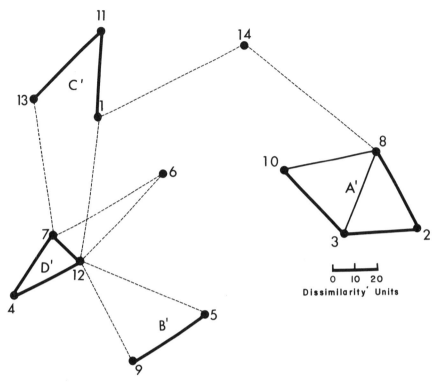

Fig. 3. Cluster analysis diagram based on similarity in sapling composition. Solid lines indicate stands included within a cluster, while dashed lines indicate similarity values less than the minimum used in defining clusters. Stands most similar to each other are connected by thick, solid lines; lesser relationships are indicated by narrow lines.

Table 4. Mean relative importance values (%) by clusters for the most important sapling species and their percent presence in all stands.

| Species | Sapling cluster | | | | | | Presence (%) |
	A'	*B'*	*C'*	*D'*	6	14	
Red maple	17.7	32.7	12.2	63.4	9.8	0.0	85.7
Pawpaw	7.4	0.0	0.0	0.0	0.0	10.9	14.2
Ash	0.0	24.7	0.0	0.0	0.0	0.0	14.2
Holly	7.3	2.4	15.7	0.0	4.9	81.9	50.0
Sweet gum	0.0	1.7	9.5	16.9	75.5	0.0	42.8
Sweet bay	6.6	2.8	17.4	3.4	0.0	0.0	71.4
Black gum	3.2	8.8	28.3	16.3	4.9	0.0	71.4
Red bay	57.9	0.0	2.4	0.0	0.0	0.0	50.0

respectively), cluster D' for red maple (63.4%), stand 6 for sweet gum (75.5%) and stand 14 for holly and pawpaw (*Asimina triloba*) (81.9% and 10.9%, respectively). The absence of pawpaw, ash, and red bay from most clusters is notable. However, red bay was at least present in 50.0 per cent of the stands investigated. The principal saplings in each cluster were the same as those named above, except for cluster B', in which it was red maple (32.7%) rather than ash.

Stand 14 was unique, and hence solitary, with regard to sapling composition (Fig. 3) as well as tree composition (Fig. 2). This stand's total dissimilarity (value of 100) to stands 3, 4, 7, 10, and 13 was extraordinary. Its least dissimilarity was to stand 1, with a value of 74, followed closely by stands 8 and 11.

The model based on sapling composition exhibited greater complexity than that for tree composition. Whereas clusters based on tree composition generally had a common soil type (either peat or mineral soils), all clusters (except A) based on sapling composition included stands occurring on both substrata.

The sapling composition of certain stands in cluster A' was like that of stands in the other clusters, although the cluster diagram has not been designed to emphasize these minor relationships. In addition to the relationships indicated in the model (Fig. 3) stand 2 of cluster A' and 12 of D' had a dissimilarity of 53, while stand 10 of cluster A' and the stands of cluster C' had dissimilarities of 50.

The mean relative frequencies in both size classes of saplings were computed for each sapling cluster (Table 5), including the most important species. In general, the principal saplings and seedlings in size class I were the same. However, there was more divergence in the smaller size class, II. Trends included an increase in the importance of red maple in stand 6, red bay in cluster C', holly in cluster D', and the appearance of sweet gum in cluster A'. Although pawpaw and red bay were present in many clusters as seedlings, they were rarely represented by saplings.

The index of similarity (reciprocal of dissimilarity) based upon RIV and RIV$_s$ was used to compare all species of the tree layer to those of the sapling layer within each stand, so as to elucidate relationships between present and potential canopies. Stands within which the tree and sapling compositions were the most similar were nos. 11, 12, and 9 with values of 0.78, 0.76, and 0.69, respectively. Those having the least similarity between these two strata were stands 3, 2, 14, and 13 with values of 0.11, 0.13, 0.33, and 0.38 (Table 6).

RIV and per cent presence in all stands for the 28 species with tree-sized individuals are summarized in Table 7. This represents an overview of the relationships revealed by the entire study. A similar overview is given for saplings in Table 8.

Table 5. Mean relative frequencies by clusters of the most important seedlings based on sapling composition

Species		Sapling cluster					
	A'	B'	C'	D'	6	14
Red maple						
Class I*	17.6	44.2	10.7	44.5	46.2	3.3
Class II	42.5	27.0	17.9	38.1	24.2	7.8
Pawpaw						
Class I	10.6	0.0	2.2	1.6	0.0	33.3
Class II	4.9	0.0	6.6	2.1	0.0	37.3
Ash						
Class I	0.0	20.5	0.0	0.0	0.0	0.0
Class II	0.0	21.6	0.5	0.0	0.0	0.0
Holly						
Class I	2.8	7.7	12.5	23.9	7.7	60.0
Class II	8.3	3.6	8.2	12.5	15.2	27.5
Sweet gum						
Class I	5.6	7.3	2.3	17.9	34.6	3.3
Class II	0.0	6.8	2.0	13.6	30.3	3.9
Sweet bay						
Class I	3.8	1.2	16.8	1.6	7.7	0.0
Class II	5.6	0.0	13.6	9.0	12.1	0.0
Black gum						
Class I	0.0	1.2	21.1	2.0	0.0	0.0
Class II	4.5	12.1	4.0	5.6	3.0	0.0
Red bay						
Class I	58.6	0.0	19.6	3.6	3.9	0.0
Class II	30.7	1.9	35.3	2.9	12.1	0.0

* Two size classes defined in Methods.

DISCUSSION OF INDIVIDUAL CLUSTERS AND STANDS

The cluster diagrams (Figs. 2 and 3) show relatively distinct communities existing in the study area. Furthermore, the lack of similarity between tree and sapling layers within some of these communities (Table 6) suggests that changes occurring in the Swamp's microclimate may be indicated by these gradual changes in forest composition.

Cluster *A* (Fig. 2)

All stands in cluster *A* occurred on soils with high peat content. Stands 2 and 3 had among the highest WRC values, while 4 and 10 had

Table 6. Index of similarity between tree and sapling strata within each stand.

Stand no.	Index of similarity*
1	0.58
2	0.13
3	0.11
4	0.59
5	0.49
6	0.52
7	0.56
8	0.59
9	0.69
10	0.44
11	0.78
12	0.76
13	0.38
14	0.33

* Reciprocal of dissimilarity.

nearly the lowest recorded on peat substrata (Table 2). This wide range of WRC values suggests that moisture-holding capacity in itself is not a major determinant of the composition of the stands in cluster *A*.

Russell (1961) observed that salts accumulating in saturated peat substrata would mimic dry conditions by inhibiting water absorption. An average soil salt concentration of 331 ppm for cluster *A* was higher than that for other clusters and isolated stands (110-274 ppm). Probably the salt effect observed by Russell is operating most strongly in this cluster.

Stands 2 and 3, which had high WRC values, were more like each other than stand 10, and to a lesser extent stand 4, which had lower WRC values. The current similarity of stands 2 and 3 is most likely due to these factors: (1) their initial similarity in composition; (2) similar substrates; (3) proximity to each other (both are located on Middle Ditch); and (4) similar history of disturbance. These stands were cut at the same time, in the mid 1950s subsequent to the excavation of Middle Ditch. The desiccating influence of the newly constructed ditch most likely prevented Atlantic white cedar from regenerating on the sites and favored the euryhydric species instead.

The difference between stand 10 and nos. 2 and 3 was minor. The location of stand 10 on Jericho Ditch suggests that it was cut at a different time, and this alone may explain the compositional differences.

Stand 4, the least like others in cluster A, was the closest to Lake Drummond and occurred adjacent to Washington Ditch (Fig. 1). Its uniqueness can be attributed in part to its remoteness from stands 2, 3, and 10, but the seasonally high water level at the end of this major ditch was also an important factor. That this stand is less subject to desiccation than the others is further substantiated by the presence of American elm (*Ulmus americana*), laurel oak (*Q. laurifolia*), ash, and ironwood (*Carpinus caroliniana*), all of which generally require uniform soil moisture.

This cluster had a low species diversity (10 species, 2 in common). The few individuals of Atlantic white cedar occurring in stands 3 and 10 are probably remnants of purer stands that were selectively cut. The species tends to form almost impenetrable stands of similarly aged individuals. Cutting followed by a light burn improves its success as germination and seedling growth are retarded by shade (Little 1950). Hence, such a history of disturbance would account for the low species diversity of cluster A (10 tree-sized spp., 2 in common to all stands; Table 7).

Cluster B (Fig. 2)

Although stand 5 was on mineral soil and 9 on peat, both included large proportions of clay and hence were poorly drained. These sites always occurred in depressions 3 feet below the road level and appeared wetter than those in cluster A, which lacked a perched water table. This relatively constant moisture level, which produces a less rigorous environment than does a greatly fluctuating level, would account for the higher species diversity in cluster B (15 tree spp., eight in common; Table 7).

Cluster C (Fig. 2)

The stands in cluster C were on sandy loams, with relatively low WRC values and portions inundated during the winter and early spring. However, unlike the stands in cluster B, those in C did not occur in noticeable depressions. At stand 11 the water table during summer lay below the bottom of the adjacent ditch, hence this area experienced moisture extremes. Likewise, stand 1 occurred on a system of ridges and runs with small portions depressed and periodically inundated. Tolerance to moisture fluctuations is apparently a common requirement of the tree species in clusters C and A, but the species diversity in C is higher (19 species, 10 in common;

Table 7. Relative importance values for species with tree-sized individuals, the number of stands in which they occurred, and mean number of trees per stand

Cluster designation	A				B		C		D			Isolated stands			No. of stands in which occurred
Stand number	2	3	4	10	5	9	1	11	6	7	12	8	13	14	
Species															
Red maple	64.8	61.4	52.9	43.9	22.6	16.7	16.8	15.5	24.7	25.2	42.8	36.5	15.1	32	14
Black gum	25.2	32.4	6.0	44.4	14.7	23.3	9.7	21.0	3.6	22.5	7.5	2.4	12.7	10.8	14
Sweet gum	3.7	–	–	–	10.2	10.9	16.4	15.9	38.6	8.3	39.3	–	–	2.3	9
Sweet bay	–	0.9	–	7.8	–	0.6	6.3	13.6	–	–	2.5	–	8.9	–	7
Yellow poplar[1]	6.0	3.7	–	0.8	0.5	–	5.5	7.9	–	–	3.4	10.5	–	–	7
Loblolly pine	–	–	–	–	0.7	–	2.5	–	33.2	44.0	3.6	3.6	–	0.8	6
American elm[2]	–	–	11.7	–	5.6	4.3	0.7	–	–	–	–	–	–	6.7	6
Laurel oak[3]	–	–	1.0	–	10.3	2.1	3.2	3.1	–	–	–	–	–	–	5
Water gum[4]	–	–	–	–	7.0	16.1	1.8	–	–	–	–	–	–	19.0	4
Bald cypress[5]	–	–	–	–	9.3	3.4	1.2	–	–	–	1.0	–	2.9	–	4
Holly	–	–	–	–	–	–	8.6	13.8	–	–	–	12.8	–	26.2	4
Ash	–	–	27.0	–	8.0	22.6	–	–	–	–	–	–	–	3.1	4
Swamp chestnut oak	–	–	–	–	–	2.2	2.6	1.4	–	–	–	–	–	–	3
Atlantic white cedar	–	1.7	–	–	–	–	–	–	–	–	–	–	58.2	–	3
Ironwood	–	–	1.4	3.1	1.0	–	–	–	–	–	–	–	–	–	2
Red bay	–	–	–	–	–	–	–	–	–	–	–	28.4	1.3	–	2
Beech[6]	–	–	–	–	–	–	1.4	0.8	–	–	–	–	–	–	2
Water oak[7]	–	–	–	–	–	–	9.5	7.0	–	–	–	–	–	–	2
White oak	–	–	–	–	–	–	3.5	–	–	–	–	–	–	–	1

Spanish oak	—	—	—	—	—	—	0.8	—	—	—	—	—	—	1
Black oak	—	—	—	—	—	—	1.4	—	—	—	—	—	—	1
Sourwood	—	—	—	—	—	—	6.5	—	—	—	—	—	—	1
Sassafras	—	—	—	—	—	—	1.3	—	—	—	—	—	—	1
Willow oak	—	—	—	—	0.7	—	—	—	—	—	—	—	—	1
Black willow	—	—	—	—	3.8	—	—	—	—	—	—	—	—	1
Pawpaw	—	—	—	—	—	—	—	—	—	—	—	9.3	—	1
Mean no. of trees/ha.	773	1005	652	865	1166	857	588	768	692	798	672	277	953	556

[1] *Liriodendron tulipifera.* [2] *Ulmus americana.* [3] *Quercus laurifolia.* [4] *Nyssa aquatica.* [5] *Taxodium disticum.* [6] *Fagus grandifolia.* [7] *Q. nigra.*

Table 8. Relative importance values for species with sapling-sized individuals, the number of stands in which they occurred, and mean number of saplings per stand

Cluster designation	A'				B'		C'			D'			Isolated stands		No. of stands in which occurred
Stand number	2	3	8	10	5	9	1	11	13	4	7	12	6	14	
Species															
Red maple	—	10.1	10.8	50.0	41.4	33.2	7.3	9.9	15.7	83.8	45.1	56.3	9.8	—	12
Black gum	12.7	—	—	—	4.2	15.6	2.2	22.8	60.4	16.2	22.6	10.3	4.9	—	10
Sweet bay	12.7	10.1	7.0	—	—	5.5	7.3	16.5	23.8	—	—	10.3	—	—	8
Holly	18.3	—	10.8	—	2.9	—	24.1	24.4	—	—	—	—	4.9	81.8	7
Sweet gum	—	—	—	—	5.0	—	15.5	13.2	—	—	32.2	23.0	75.4	—	6
Red bay	56.3	79.8	38.0	50.0	—	—	2.2	3.2	—	—	—	—	—	—	6
Laurel oak	—	—	—	—	7.9	8.2	—	3.2	—	—	—	—	—	7.3	3
American elm	—	—	—	—	11.4	8.2	—	—	—	—	—	—	—	—	3
Pawpaw	—	—	33.4	—	—	—	—	—	—	—	—	—	—	10.9	2
Yellow poplar	—	—	—	—	—	—	4.2	3.2	—	—	—	—	—	—	2
Ash	—	—	—	—	19.3	17.2	—	—	—	—	—	—	—	—	2
Swamp white oak	—	—	—	—	2.1	—	6.4	—	—	—	—	—	—	—	2
June berry[1]	—	—	—	—	—	—	—	3.2	—	—	—	—	—	—	1
Water gum	—	—	—	—	3.7	—	—	—	—	—	—	—	—	—	1
Black oak	—	—	—	—	—	—	—	—	—	—	—	—	4.9	—	1
Water oak	—	—	—	—	2.1	—	—	—	—	—	—	—	—	—	1
Sourwood	—	—	—	—	—	—	14.2	—	—	—	—	—	—	—	1
Beech	—	—	—	—	—	—	4.2	—	—	—	—	—	—	—	1
Mean no. of saplings/ha.	91	111	405	41	637	445	587	334	971	283	486	213	283	408	

[1] Amelanchier arborea.

Table 7). This diversity could result from two factors: first, the distal location from Lake Drummond and its dominating influence on the water table, and second, the sandy loam substrate, which has good internal drainage providing optimal conditions for a great number of tree species.

The proximity of stands 1 and 11 suggests that they have a similar history of cutting and other forms of disturbance (Fig. 1).

Cluster *D* (Fig. 2)

The vegetational composition of cluster *D* was comparable to seral stages of typical southeastern "old-field" succession in which pine is replaced by shade-tolerant hardwoods. The presence of loblolly pine in stands 6, 7, and 12 shows that they are probably drier than others on mineral soils. Stands composing cluster *D* were located on well-drained sandy loam soils.

The aggregation of red maple in stand 12 indicated vegetational heterogeneity that was confirmed by the t-test. However, this aggregation was not generally correlated with substrate heterogeneity; rather, it was due to the occurrence of trees in small clumps, undoubtedly stump sprouts in the aftermath of fire.

The northern edge of the Swamp, where cluster *D* occurred, may have been cleared at one time for agriculture, or burned frequently due to proximity to the Norfolk and Western rail line.

Isolated Stands of Trees (Fig. 2)

Although occurring on peat with high WRC values, stands 8, 13, and 14 showed no significant similarity to cluster *A* or to one another.

Selective logging appears the major reason for stand 8 being excluded from cluster *A*. The scattered islands of trees, low average density and dominance, and high mean basal area document a history of intense but erratic logging. The importance of small tree species (e.g., red bay) also suggests that taller species were selectively cut.

Stand 13, being almost pure Atlantic white cedar, was extremely different from any other stand, even though the soil characteristics were basically like those of other peaty soils. This is an important remnant of the formerly extensive Atlantic white cedar forests.

Stand 14 undoubtedly included the oldest undisturbed vegetation in this study, the mean basal area of the trees being the highest value obtained (108.5 in^2 vs 31.0-93.0 in^2 for other stands). Extremes of the WRC plus conspicuous inundation showed this stand to be extremely wet in certain areas. A compositional similarity to stands within cluster B is probably due to the uniform moisture conditions in both areas, produced by their mutual proximity to Lake Drummond.

Sapling Clusters: General Considerations (Fig. 3)

Cluster composition among saplings was not determined so much by soil characteristics. The sapling composition of stands 4, 9, and 13 on peat was quite similar to that of all stands on mineral soils. In addition, certain stands in cluster A' (on peat) were somewhat similar to others in clusters C' and D', although these lesser relationships are not shown in Figure 3.

The higher degree of similarity among sapling clusters than among tree clusters and the greater difficulty of segregating stands of saplings into clusters suggest that successional changes throughout the study area are toward a more uniform forest cover.

Cluster A' (Fig. 3)

Cluster A' differs from cluster A (Fig. 2) only with respect to stands 4 and 8. The sapling layer in stand 8 is more like the overstory than in stands 2, 3, and 10 (Table 6). Hence, it is presumed that the last three may eventually be dominated by tree-sized individuals of red maple, red bay, and pawpaw (compare Tables 7 and 8).

Large numbers of saplings in the understory of stand 8 are probably the result of previous logging, and selective cutting must have been responsible for the high degree of similarity between sapling and over-story species. On the other hand, the comparatively small number of saplings in stands 2, 3, and 10 may be due to the inhibition of seed germination and seedling growth by the cold, water-logged peaty substrate (Hillel 1971). Although stand 8 is also in peat, it contains many openings in the cover where sunlight can penetrate and warm the soil. If stands like 2, 3, and 10 were selectively cut, leaving species like red maple and red bay, they would certainly be expected to develop like stand 8.

Cluster B' (Fig. 3)

Stand 9 supported a greater similarity of tree and sapling species, but a lower sapling density than stand 5 (Tables 6 and 8). Stand 5 may be developing into a community like stand 9 containing tree-sized red maple, black gum, and ash (Table 7). Neither stand showed evidence of recent disturbance in substrate or moisture relations and may be among the most stable in the study area.

Cluster C' (Fig. 3)

Cluster C' differs from cluster C (Fig. 2) by the inclusion of stand 13, which had a lower tree-to-sapling similarity than stands 1 and 11 (Table 6). Stand 11 had the greatest tree-to-sapling similarity of any investigated. Thus, it appears that stands 13 and 1 are becoming more like stand 11, containing tree-sized holly, black gum, and sweet bay (compare Tables 7 and 8).

The leading dominant in stand 13, Atlantic white cedar, is dependent upon fire to clear areas where seedlings can germinate and grow (Buell and Cain 1943). Because fire is generally controlled by man in the Swamp, a change in composition seems inevitable. Being located in thick peat with a high WRC, stand 13 might be expected to develop more like cluster A' rather than C'. The pattern of development in stand 13 seems somewhat like that of the stands on mineral soils having low WRC values, owing possibly to the extremely uneven topography. Such uneven relief provides relatively dry hummocks for the germination and growth of species tolerant to overstory shading.

Cluster D' (Fig. 3)

Cluster D' differs from cluster D (Fig. 2) only with respect to stands 6 and 4. Stand 12 showed the greatest degree of similarity between the tree and sapling layers. Stands 4 and 7 will probably become dominated by red maple and sweet gum, as in stand 12 (compare Tables 7 and 8).

Stand 4 appeared similar to 8, undoubtedly due to cutting and burning. Clearing may have accelerated seedling and sapling growth. Burning of the upper peat layer could account for the mean WRC being lower in stand 4 than in other stands with a similar tree composition (cluster A). This change from a wet to a relatively drier situation may explain some of stand 4's similarity to stands 7 and 12.

The only saplings in stand 4 were red maple and black gum, with a RIV_s value of 83.8 percent for the former. Since this species is capable of withstanding extremely wet or dry conditions, stands with different soil moisture could have similarly high RIV_s values for red maple. Owing to the low species diversity, it is difficult to surmise whether stand 4 will become more like stands 7 and 12.

Isolated Stands

The tree stratum of stand 6 was most like that of nos. 7 and 12, and the sapling layer had similarity indices of 42 to stand 7 and 38 to stand 12.

The major soil difference was that stand 6 had a lower mean WRC than 7 or 12. The three stands appeared to be undergoing similar "old-field" succession, but with sweet gum the leading sapling in stand 6 rather than red maple as in nos. 7 and 12.

Sapling composition relationships of stand 14 were as difficult to evaluate as those based on its tree layer. The sapling and tree layers were dissimilar, indicating that the stand should undergo great compositional change. There were no saplings of red maple, the leading tree species, but holly exhibited high reproduction. Stand 14 had no appreciable similarity to any of the other 13 stands, including stand 6 and cluster D'. Its greatest similarity index of 26 to stand 1 of cluster C' may indicate that extremes in wetness and dryness are important factors in determining its composition. Yet this similarity value was so low as to seem insignificant, as did the values of 22 to stand 8 and 21 to stand 11. More study is needed to clarify successional relationships of stand 14, including examination of the low reproductivity of red maple and high reproductivity of holly. It is possible that active or passive alleopathy is being produced by holly against red maple.

CONCLUSIONS

The individual characteristics of all stands must be analyzed in order to perceive and explain the apparent similarity of successional trends among so many stands having different soil and moisture conditions. Stands on mineral soils with low WRC values may have wet areas due to topographic variations or to a perched water table. Conversely, hummocks in stands on peat provide drier areas. In addition, peat may become very wet or very dry, depending on rainfall, and at times can withhold moisture from plants. The influence of such factors on the future composition of communities must be considered in much greater detail. In many areas, detailed studies of tree reproduction rates and the response of these rates to moisture relations will be required.

The present forest canopy includes two major community types divisible by substrate, either peat or mineral soils. These groups can be further subdivided into clusters based on soil texture and topography, with a past history of disturbance also an important determinant. Clusters are interrelated along a moisture gradient, except for those having been greatly disturbed. Most of the latter occur on peat. Cluster A (Fig. 2) includes several disturbed stands that were probably pure stands of Atlantic white cedar before logging. Other stands resulting from disturbance contain remnants of the Atlantic white cedar with a few clear-cut areas. These stands exhibit few interrelationships to those of clusters *B, C,* and *D,* in which comparatively undisturbed stands were related along a moisture gradient.

The most prevalent community type throughout the Swamp is dominated by red maple and black gum. Many stands of this type, which occur on peat, have resulted from removal of Atlantic white cedar. Those areas with predominantly mineral soils, however, support a mixed deciduous swamp with evidence of less recent and less severe disturbance.

Red maple and black gum are important species, but their relative importance values are not as great in stands on mineral soil as in those on thick peat. Greater diversity exists in the mixed deciduous swamp, with ash more important in the wetter areas and sweet gum and loblolly pine in drier.

The relative ease of separating clusters based on the tree canopy as opposed to those based on saplings indicates that present adult communities are more distinct than their sapling layers. Logging and burning particularly have simplified or isolated communities and altered seed availability. Successional trends and interrelationships among saplings are complex, but seem mostly related to moisture conditions determined by edaphic and topographic factors.

Within the 4 sapling clusters (Fig. 3), stands 8, 9, 11, and 12 are focal types, with 9 the wettest community, 12 the driest, and 8 and 11 exhibiting fluctuations between these moisture extremes. Although stands 6 and 14 were isolated from the clusters, 6 is relatively dry and 14 exhibits wide moisture fluctuations. The relative important values of saplings from the four clusters and from stand 6 suggest that future vegetation will exhibit a continuum with ash more important in wetter areas, red maple in both wet and dry situations, sweet gum in dry, and holly, black gum, and red bay in areas with wide moisture fluctuations. The uniqueness of 14 makes it impractical to include this stand in the foregoing analysis.

Although the conditions within each stand must be considered individually, each appears to be a continuation of the other stands showing an overlap in species composition. Populations increase or decrease in importance along a moisture gradient in accordance with Whittaker's climax-pattern hypothesis (Whittaker 1953). Instead of a single community type, or even several distinct community types, communities exhibit increasing intergradations based on the overlap in species composition as a direct result of the tolerance of individual populations.

The general overall trend is characterized by moisture fluctuation with a definite drying trend most evident in the northern portion of the study area. This trend is typified by stands 1, 6, 7, 11, and 12

(Fig. 1). In these stands such mesic and submesic species as black oak (*Quercus velutina*), white oak (*Q. alba*), yellow poplar, ironwood, sourwood (*Oxydendron arboreum*), and sweet bay are becoming frequent in the understory. A recent, detailed study of stand 1 (Janszen 1974) concludes, "Beech which is very shade tolerant, may attain canopy importance." Janszen states further that this stand is undergoing fairly rapid succession with red maple increasing its dominance. This would suggest that some areas of the Swamp are ultimately capable of becoming red maple–beech communities. Such vegetation, as is well known, is generally considered typical of the northeastern United States, and not at all like the southeastern swamps.

SUMMARY

Vegetational composition and soil characteristics were analyzed for 14 wooded stands located in the Dismal Swamp National Wildlife Refuge. Cluster diagrams based on the index of dissimilarity were used to evaluate relationships among the stands. Present vegetation was divisible into rather distinct communities caused in part from disturbance.

The most prevalent community type occurs on peat and is dominated by red maple (*Acer rubrum*) and black gum (*Nyssa sylvatica*) with few additional species present. This community type has probably resulted from selective cutting of Atlantic white cedar (*Chamaecyparis thyoides*).

In the mixed deciduous swamp, which generally occurs on mineral soils, red maple and black gum are less important and species diversity is greater. Ash species (*Fraxinus* spp.) are more important in wetter areas, and sweet gum (*Liquidambar styraciflua*) and loblolly pine (*Pinus taeda*) in the relatively drier ones.

Clusters based on sapling composition showed the stands to be basically more similar, regardless of substrate type, than when only tree-sized individuals were considered.

It was concluded that future vegetation will be a continuum of integrated populations with red maple important throughout, ash in areas with hydric substrates, sweet gum in relatively dry areas, and holly (*Ilex opaca*), black gum, and red bay (*Persea borbonia*) important in those that fluctuate between wetter and drier extremes.

ACKNOWLEDGMENTS

This study is based in part on Susan Walker's masters thesis and was supported by a grant from the Old Dominion University Research Foundation. The authors wish to thank Professor Grant Cottam, Department of Botany, University of Wisconsin, for reading the manuscript and making valuable suggestions. Assistance of the Virginia Truck and Ornamentals Experimental Station in Virginia Beach with the soil nutrient analysis is also gratefully acknowledged.

REFERENCES CITED

Bouyoucos, G. J. 1936. Directions for making mechanical analysis of soils by the hydrometer method. *Soil Sci.* 421:225–229.

Bray, J. R., and J. T. Curtis. 1957. An ordination of the upland forest communities of southern Wisconsin. *Ecol. Monographs* 27:325–349.

Buell, M. F., and R. L. Cain. 1943. The successional role of southern white cedar, *Chamaecyparis thyoides,* in southeastern North Carolina. *Ecology* 24:85–93.

Dean, G. W. 1969. Forests and forestry in the Dismal Swamp. *Va. J. Sci.* 20:166–173.

Grosenbaugh, L. R. 1952. Plotless timber estimates, new, fast, easy. *J. Forestry* 50:32–37.

Henry, E. F. 1970. Soils of the Dismal Swamp of Virginia. *Va. J. Sci.* 21:41–46.

Hillel, D. 1971. *Soil and water: physical principles and processes.* Academic Press, New York. 288 pp.

Janszen, T. A. 1974. Studies on the causes of tree distribution in a forest type in the Dismal Swamp National Wildlife Refuge. Masters Thesis Old Dominion Univ. 32 pp.

Kearney, T. H. 1901. Report on a botanical survey of the Dismal Swamp region. *Contrib. U.S. Natl. Herbarium* 5:321–550.

Levy, G. F. 1970. The phytosociology of northern Wisconsin upland openings. *Amer. Midl. Nat.* 83:213–237.

Levy, G. F., and Susan W. Walker. 1971. The combined Bitterlich-rangefinder circular quadrat method in phytosociological studies. *Jeffersonia* 5:37–39.

Lindsey, A. A., J. D. Barton, Jr., and S. R. Miles. 1958. Field efficiencies of forest sampling methods. *Ecology* 39:428–444.

Little, S. 1950. Ecology and silviculture of white cedar and associated hardwoods in southern New Jersey. *Yale Univ. School Forestry Bull.* 56. 103 pp.

McGinnies, W. G. 1934. The relation between frequency index and abundance as applied to plant populations in a semi-arid region. *Ecology* 15:263–282.

Meanley, B. 1968. Notes on Dismal Swamp plants. *Atlantic Nat.* 23:78–82.

Mueller-Dombois, D., and H. Ellenberg. 1974. *Aims and methods of vegetation ecology.* John Wiley & Sons, New York. 547 pp.

Musselman, L. J., D. L. Nickrent, and G. F. Levy. 1977. A contribution towards a vascular flora of the Great Dismal Swamp. *Rhodora* 79:240–268.

Penfound, W. T. 1952. Southern swamps and marshes. *Bot. Rev.* 18:413–446.

Radford, A. E., H. E. Ahles, and C. R. Bell. 1968. *Manual of the vascular flora of the Carolinas.* Univ. North Carolina Press, Chapel Hill. 1183 pp.

Ramsey, E. W., K. R. Hinkle, and L. E. Benander. 1970. Waters of the Dismal Swamp. *Va. J. Sci.* 21:81–83.

Russell, E. W. 1961. *Soil conditions and plant growth.* John Wiley and Sons, New York. 688 pp.

U.S. Dept. Agriculture, Soil Conservation Service, Northeast Technical Service Center, Soil Correlation Unit, Upper Darby, Pa. 1974. Great Dismal Swamp and Dismal Swamp Canal study. Report on ascertainment of soil types and agricultural information. 14 pp.

U.S. Dept. Commerce. 1970. *Statistical abstract of the United States.* 91st ann. ed. 1018 pp.

Waters, S. B., Rebecca D. Bray, and G. F. Levy. 1974. A taxonomic survey of the spring vascular flora of the Nansemond County, Virginia, portion of the Great Dismal Swamp. *Castanea* 39:82–95.

Wells, B. W. 1942. Ecological problems of the southeastern coastal plain. *Bot. Rev.* 8:533–561.

Whitehead, D. R. 1972. Developmental and environmental history of the Dismal Swamp. *Ecol. Monographs* 42:301–315.

Whittaker, R. H. 1953. A consideration of climax theory: the climax as a population and pattern. *Ecol. Monographs* 23:41–78.

LOG FERNS (*DRYOPTERIS CELSA*) AND THEIR RELATIVES IN THE DISMAL SWAMP

W. H. Wagner, Jr., and Lytton J. Musselman

The ferns of the Dismal Swamp are still not entirely known. About 30 species occur in or near the Swamp, the most abundant being the cinnamon fern (*Osmunda cinnamomea*), royal fern (*O. regalis*), sensitive fern (*Onoclea sensibilis*), Virginia chain fern (*Anchistea virginica*), and narrow chain fern (*Lorinseria areolata*). Some species are near their southern limits on the coastal plain in the Dismal Swamp area, e.g., fancy fern (*Dryopteris intermedia*). Another, the very interesting epiphytic resurrection fern (*Polypodium polypodioides*) is nearing its northern limits. Of all the ferns and fern allies of the Dismal Swamp, however, unquestionably the most interesting is the log fern (*Dryopteris celsa*) and its hybrids (Fig. 1).

Log fern is one of the rarest and most localized of eastern American ferns. Nowhere is it more common than in the Dismal Swamp. The species has attracted much attention from biosystematists, as will be discussed below, and its evolutionary origin has been worked out with a high degree of confidence. Log fern is noted for its ability to hybridize with other species of *Dryopteris*. In 1938 Small wrote that "the Great Dismal Swamp within this century has furnished the clues to and the type specimens of three species of *Dryopteris—D. celsa, D. atropalustris,* and *D. separabilis.*" Since Small wrote this, we have learned much about the nature of these "species." However, the plant known as *D. atropalustris* still remains a mystery.

The name *Dryopteris celsa* means, approximately, the "exalted oak fern." The genus *Dryopteris* is "oak fern" (= woodland fern or woodfern) and the epithet *celsa* ("exalted") comes from the habit of the original plants, perched upon logs. The log fern is a tall, showy plant, ideal for gardens, but it is impossible to obtain from ordinary garden suppliers because of its rarity. Horticulturists are generally unaware of the plant.

Log fern was discovered first in the late 1800s by William Palmer near the head of Washington Ditch. He described it (Palmer 1899)

Fig. 1. Log fern (*Dryopteris celsa*) fronds showing variations. Upper left: Nansemond County, Va., northeast of junction of Drummond Methodist Church Road and Drummond Causeway, east of Wallaceton, *Wagner 70512* (MICH). Others: Nansemond County, Lake Drummond, northeast of Spillway, *Wagner 70510* (MICH). Scale = 5 cm.

as a subspecies of Goldie's woodfern (*D. goldiana*). In 1938 J. K. Small recognized it for the first time as a wholly distinct species, and he described two other relatives of the log fern from the Dismal Swamp. The history of log fern and its relatives has been one of great confusion practically since its original description. According to our present knowledge, even William Palmer himself was confused. He wrote (1902) as follows:

In June, 1896, at the head of Washington Ditch, in the Dismal Swamp of Virginia, I found a few imperfect fern fronds which I thought at the time might be *Dryopteris cristata Clintoniana*. The following year at the same place I found a few more but none of them perfect. Never having seen Clinton's fern growing I with some doubt concluded my specimens belonged to that subspecies. On June 8, 1899, however, while examining another part of the swamp, about eight miles distant, I found the same fern abundant, growing about the bases of large trees and on huge, partially rotten logs, and at once satisfied myself of its distinctness from the fern mentioned. This view was confirmed soon after my return to Washington, on finding near Lincolnia, Fairfax County, Virginia, on July 9, a large colony of Clinton's fern, and later a small colony near Glen Echo, Maryland. Comparison then of a large amount of fresh material of these two forms, my own and the collection in the National Herbarium, convinced me not only of their distinctness from each other, but from other species of Eastern North America as well.

According to our studies, there is no plant referable to what is generally called *D. clintoniana* (D. C. Eat.) Dowell that is found south of Pennsylvania. All records from Maryland and Virginia and southward pertain to *D. celsa* rather than *D. clintoniana*.

L. M. Underwood (1908) added to the confusion by reducing taxon *celsa* to a synonym of *clintoniana*. Furthermore, in the area of New York, New Jersey, and Pennsylvania, where both taxa are known, the identifications given these plants have been chaotic, largely because their differences had not been elucidated. The taxonomy of these plants broke down almost completely in connection with the fern known as *D.* X *leedsii* Wherry in its occurrences in Harford County, Maryland. (X denotes hybrid origin of the plant. See *Taxon* 24:296, 1975). What later turned out to be typical *D. celsa* was confused with *D. celsa* x *marginalis*, of which it was regarded as the fertile tetraploid form, and the *D. celsa* x *marginalis* was interpreted as *D. goldiana* x *marginalis* (see Wherry 1942, Walker 1962 *a* and *b*, Wagner and Wagner 1966, Wagner and Taylor 1976).

It is perhaps no surprise that the hybrids involving *D. celsa* have caused confusion (see Wagner 1970, p. 175), but the differences between log fern and so-called Clinton's fern are sufficiently well defined that they should no longer be confused. *D. celsa* more closely resembles *D. goldiana,* and *D. clintoniana* resembles *D. cristata. D. celsa* (Fig. 1) has a frond outline which is ovate-lanceolate, while that in *D. clintoniana* is narrower. The pinnae of *D. celsa* are relatively longer than those of *D. clintoniana* and tend to be more deeply cut and to have smoother margins. The lower pinnae of *D. celsa* provide the strongest contrast, being lanceolate and commonly provided with stalked pinnules at the base; in *D. clintoniana* the basal pinnae are more triangular, and the basal pinnules are usually adnate. The scales at the petiole base in *D. celsa* tend to be blackish and glossy, rather than tan or brown and dull as in *D. clintoniana*. Also, the spores of *D. celsa* average around 38 microns in exospore length (range of averages of different collections is 36–40.5), while those of *D. clintoniana* average around 45 microns (range 40.5–48.5). Cytologically, *D. celsa* is a tetraploid, and *D. clintoniana* is a hexaploid, as was originally established in the work of Stanley Walker.

Walker did most of his studies at the University of Leeds, England, in association with Professor Irene Manton. The results of his investigations (1962 *a* and *b*, 1969) were most remarkable in relation to the occurrence of the log fern in the Dismal Swamp, for he postulated that the log fern originated as a sterile hybrid of the Louisiana, or "Florida," woodfern (*D. ludoviciana*) and the Goldie's, or "giant," woodfern (*D. goldiana*). The former is known only from the outer coastal plain in the Gulf States and on the eastern coast as far north as the Carolinas (where it is extremely rare and sporadic), and the latter is a widespread northern species occurring down the Appalachian mountain chain to Georgia. Nowhere do these hypothesized parental species grow together today. Neither *D. ludoviciana* nor *D. goldiana* has been found to occur in the Dismal Swamp. Nevertheless, *D. celsa* is widespread there, as it is in a number of places where neither parent is found.

Walker postulates (1962*a* and *b*, 1969) that the original hybrid, which must have formed at some time in the past when the parents grew together, had the cytogenetic constitution of GL, i.e., one whole genome each from *D. goldiana* (GG) and *D. ludoviciana* (LL). Then, through accidental misdivisions of certain cells and resultant doubling of the chromosome complement, a tetraploid fern appeared with the cytogenetic constitution of GGLL. Thus the original sterile hybrid, in which the chromosomes failed to pair normally, became converted to a fertile hybrid in which the chromosomes paired and normal spores were produced. Through this mechanism the modern form of *D. celsa* originated and through the years spread itself by spores.

After the completion of Walker's initial papers, a number of relevant investigations have been made on various aspects of the nature of *D. celsa* (e.g., Wagner and Chen 1965, Wagner and Wagner 1965, 1966, Wagner et al. 1969, Wagner 1970, Thomas et al. 1974, Wagner and Taylor 1976). Most of these have been new discoveries regarding the geographical range of this fern, and we now know that it extends as far north as New York and Michigan and south into Georgia and Louisiana.

The concentration of *D. celsa* in the Dismal Swamp area makes one wonder whether the fern originated there sometime in the past. We have records from throughout the area. The best known populations are those around Lake Drummond, where it is very common. In addition, we have other records for four counties, these collections in the herbaria of Harvard University, New York Botanical Garden, University of Michigan, U.S. National Museum, and Old Dominion University. They include Surry County (5 localities), Norfolk County (3), Nansemond County (3), and Southampton County (1). In addition, we have found a very large population in nearby Gates County, North Carolina, the first record for that part of the state. The plants occur there in two extensive colonies of hundreds of plants, including examples of the hybrid *D.* X *separabilis* (see below), the latter being the first records for the Carolinas.

In addition, several new hybrids have been confirmed involving this fern in a number of localities. The total list is as follows:

1. *D. celsa* x *cristata*—Michigan, New York

2. *D. celsa* x *goldiana*—Michigan, New York, Pennsylvania, Tennessee

3. *D. celsa* x *intermedia* (= *D.* X *separabilis* Small)—Maryland, Michigan, New York, Virginia

4. *D. celsa* x *marginalis* (= *D.* X *leedsii* Wherry)—Arkansas, Maryland, New York, Pennsylvania

5. *D. celsa* x *ludoviciana* (= *D.* X *australis* Wherry)—Alabama, Georgia, Louisianna, South Carolina

Two other hybrids are postulated, but strong support for their actual occurrence is still lacking. These are *D. celsa* x *clintoniana* (to be sought in the Great Lakes region and in eastern New York, Pennsylvania, and northern New Jersey), and *D. celsa* x *spinulosa* (to be sought especially in the northern part of the range of *D. celsa*, where it comes in contact with *D. spinulosa*, including the Dismal Swamp region—see below).

A very striking log fern hybrid in the Dismal Swamp has been found a number of times by one of us (Musselman) in connection with his efforts to find new colonies and variations of *D. celsa*. This is *D.* X *separabilis*, a very distinctive and showy fern that occurs side-by-side with its parents. In his early studies Walker (1959, p. 110) first determined the chromosome situation in this plant from Dismal Swamp materials, and he wrote as follows: "*D. separabilis* Small is considered by most authors to be the hybrid between *D. goldiana* and *D. intermedia*, both of which are diploid. Cytological investigation of a number of specimens certainly show its hybridity but it cannot have the considered parentage since it is triploid. I believe that it may well be the hybrid between *D. celsa* and *D. intermedia*, which are tetraploid and diploid respectively, as this would account for its chromosome complement and also for its morphology." All evidence since has tended to support his conclusion, and there seems to be no question that this is a log fern hybrid. In the Dismal Swamp we have no evidence of *D. goldiana* being present, so its participation in the hybridization is obviously very unlikely. Furthermore, *D.* X *separabilis* is so predictable in its appearance that we have found it everywhere the possible parents were encountered together. It is very readily separated from *D. goldiana* x *intermedia* (cf. Walker 1959, Fig. 11, right; Evans and Wagner 1964, pl. 1302), which differs in having broader, more divided leaves and only the diploid complement of chromosomes.

The greatest problem involving log fern and its allies in Dismal Swamp has to do with the plant known as *D. atropalustris,* described by J. K. Small in 1938. He contrasted this new species with two others in his diagnosis as follows: "*Dryopteridem Goldianam* atque *D. celsam* referente, a quibus dignoscitur lamina brevi lataque, facie triangulari: foliolis paucis, distalibus rare fertilibus: venis segmentorum fertilium semel dichotomis: soris medianis vel extramedianis. Great Dismal Swamp, ad Lake Drummond, Octobri 2, 1921, E. Jerome Grimes, typus in herb. Hort. Bot. Noveboracensis." Thanks to Dr. J. T. Mickel, we have been permitted to borrow and study this type specimen (Fig. 2). Unfortunately the sori of this specimen are imperfectly formed, so that it is not possible to determine from it whether the spores are normal or abortive, indicating whether it is a species or a sterile hybrid. For this reason we have made efforts to rediscover plants of this description in and around the Dismal Swamp since 1970.

The other specimens cited by Small (1938) under his original description of *D. atropalustris* were from Kent County, Delaware, Lorain County, Ohio, and Santee Canal, South Carolina. The specimens we have seen from these localities appear to be merely *D. celsa* forms. For example, the one from Santee Canal collected by Ravenel is a large specimen of *D. celsa* that is slightly more divided than usual. It is shown in Figure 3.

One real possibility suggested by the type specimen of *D. atropalustris* is that it is indeed the sought-for hybrid of *D. celsa* and *D. spinulosa,* both of which occur together in various localities in the Swamp. Because the hybrid *D. celsa* x *intermedia* (= *D.* X *separabilis*) frequently occurs in the colonies of *D. celsa,* we fully expect to find the hybrid of *D. celsa* and *D. spinulosa.* Furthermore, certain of the character states of Small's taxon *D. atropalustris* are suggestive of *D. spinulosa* being a

Fig. 2. Type specimen of *Dryopteris atropalustris* Small. (N.B. Apparently the author originally intended to name the plant *Dryopteris atropaludis* but changed his mind.) Specimen is mounted on standard 12″ × 18″ herbarium sheet.

Fig. 3. Specimen collected by Ravenel in South Carolina and determined by J. K. Small as *D. atropalustris*. Mounted on standard 12″ × 18″ herbarium sheet.

possible relative, notably (1) the frond outline, (2) the vein branchings, and especially (3) the medial to supramedial soral position, which is common in *D. spinulosa*.

On the basis of three sources of evidence, however, we now conclude that *D. atropalustris* is probably an extreme growth form of *D. celsa,* and not a hybrid or a distinct species. The bases of our conclusions are as follows:

1. In December 1970 one of us (Wagner), in company with B. W. McAlpin, studied two localities—along Lake Drummond, northeast of the spillway, and east of Wallaceton—and discovered unexpectedly great variation, as illustrated in Fig. 1. Among the forms we found were ones nearly as narrow as northern crested woodfern (*D. cristata*) and others as broad as *D. atropalustris*.

2. In June 1953 the late C. V. Morton made a remarkable collection of basal pinnae from a number of plants of *D. celsa* at the head of the Feeder Ditch at the entrance of Lake Drummond, in which variations from more or less "typical" *D. celsa* to *D. atropalustris* are illustrated. These specimens are on deposit in the National Herbarium and were sent to us (mounted on three sheets) in connection with the present study.

3. In June 1974 one of us (Musselman) discovered several plants having characters of *D. atropalustris,* as shown in Fig. 4. Not only is the frond outline very wide, but the sori are clearly medial to supramedial. Fortunately, this specimen has well-developed (although young) sori, and some of the sporangia are mature enough to yield fully developed spores. Examination of these spores reveals that they are normal in shape, fairly uniform in size, and possess typical perispores. Thus there is no question that there can be forms of *D. celsa* that resemble *D. atropalustris* type material in the essentials of frond outline, pinnae outline, pinnule shape, and soral position. There is no reason to conclude that the specimens taken by Musselman are of hybrid origin involving *D. celsa* and *D. spinulosa*.

Dryopteris celsa x *spinulosa* has still not been found and remains unknown morphologically and cytologically. For a number of reasons this is a "key" hybrid, and the Dismal Swamp is an ideal place for it to form, as the parents coexist here in considerable numbers.

CONCLUSIONS

In spite of a history of taxonomic confusion, the log fern (*Dryopteris celsa*) has proved to be a distinct sexual tetraploid species. Described originally from the Dismal Swamp, it is, so far as we know, still more

Fig. 4. Unusual form of *D. celsa* showing extremely dissected condition with sori terminal on frond and submarginal in relation to the segments. City of Chesapeake, Va., 0.5 mi. east of Lake Drummond, *Musselman 4777 dup* (MICH). Scale = 5 cm.

common there than in any other locality. Elsewhere it is a rare and sporadic species, often overlooked and commonly confused with other woodferns, especially Goldie's woodfern (*D. goldiana*) and Clinton's woodfern (*D. clintoniana*). The former of the presumed "look alikes" is a diploid species, and the latter a hexaploid. *D. clintoniana* does not occur in the South, so far as we have been able to determine; all of its occurrences are north of the bordering line of the Wisconsin glaciation. According to Walker (1962 *a* and *b*, 1969), *D. celsa* originated sometime in the past as the natural hybrid of *D. goldiana* and the Louisiana woodfern (*D. ludoviciana*), two species which today do not coexist but are separated by long distances. The former is in the northern mountains, the latter in the southeast along the coastal plain.

In the Dismal Swamp and elsewhere, the log fern is noted for its remarkable ability to form hybrids with other species, and five of these are well known. In the Swamp, however, we have only one definite hybrid (*D.* X *separabilis* = *D. celsa* x *intermedia*), and the possibility of another, *D. celsa* x *spinulosa*. The latter has not been found in any locality, but the plant described from the Dismal Swamp as *D. atropalustris* Small was a possible candidate. Examination of the type specimen of *D. atropalustris* shows several suggestive characters, such as frond outline, pinnae, and soral position. However, efforts by the authors to rediscover *D. atropalustris* have revealed that *D. celsa* has the ability to develop forms with characters similar to *D. atropalustris*. One specimen in particular, that taken by Musselman in June 1974 and shown in Figure 4, has certain features of *D. atropalustris,* but has normal spores, indicating that it is not a hybrid involving two species. All the evidence points to the interpretation of *D. atropalustris* as merely a sporadic form of *D. celsa.*

Our studies of the log ferns and their relatives in the Dismal Swamp will not be complete until we have discovered the hybrid *D. celsa* x *spinulosa*. This hybrid should have considerable interest not only for its morphology but for its cytology as well, the latter of significance in understanding the evolution of this group of plants. *D. celsa* x *spinulosa* has not been collected anywhere that the ranges of the parents overlap. At least, plants that unquestionably represent this combination have not been established. Because of the coexistence of the parents in the Dismal Swamp, this should be an ideal place to search for the hybrid.

ACKNOWLEDGMENTS

We are indebted to various individuals for their help in this study, including David B. Lellinger, U.S. National Museum, Rolla M. Tryon, Gray Herbarium, Bruce McAlpin, New York Botanical Garden, and E. T. Wherry, University of Pennsylvania. Some of these studies were conducted under National Science Foundation Grant GB–30918x, "The evolutionary characters of the ferns."

REFERENCES CITED

Evans, A. M., and W. H. Wagner, Jr. 1964. *Dryopteris goldiana* x *intermedia—* a natural woodfern cross of noteworthy morphology. *Rhodora* 66:255–266.

Palmer, W. 1899. Ferns of the Dismal Swamp, Virginia. *Proc. Biol. Soc. Washington* 13:61–70.

———. 1902. The log fern. *Fern Bull.* 10:37–41.

Small, J. K. 1938. *Ferns of the southeastern states.* Science Press, Lancaster, Pa. 517 pp.

Thomas, R. D., W. H. Wagner, Jr., and M. R. Mesler. 1974. Log fern *(Dryopteris celsa)* and related species in Louisiana. *Castanea* 38:269–274.

Underwood, L. M. 1908. *Our native ferns and their allies.* 6th ed., rev. Henry Holt and Co., New York. 158 pp.

Wagner, W. H., Jr. 1970. Evolution of *Dryopteris* in relation to the Appalachians. Pp. 147–192 *in* P. C. Holt (ed). The distributional history of the biota of the Southern Appalachians. Part II: Flora. *Va. Polytech. Inst. & State Univ. Res. Div. Monographs* 2.

Wagner, W. H., Jr., and Katherine Lim Chen. 1965. Abortion of spores and sporangia as a tool in the detection of *Dryopteris* hybrids. *Amer. Fern J.* 55:9–29.

Wagner, W. H., Jr. and Florence S. Wagner. 1965. Rochester area log ferns *(Dryopteris celsa)* and their hybrids. *Proc. Rochester Acad. Sci.* 11:57–71.

———. 1966. Pteridophytes of the Mountain Lake area, Giles Co., Virginia: biosystematic studies, 1964–1965. *Castanea* 31:121–140.

Wagner, W. H., Jr., Florence S. Wagner, and D. J. Hagenah. 1969. The log fern *(Dryopteris celsa)* and its hybrids in Michigan. *Michigan Botanist* 8:137–145.

Wagner, W. H., Jr., and W. C. Taylor. 1976. *Dryopteris leedsü* and its westernmost station. *Sida* 6:224–234.

———. 1962a. Further studies in the genus *Dryopteris:* the origin of *D. clintoniana, D. celsa,* and related taxa. *Amer. J. Bot.* 49:497–503.

———. 1962*b*. The problem of *Dryopteris leedsii*. *Amer. J. Bot.* 49:971–974.

———. 1969. Identification of a diploid ancestral genome in the *Dryopteris spinulosa* complex. *Brit. Fern Gaz.* 10:97–99.

Walker, S. 1959. Cytotaxonomic studies of some American species of *Dryopteris*. *Amer. Fern J.* 49:104–112.

Wherry, E. T. 1942. A woodfern hybrid deserves a name. *Bartonia* 21:2.

[Editor's note: Also see Nickrent, D. L., L. J. Musselman, Laura A. Pitchford, and D. W. Sampson. 1978. The distribution and ecology of *Dryopteris* in southeastern Virginia and adjacent North Carolina. *Amer. Fern J.* 68:45–51.]

HYDROLOGY OF THE DISMAL SWAMP, VIRGINIA–NORTH CAROLINA

William F. Lichtler and Patrick N. Walker

INTRODUCTION

The Dismal Swamp, on the border between eastern Virginia and North Carolina, is one of the few remaining large areas of wet wilderness in the eastern United States. The flora and fauna of the Swamp are predominantly southern, yet a large number of northern plants and animals are present. Recognizing the unusual character of the Swamp, Congress passed an act (P.L. 92–478) authorizing the Secretary of the Interior to determine the feasibility and desirability of protecting and preserving the Swamp and the Dismal Swamp Canal. The U.S. Geological Survey is one of eight Federal agencies participating in the determination.

Purpose and Scope

The purpose of this report is to summarize and interpret information on the hydrology of the Dismal Swamp area and the related geology and to suggest aspects of the hydrology that need further study. Several reconnaissance trips were made to the Swamp to observe groundwater and surface-water conditions and to hand-auger shallow holes through the peat, but time did not permit extensive field work.

DESCRIPTION OF THE AREA

Location and Extent

The Dismal Swamp, as used in this report, comprises about 210,000 acres between Chesapeake, Virginia, and Elizabeth City, North Carolina, and is almost equally divided between the two states (Fig. 1). The study area in Virginia is within the independent cities of Chesapeake and Suffolk (the latter shown as Nansemond City in Fig. 1). The North Carolina study area includes parts of Currituck, Camden, Gates, Perquimans, and Pasquotank counties.

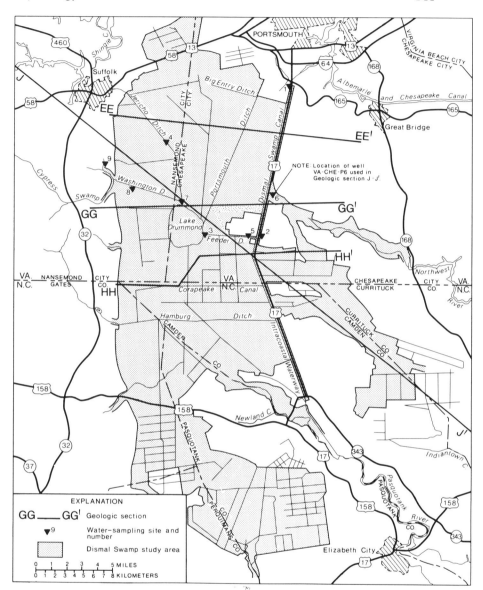

Fig. 1. Dismal Swamp study area showing location of geologic sections and water sampling sites. Sections *EE-EE'*, *GG-GG'* and *HH-HH'* are equivalent to sections *B*, *C* and *D*, respectively, in Figs. 2 and 3 Oaks and Whitehead (this volume).

Estimates of the original size of the Swamp range widely and include some estimates of as much as 1 million acres. The high figures probably included large wet areas that are not generally considered to be part of Dismal Swamp.

Topography and Physiography

Morphologic subdivisions in the report are those used by Oaks and Coch (1973, pp 14–24) and also by Oaks and Whitehead in the present volume. Several of the latter's figures will be referred to rather than duplicating them in our report.

The surface of Dismal Swamp slopes gently eastward at about 1 foot per mile from an altitude of 25 feet near the toe of the Suffolk Scarp to 15 feet near Deep Creek Swale (Oaks and Whitehead, Figs. 2 and 3). At the west edge of the Swamp the Suffolk Scarp rises abruptly to an altitude of 60 to 70 feet on its undissected crest. The face of the scarp slopes eastward as much as 130 feet to the mile (Oaks and Whitehead, Fig. 3).

The Suffolk Scarp can be traced continuously for at least 210 miles from the Potomac River in northern Virginia to the Neuse River in North Carolina. It was formed as a shoreline feature during the Pleistocene Epoch when sea level was approximately 45 feet higher than it is at present.

Deep Creek Swale bounds the Dismal Swamp on the east (Oaks and Whitehead, Fig. 3). The axis of the swale trends north-south, and the land surface rises from the center westward to the Dismal Swamp and eastward to the Fentress Rise. The altitude of the swale ranges from about 10 feet near the center to about 15 feet near the Swamp and the Fentress Rise. The fact that Deep Creek Swale is lower than the Dismal Swamp yet is not a part of it is significant, and is discussed in the section on the origin of the Dismal Swamp.

The Fentress Rise consists of five large remnants of a gently westward-sloping surface that rises eastward from the Deep Creek Swale to a flat crest with an altitude between 20 and 25 feet (Oaks and Coch 1973, p. 19). The rise extends from Norfolk, Virginia, on the north almost to Albemarle Sound in North Carolina. It is broken by the four east-west–trending valleys of the Eastern and Southern branches of the Elizabeth River, the Northwest River, and Indiantown Creek. The eastern boundary of the Fentress Rise is the Hickory Scarp (Oaks and Whitehead, Figs. 2 and 3).

Climate

The climate of Dismal Swamp is temperate, characterized by long, humid summers and mild winters. The average annual rainfall at Wallaceton–Lake Drummond station at the control structure on the Feeder Ditch is 50.42 inches (U.S. Weather Bureau, 1965). The average annual rainfall is 47.19 inches at Suffolk's Lake Kilby and 44.94 inches at Norfolk airport. The wettest months at Wallaceton–Lake Drummond station are July and August, with 6.73 and 5.92 inches of rainfall, respectively. The driest are October and December, with 3.20 and 3.28 inches, respectively (Table 1).

Average annual temperature is 59.0°F at Lake Kilby and 59.7°F at Norfolk airport. Temperature is not recorded at Wallaceton–Lake Drummond station.

GEOLOGY

Geologic formations underlying Dismal Swamp range in age from Precambrian to Holocene. Approximately 2800 feet of unconsolidated or poorly consolidated sedimentary rocks overlie the crystalline "basement" rocks of Precambrian or Paleozoic age (Fig. 2). The unconsolidated rocks range in age from Late Jurassic(?) and Cretaceous to Holocene.

Cretaceous Rocks

Approximately half the total thickness of the unconsolidated rock is of Early Cretaceous age (Fig. 2). These rocks are mostly of continental origin and consist of alternating sand and clay layers. The sand beds form some of the most productive aquifers in the coastal plain of Virginia; however, beneath Dismal Swamp most of them contain salty water.

Rocks of Late Cretaceous age overlie rocks of Early Cretaceous age (Fig. 2). They range in thickness from about 200 feet on the west side of the Swamp to about 600 feet on the east. In general, the Late Cretaceous rocks are of marine origin and contain a higher percentage of clay and fine sand than the Early Cretaceous sediments. Thin, waterbearing limestone beds and sand layers occur at some locations.

Paleocene-Eocene Rocks

Rocks of Paleocene age overlie the rocks of Late Cretaceous age (Fig. 2). In a large part of the coastal plain, Paleocene rocks are thick and

Table 1. Normal precipitation (in inches)

	Jan.	Feb.	Mar.	Apr.	May	June	July	Aug.	Sept.	Oct.	Nov.	Dec.	Annual
Norfolk W.B. Airport	3.33	3.21	3.45	3.16	3.36	3.61	5.92	5.97	4.22	2.92	3.05	2.74	44.94
Suffolk Lake Kilby*	3.36	3.53	3.50	3.12	3.89	4.15	5.86	5.67	3.98	3.39	3.58	3.16	47.19
Wallaceton Lake Drummond	3.64	3.65	3.95	3.76	3.98	4.49	6.73	5.92	4.37	3.20	3.45	3.28	50.42

NOTE: Data from Climatic summary of the United States, supplement for 1951–60.
* Record years 15 to 18 years

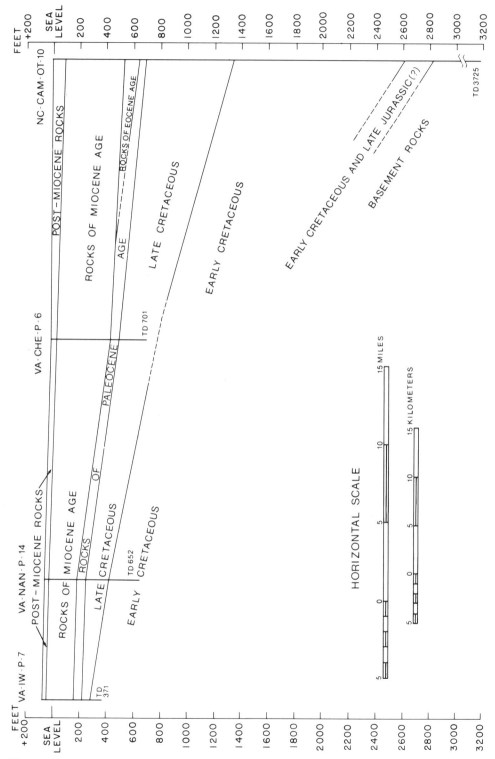

Fig. 2. Geologic section showing rock units under Dismal Swamp. Post-Miocene rocks include those of Pliocene, Pleistocene, and Holocene ages (after Brown et al. 1972).

clayey, and act as a confining bed between Eocene and younger aquifers, and the Cretaceous aquifers. However, in the Dismal Swamp area Paleocene rocks are only 25 to 30 feet thick and are composed mostly of glauconitic sand and limestone of low permeability.

Rocks of Eocene age occur under the easternmost part of Dismal Swamp but pinch out to the west. In the area of the Swamp, Eocene rocks are mostly glauconitic limestone with a maximum thickness of 100 feet.

Miocene Rocks

Rocks of Miocene age include the Calvert, Choptank, and St. Marys Formations. They consist of alternating sand and clay layers overlying the Eocene and older rocks and in the Dismal Swamp area are 400 to 500 feet thick (Fig. 2). More than half the Miocene section is composed of tight clay; some clay beds as thick as 100 feet occur in the lower part.

Miocene and Pliocene Rocks of the Yorktown Formation

The Yorktown Formation is the uppermost formation of the Miocene Series. Recent studies of the microfossils contained in the Yorktown Formation (McLean 1966, p. 28) as well as studies of the vertebrate fossils by the U.S. Geological Survey indicate that the upper part of the Yorktown is of early Pliocene age. The Yorktown Formation extends to within 50 feet or less of the land surface and is exposed in sand pits, where it can be recognized by its characteristic blue-gray color in unweathered sections and by the yellowish-orange and dark reddish-brown saprolite above the unweathered section.

The upper surface of the Yorktown Formation is an irregular erosional surface that slopes gently eastward from about 130 feet near Petersburg, Virginia, to below sea level in the Dismal Swamp (Oaks and Whitehead, Figs. 3 and 4). Present-day drainage channels generally follow the old post-Miocene channels.

Pliocene and Pleistocene Formations

Post-Yorktown geology is much more complicated than once supposed, as explained in detail by Oaks and Whitehead, and Whitehead and Oaks in this volume and in their other published works concerning this subject. Equally thorough studies have not been made of the North Carolina part of the Swamp, but it is assumed that the geology is similar to the Virginia section. It is our purpose now merely to review briefly those formations that underlie the Dismal Swamp and seem particularly relevant to its groundwater hydrology. The formations are outlined in Table 2, and the geologic sections are shown in Oaks and Whitehead's Figure 3 on p. 6.

The Sedley Formation probably extended originally from the present coastline to the vicinity of Petersburg, Virginia. However, subsequent erosion has removed the Sedley from several places, especially east of the Suffolk Scarp, where it is present only as thin, isolated remnants that extend less than a mile eastward from the scarp in the subsurface (Oaks and Coch 1973, p. 51). The age of the Sedley Formation is uncertain, but it is probably late Pliocene and/or early Pleistocene. The Sedley unconformably overlies the Yorktown Formation and is overlain by younger formations in several small areas in the western part of the Dismal Swamp (see Oaks and Whitehead, Fig. 3, geologic sections *B* and *D*).

The Windsor Formation extends from the Surry Scarp eastward to the Suffolk Scarp. It is thickest (as much as 35 feet) near the Suffolk Scarp, where it unconformably overlies remnants of the Sedley Formation or the Yorktown Formation. The Windsor Formation, of middle Pleistocene age, terminates to the east rather abruptly at the Suffolk Scarp (see Oaks and Whitehead, Fig. 3). There is evidence that a protracted period of subaerial erosion followed deposition of the Windsor Formation. This erosion and strong headland retreat of the Suffolk Scarp caused by wave action during submergence probably removed all traces of the Windsor Formation east of the scarp.

The Great Bridge Formation overlies the Yorktown from the Deep Creek Swale eastward to the ocean. Its age is probably late Pleistocene, but exact dating is uncertain, as radiocarbon dating of wood fragments in the formation shows its age to be greater than the age limit of this technique (47,000 years).

The Norfolk Formation unconformably overlies the Yorktown beneath most of the Dismal Swamp, the southern part of the Deep Creek Swale, and the northern segment of the Fentress Rise (see Oaks and Whitehead, Fig. 3). In part of the Deep Creek Swale and the Fentress Rise, the Norfolk Formation conformably overlies the Great Bridge Formation. Its average thickness is 30 feet at the Fentress Rise, becoming thinner to the east and the west (Oaks and Coch 1973, p. 72). The present topography east of the Suffolk Scarp is a subdued reflection of the top of the Norfolk Formation (see Oaks and Whitehead, Fig. 5). Norfolk sediments are unconformably overlain by the Londonbridge Formation in the Deep Creek Swale, in parts of the Dismal Swamp, and in northern segments of the Fentress Rise, and by the Sand Bridge Formation in westernmost Dismal Swamp. Sediments of Holocene age overlie the Norfolk Formation, where other post-Norfolk units are absent (Oaks and Coch 1973, p. 73).

The Norfolk Formation is composed of a lower member and a highly variable upper member. The lower member consists of bluish-gray, subangular to subrounded, fine to a very coarse quartz sand containing from a trace to 20 percent fine pebble gravel. The lower member is present through virtually the entire area of the Dismal Swamp and is a useful stratigraphic marker (Oaks and Coch 1973, p. 73).

The upper member of the Norfolk Formation consists of eight facies (Table 2). The coarse-sand facies (Qn_1) is present under the Suffolk Scarp and the extreme western part of Dismal Swamp, where it is the principal aquifer for domestic and other small to moderate, 5 to 20 gpm (gallons per minute), water supplies. The coarse-sand facies grades eastward under Dismal Swamp into the medium-sand facies (Qn_5) (see Oaks and Whitehead, Fig. 3). The medium-sand facies underlies most of the Dismal Swamp and, in turn, grades into the fine-sand facies (Qn_8) beneath most of the area east of the Dismal Swamp as shown in our Figure 3. The coarse-sand facies (Qn_1) of the upper member crops out at altitudes between 25 and 70 feet, in a belt less than one mile wide that trends north-south along the Suffolk Scarp (Oaks and Coch 1973, p. 73). It ranges in thickness from a veneer to 50 feet or more in undissected parts of the Suffolk Scarp. These three facies $(Qn_1, Qn_5, \text{and } Qn_8)$ of the Norfolk Formation probably play an important role in the hydrology of the Dismal Swamp, as will be explained later.

The Londonbridge Formation occurs in the subsurface beneath most of Deep Creek Swale and the eastern part of the Dismal Swamp. It also occurs as small remnants in breaches of the Fentress Rise, where the Norfolk Formation is high in the Deep Creek Swale, and beneath most of the western part of Dismal Swamp. In the area of the Dismal Swamp, the Londonbridge Formation is a clayey silt that unconformably overlies the Norfolk Formation. The Londonbridge underlies the Sand Bridge Formation except along pre-Holocene channels in the Dismal Swamp where both formations are missing (see Oaks and Whitehead, Figs. 3 and 6).

The Sand Bridge Formation is composed of a lower member of homogeneous sand and an upper member that is variable in some areas but fairly homogeneous in the Dismal Swamp. The lower member forms a blanket of silty sand 2 to 8 feet thick beneath low areas east of the Suffolk Scarp and pinches out near the scarp and the Fentress Rise. It generally overlies the Londonbridge Formation where present, or unconformably overlies the Norfolk Formation (see Oaks and Whitehead, Figs. 3 and 7).

The upper member is a sheetlike deposit, averaging 2 to 6 feet in thickness throughout much of the Dismal Swamp (see Oaks and

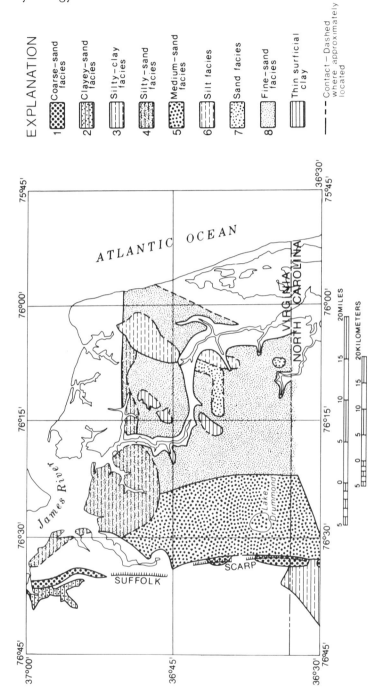

Fig. 3. Distribution of major sediment facies of Norfolk Formation, southeastern Virginia (after Oaks and Coch 1973).

Table 2. Descriptions of units shown in Oaks and Whitehead Figure 3

Holocene
Qhu-Undivided sediments
Beach, marsh, swamp, and stream sediments

Pleistocene
Qsb-Sand Bridge Formation
Upper member: (facies designated by numbers in geologic sections)
    (1) Estuarine and tidal channel: clayey-sand facies
    (2) Fluvial and lagoon: silty-sand facies
    (3) Marsh and tidal flat: silty-clay facies
    (4) Barrier: sand ridge and mud flat complex
Lower member: Coastal sand, silty sand, and clayey sand (exposed only as narrow bands along streams; shown in cross sections as *Qsbl*).
Ql-Londonbridge Formation
Beach and dune sand and gravel in Oceana Ridge; lagoon clayey silt westward nearly to Suffolk Scarp.
Qn-Norfolk Formation
Upper member: (facies designated by numbers in geologic sections)
    (1) Beach and dune: coarse-sand facies
    (3) Marsh and lagoon: silty-clay facies
    (4) Brackish-marine: silty-sand facies
    (5) Shoreface: medium-sand facies
    (6) Shelf: silt facies
    (7) Shelf: sand facies
    (8) Shelf: fine-sand facies
Lower member: Beach sand and gravel (combined with upper member)
Ogb-Great Bridge Formation
Upper member: (facies designated by numbers in geologic sections)
    (1) Beach sand and gravel near present coast
    (2) Lagoon silty clay in west
Lower member: Fluvial sand, gravel, and freshwater peat along channels in top of Yorktown Formation
Qw-Windsor Formation
Upper member: Lagoon silty sand
Lower member: Beach- and nearshore-marine sand and gravel

Pliocene and/or Pleistocene
QTs-Sedley Formation
Marine and estuarine clay, silt, and fine sand

Miocene and Pliocene
Ty-Yorktown Formation
Fossiliferous marine clay, silt, sand, and coquinite

Whitehead, Figs. 3 and 8). The upper member overlaps the lower, so as to overlie the Londonbridge Formation in the southern part of Dismal Swamp and the Norfolk Formation along the western part of Fentress Rise and the western part of Dismal Swamp. Beneath the Swamp and Deep Creek Swale, the upper member of the Sand Bridge Formation is composed of silty clay (Oaks and Coch 1973, p. 94). In most places, the silty clay is very light gray to dark gray, has a blocky, massive texture, and is cohesive.

The Sand Bridge Formation is late Pleistocene in age and is at least as old as mid-Wisconsin. It probably belongs to the same major submergent episode as the Londonbridge Formation. A surface drainage pattern was eroded into the surface of the Sand Bridge or older formations before the emplacement of Holocene deposits (see Oaks and Whitehead, Fig. 9).

The Holocene in the Dismal Swamp consists of a basal inorganic layer, generally not more than 1 foot thick, and the overlying organic peat. The inorganic layer, commonly found only beneath thick peat layers, consists of white, angular, fine to medium sand presumably of fluvial origin. It is overlain by soft, light-blue clay containing organic fragments and freshwater microfossils (Oaks and Coch 1973, p. 105). The Dismal Swamp Peat is "a soft, wet, sponge-like mass of decaying organic material, chiefly leaves, twigs, rooted stumps and fallen logs" (Oaks and Coch 1973, p. 106). Its color ranges from dark brown near the surface to brownish black at depth. The thickness is highly variable within the Swamp and ranges from a featheredge to more than 12 feet. The surface of the peat slopes gently eastward from an altitude of 25 feet at the base of the Suffolk Scarp to 15 feet along the west side of the Deep Creek Swale. Natural surface drainage is poor, and there are no well-developed streams.

The Dismal Swamp Peat is entirely of freshwater origin. The oldest radiocarbon age of five specimens of the peat is 8900 ± 160 years B.P. (before present) (Oaks and Coch 1973, p. 106).

Radiocarbon ages of freshwater peat found between 70 and 89 feet below present sea level in the mouth of Chesapeake Bay ranged between 8135 ± 160 and 15,280 ± 200 years B.P. (Harrison et al. 1965, pp. 217–221). Therefore, the oldest known peat in the Dismal Swamp began forming while sea level was 60 to 70 feet or more below its present level. Sea level probably has not been significantly higher since that time than it is at present.

HYDROLOGY

The hydrology of the Dismal Swamp area has been important in the formation of the Swamp and will obviously play an important role in its future. The climate, topography, and geology of the area, as previously discussed, are principal factors controlling the hydrology.

Review of Theories on the Origin and Development of Dismal Swamp and Lake Drummond

The basic hydrologic requirements for the formation and development of large peat swamps are a humid climate with reasonably uniform rainfall throughout the year and restricted drainage, both surface and subsurface. The Dismal Swamp has a warm, humid climate, an average annual rainfall of 45 to 50 inches, and an average annual temperature of 59° to 60°F. Average monthly rainfall ranges from 3.20 inches in October to 6.73 inches in July. Average monthly temperature ranges from 41.2°F in January to 78.8°F in July.

The thick, rather impervious clay of the Miocene and Pliocene Yorktown Formation which underlies the entire area (see Oaks and Whitehead, Figs. 3 and 4) is an effective seal preventing either downward or upward movement of water. The Miocene and Pliocene sediments constitute a confining bed, and water in the underlying Upper Cretaceous is under sufficient head to flow at the land surface. Therefore, if appreciable exchange of water could occur between the Upper Cretaceous aquifers and the Swamp, it would be upward into the Swamp rather than downward to the Upper Cretaceous aquifers.

The pre-peat surface is fairly flat (see Oaks and Whitehead, Fig. 9). Surface drainage is restricted by the sharp rise of the Suffolk Scarp on the west and by the Fentress Rise on the east. To the north, the flat surface of the Churchland Flat inhibits surface flow, and the flat gradient to the south also inhibits flow. Most surface drainage from the pre-peat surface of the Dismal Swamp area was apparently to the east via the ancestral Northwest River, which flowed through a gap in the Fentress Rise, and to the southeast via the Pasquotank River.

The general hydrologic conditions necessary for the formation of a swamp existed in the Dismal Swamp area before peat began to form. However, normal dendritic stream drainage patterns were incised on the Sand Bridge Formation before the peat began to form about 9000 years ago (see Oaks and Whitehead, Fig. 9). Studies by Whitehead (1972, p. 301) show that the peat began to form in topographic lows along the stream channels. This, plus the fact that the stream channels had formed, indicates that there was not area-wide ponding in the Dismal Swamp when the peat began to form.

As previously stated, analyses of freshwater peat from the mouth of Chesapeake Bay show that sea level was 60 to 70 feet or more below present sea level. Therefore, the following questions arise: (1) Why did downcutting of the drainage channels of the ancestral Northwest River west of and through the Fentress Rise cease, and (2) why didn't peat form in Deep Creek Swale? This swale is in a topographic setting similar to the Swamp, and surface altitudes are lower than in many areas of Dismal Swamp covered with peat.

A plausible explanation may be found in the geology of the region, as interpreted by Oaks and Coch (1973) and Oaks and Whitehead. The latter's Figure 3 shows that the permeable coarse-to medium-sand facies of the Norfolk Formation crop out on the Suffolk Scarp and dip under the Dismal Swamp. East of the Swamp and under Deep Creek Swale the Norfolk Formation grades into facies that are much less permeable, and these facies act as a barrier to further eastward movement of water through the Norfolk Formation. The Sand Bridge Formation, which acts as a confining layer, is absent from most of the Swamp area. However, the Sand Bridge actually overlies the Norfolk Formation except along topographic lows, such as broad stream channels (see Oaks and Whitehead, Fig. 8).

Before development of the drainage pattern on the surface of the Sand Bridge Formation (Oaks and Whitehead, Fig. 9) the water in the Norfolk Formation was under artesian pressure caused by recharge in the outcrop area on top of the Suffolk Scarp, but was trapped by the fine-sand facies of the Norfolk Formation to the east and by the overlying silty-clay facies of the Sand Bridge. As downcutting of the broad shallow valleys of the drainage system proceeded, the silty-clay confining layer of the Sand Bridge was removed, thereby allowing upwelling of water from the medium-sand facies of the Norfolk Formation. The addition of this water in an area of poor surface drainage may have been sufficient to trigger the accumulation of peat.

The groundwater, although a small percentage of the total water budget of the area, would be especially significant because the relatively constant quantity would keep the area wet even during dry periods. Once started, the formation of peat would be self-perpetuating. As the peat accumulated, it would tend to block the stream channels, slow surface drainage, cause local ponding, and hold the upwelling groundwater. The groundwater would be distributed by artesian pressure and by capillary action, and the peat would gradually spread to cover the interfluve areas.

The origin of Lake Drummond is unknown. Whitehead (1972, p.

314) states that C^{14} (radiocarbon) dates from the base of the gel-mud in the lake indicate that Lake Drummond is a comparatively young feature of the Swamp (originating about 4000 years ago), whereas the peat began to form about 9000 years ago. The lake has no apparent relation to peat thickness or pre-peat topography (Oaks and White-head, Fig. 9), nor does it seem to be the remnant of a larger body of water.

Whitehead (1972, p. 314) states that the most likely explanation for the lake, based on evidence at hand, is a deep burn about 4000 years ago, when the peat layer was thinner. Subsequent wave erosion of un-burned peat would tend to smooth shoreline irregularities and account for the present almost circular shape of Lake Drummond.

It is possible that upward flow of water from the Norfolk Formation into the bottom of the lake has helped to keep fine sediments from settling in the bottom. The upwelling water would help to keep bottom sediment in suspension and allow sediment to float into the surrounding Swamp when the lake extended beyond its normal shoreline. This would partly account for the clean sand bottom that was reported to exist in most of the lake before ditches were dug from the lake into the Swamp. Part of the bottom of the lake has been covered by sediment, but approximately 30 percent is still sand (Mary Keith Garrett, pers. comm.; also see Marshall and Robinson, this volume).

Groundwater and Surface-Water Relationships

Groundwater and surface water are more closely interrelated in a Swamp than in most environments. The dividing line is not always clearly defined. Groundwater out of sight below organic litter becomes surface water when the litter is compressed by a footstep. As suggested previously, the formation of the Swamp may have been initiated by seepage of water from the Norfolk Formation. This seepage has probably continued, in modified form, to the present day.

Ditches designed to remove surface water and lower the water table in the peat often intersect underlying aquifers and may deplete groundwater resources if heads in the aquifers are above water levels in the ditches. If heads in the aquifers are below water levels in the ditches, surface water may drain into the aquifers. Rain falling on and near the Swamp may stand on the surface before soaking into the peat and underlying formations. It then moves laterally toward areas of discharge, such as canals or ditches, and becomes surface water again.

The interrelationships between surface water and groundwater are basic to an understanding of the hydrology of the Dismal Swamp.

Especially significant is the present hydrologic connection between the Norfolk Formation and the peat.

Modifications of the Hydrology

Many modifications have been made to the surface-water and ground-water systems of the Swamp. The construction of canals and ditches has made the most change in the hydrology. Starting in prerevolution-ary days, ditches were dug to drain land for farming, to provide access for water-borne transportation, or to float timber from the Swamp. Many wells located along the Suffolk Scarp draw water from the Norfolk aquifer (water-bearing sand in the Norfolk Formation) that underlies the Swamp, reversing the potentiometric gradient and hence the direction of groundwater movement (Fig. 4). Ground-water withdrawal from the Norfolk Formation in other areas adja-cent to the Swamp may also influence the hydrology.

Surface Water: General Considerations

Estimates of the original size of the Dismal Swamp are as much as 1 million acres. This figure may be high, and the 210,000 acres pres-ently considered to be viable swamp (Fig. 1) probably represent more than half the original. The remainder has been developed by ditching and diking to remove excess surface water. This has caused a general lowering of the water table, so that upland forest assemblages have replaced swamp vegetation in much of the drained area that is not being used commercially (see Levy and Walker, this volume). The present 210,000 acres probably represent the "heart" of the original Swamp, as it is logical to assume that the developed acreage was more easily drained than that remaining. Development of the adjacent former swampland undoubtedly affects the hydrology of the present Swamp, but the effect is probably minimal due to the flat terrain and low permeability of the near-surface material in most of the area. Modification of surface drainage into the Swamp from the high land to the west, plus the numerous drainage ditches that eventually dis-charge to the Dismal Swamp Canal, undoubtedly have the greatest impact.

Continuous records of stream or ditch flow for several years are needed to assess surface-water conditions in the Swamp adequately, but owing to the short time available, flow data were obtained on only two occasions—early July and late September 1973. Numerous sites were visited and estimates of flow made where possible (Table 3 and Fig. 5). "No flow" in Table 3 indicates that a dry section of channel was observed.

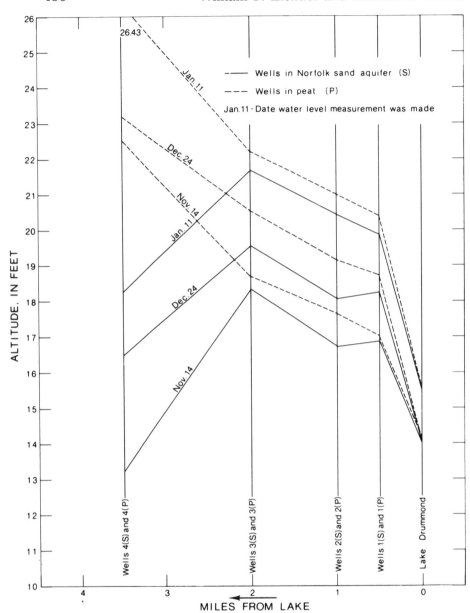

Fig. 4. Profiles of water levels near Washington Ditch. Data years late 1970 and early 1971 (from Main, Inc., 1971).

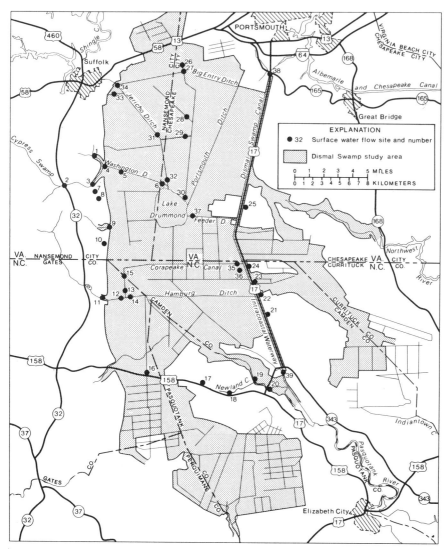

Fig. 5. Dismal Swamp study area showing where surface-water flow estimates were made.

The flow varied considerably during the mid and late parts of the growing season when these estimates were made (Table 3). During other parts of the year, very different flow rates would probably have been observed. Figure 6 illustrates the variability in flow recorded at the gauging station on Cypress Swamp at Cypress Chapel, Virginia (site 2 in Table 3). These data suggest that during the summer, average surface inflow to the Dismal Swamp from uplands west of the Suffolk Scarp is probably very small, while average winter inflow to the Swamp may be three or four times greater.

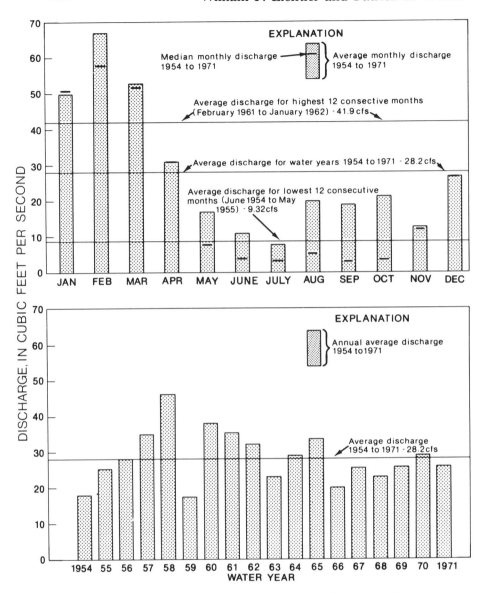

Fig. 6. Discharge of Cypress Swamp at Cypress, Va., site no. 2 in Fig. 5.

Surface-Water Inflow

Surface inflow to the Dismal Swamp occurs through numerous small streams and sloughs that enter from the Suffolk Scarp on the west. Most inflow enters the Swamp through two watercourses, Cypress Swamp and Hamburg Ditch. Only a few discharge measurements have been made on Hamburg Ditch, but a continuously recording stream gauge was maintained on Cypress Swamp from October 1953 to September 1971 (U.S. Geological Survey, 1972). The gauge was on State Highway 32, about 2 miles upstream from the Suffolk Scarp. The drainage area above the gauge is 23 square miles, or 61 percent of the 38 square miles of upland that reportedly drains into Lake Drummond (Main, Inc., 1971, p. 7). Streamflow records for Cypress Swamp show that runoff varies greatly from season to season and from year to year (Fig. 6). The minimum consecutive 12-month discharge averaged 9.32 cfs (cubic feet per second), or 33 percent of the long-term average of 28.2 cfs. The maximum consecutive 12-month discharge was 41.9 cfs, or 149 percent of the long-term average.

Runoff measured at the Cypress Swamp gauge is probably a good indication of runoff to Dismal Swamp from the upland area west of the Suffolk Scarp. However, study of aerial photographs shows that the other major inlet, Hamburg Ditch, runs through the Swamp and drains an unknown amount of water into the Pasquotank River. Little, if any, of the runoff from the upland area drained by Hamburg Ditch is retained in the Swamp or enters Lake Drummond.

About 113 square miles of upland area is a potential source of inflow to the Swamp. Using Cypress Swamp records as a base, and using median flow values rather than the average, this upland area could furnish about 95,000 acre-feet or 31,000 MG (million gallons) of inflow per year. About 90 percent of this inflow could be expected during November through April, the remainder during May through October.

Presently, only about 13,100 MG of upland flow enters Lake Drummond annually (Main, Inc., 1971, p. 7). Approximately another 18,000 MG that is potentially available to the Swamp is intercepted and drained away by the ditches in the southern part of the area.

Drainage ditches along the Suffolk Scarp have not affected the quantity or pattern of surface-water flow from the scarp into Dismal Swamp, except as noted. It is likely that the streams and sloughs have always dried up during even moderate droughts.

Surface-Water Outflow

The principal outflow of surface water from the Dismal Swamp occurs through the Dismal Swamp Canal. Other outlets are Jericho,

Table 3. Estimates of surface-water flow in the Dismal Swamp area

Site number (Fig. 5)	Date	Estimated discharge (cubic ft/sec)	Site	Remarks
1	7/10/73	No flow	White Marsh Road	Inflow to Washington Ditch
2	7/11/73	0.98	Cypress Swamp (Cypress Chapel, Va)	At site of discontinued gauge
	9/27/73	No flow		
3	7/10/73	5	Cypress Swamp	Inflow to Washington Ditch
4	7/11/73	0.1–0.2	Washington Ditch	
	9/26/73	0.04		
5	9/26/73	0.2–0.3	Washington Ditch	
6	7/11/73	5–10	Washington Ditch	Inflow to Lake Drummond
	9/26/73	0.4		
7	7/10/73	No flow	Hoosier Road	Inflow to Railroad Ditch
	9/27/73	No flow		
8	7/10/73	No flow	Hoosier Road	Inflow to Dismal Swamp
	9/27/73	No flow		
9	7/10/73	No flow	Moss Swamp	Inflow to Dismal Swamp
	9/27/73	No flow		
10	7/10/73	0.02	No Name Swamp	Inflow to Dismal Swamp
11	7/10/73	13	Taylor Swamp	Inflow to Hamburg Ditch
	9/27/73	0.002		
12	9/27/73	0.2	Hamburg Ditch	
13	9/27/73	0.07	Sherril Ditch	Flow south to Hamburg Ditch
14	9/27/73	0.3	Hamburg Ditch	Outflow from Dismal Swamp
15	9/27/73	0.2	Sherril Ditch	Flow north to Corapeake Canal
16	9/27/73	1	Newland Drainage Canal	Outflow from Dismal Swamp
17	7/10/73	30–35	Newland Drainage Canal	
	9/27/73	2		
18	9/27/73	2	Newland Drainage Canal	
19	9/27/73	Slight	Pasquotank River	Flow upstream—tidal
20	7/10/73	15–60	Pasquotank River	Tidal
21	7/10/73	No flow	Unnamed drainage ditch	Inflow to Dismal Swamp Canal
22	7/10/73	No flow	Unnamed drainage ditch	Inflow to Dismal Swamp Canal
23	7/10/73	0.8	Unnamed drainage ditch	Inflow to Dismal Swamp Canal
24	7/10/73	0.5	Unnamed drainage ditch	Inflow to Dismal Swamp Canal
25	7/10/73	<0.1	Unnamed drainage ditch	Inflow to Dismal Swamp Canal
26	7/11/73	No flow	East Ditch	Interior drainage
27	7/11/73	0.04	East Ditch	Interior drainage
28	7/11/73	5	Hudnell Ditch	Flow to East Ditch
29	7/11/73	5–10	Cross Ditch	Flow to East Ditch

Table 3. (cont.)

Site number (Fig. 5)	Date	Estimated discharge (cubic ft/sec.)	Site	Remarks
30	7/11/73	30–50	East Ditch	Inflow to Lake Drummond
31	7/11/73	20	Jericho Ditch	Flow to south
32	7/11/73	20–30	Jericho Ditch	Inflow to Lake Drummond
	9/26/73	1		
33	7/11/73	<0.1	Jericho Lane Ditch	Outflow to Shingle Creek
34	7/11/73	3–5	Jericho Ditch	Outflow to Shingle Creek
	9/26/73	1		
35	9/27/73	<0.1	Corapeake Canal	Outflow from Dismal Swamp to Dismal Swamp Canal
36	9/27/73	0.5	Corapeake outfall	Outflow from Dismal Swamp to Dismal Swamp Canal
37	7/18/73	72	Feeder Ditch	Measured flow, one wicket gate open
38	7/10/73	—	Dismal Swamp Canal at Deep Creek	Leakage and one wicket gate open
	9/28/73	—		Leakage; no wickets open
39	7/10/73	10	Dismal Swamp Canal at South Mills	Leakage; no wickets open
	9/27/73	—		Leakage; no wickets open

Portsmouth, and Hamburg (modified) ditches (Fig. 1). Many ditches within the Swamp drain into Lake Drummond, which, in turn, drains to the Dismal Swamp Canal through the Feeder Ditch. Jericho Ditch drains northwest to Shingle Creek and southeast into Lake Drummond. Corapeake, Big Entry, and several smaller ditches drain into Dismal Swamp Canal. The Dismal Swamp Canal and most ditches in the Virginia part of the study area have water-control structures that can be used to restrict outflow from the Swamp; however, many ditches in the North Carolina part do not.

A significant amount of the outflow from the Dismal Swamp is used for operation of the Dismal Swamp Canal locks at South Mills and Deep Creek. During an average year there is a total of 2600 lockages. Each lockage requires 1.25 million gallons of water. Most lockages are during May through October (85%–90%), which is the period of lowest inflow (Main, Inc., 1971, p. 5). It is estimated that lockages required about 3250 MG annually, based on 1.25 MG per lockage, and that total annual water use by the canal was 5190 MG (Main, Inc., 1971, p. 5).

A large amount of water leaves the southern part of the Swamp via a network of canals. As pointed out previously, the Hamburg Ditch inflow is channeled through the Swamp, eventually to flow into the Pasquotank River. Newland Canal along the southern edge of the Swamp provides an efficient drainage for outflow from the heavily ditched southern part.

Outflow rates from the Swamp follow general seasonal patterns similar to inflow patterns except for the release of water from Lake Drummond to support canal operations. Outflow depends in part on the setting of the individual control structures, and to a certain extent on the pattern of precipitation. For example, a heavy rainstorm in one part of the Swamp may cause a reversal in the direction of flow in various ditches.

Surface-Water Quality

The surface water in Dismal Swamp is generally of good quality except for very high color (160–1000 units) and low pH (3.5–6.7). Although it has a distinct taste, most people consider it potable after they become accustomed to its taste. The low pH tends to inhibit growth of organisms. This characteristic made Dismal Swamp water especially desirable for long ocean voyages in the days of sailing ships. Water samples have been collected from Jericho Ditch near the fire tower, from Lake Drummond, and from Dismal Swamp Canal. Representative analyses are shown in Table 4.

Groundwater Inflow

Groundwater inflow to the Dismal Swamp is mostly from the west through the Norfolk aquifer and surficial sand that overlies the Sand Bridge confining layer. The flow within the Norfolk aquifer has been modified (Fig. 4) by withdrawal of water for domestic, stock, and irrigation uses. Ditches that intersect the Norfolk aquifer, when inadequately controlled, drain groundwater to Lake Drummond or out of the Swamp.

Groundwater moving laterally through the surficial sand overlying the confining bed seeps into the peat of the Swamp. The movement of water through the peat has not been studied. Most of the peat is sapric (well-decomposed) (Main, Inc., 1971, p. 13) and has a low hydraulic conductivity below the top few inches. However, desiccation cracks extend 1.5 to 2 feet below the surface in many parts of the Swamp. The extent of interconnection is fairly good in at least the top 1 to 1.5 feet.

When the water table is at or near the surface of the peat, water

Table 4. Chemical quality of surface water from the Dismal Swamp (results in milligrams per liter except as indicated)

No. used on Fig. 1	Location of sampling site	Date of collection	Temperature (°C)	Dissolved silica (SiO₂)	Iron (Fe)	Dissolved calcium (Ca)	Dissolved magnesium (Mg)	Dissolved sodium (Na)	Dissolved potassium (K)	Bicarbonate (HCO₃)	Carbonate (CO₃)	Dissolved sulfate (SO₄)	Dissolved chloride (Cl)	Fluoride (F)	Nitrate (NO₃)	Phosphate (PO₄)	Dissolved solids (residue at 180°C)	Hardness Calcium, magnesium	Hardness Non-carbonate	Specific conductance (micromhos at 25°C)	Laboratory pH	Color (platinum-cobalt units)
1	Dismal Swamp Canal	7/27/70	—	3.8	0.94	7.2	3.2	15	2.4	10	—	18	23	0.2	0.5	0.69	151	31	23	122	6.7	160
2	Dismal Swamp Canal	7/27/70	—	4.2	0.81	5.2	0.7	10	5.8	2	—	12	8.7	1.2	0.0	4.4	127	16	14	71	4.9	240
3	Lake Drummond	7/28/70	—	7.5	0.80	8.0	2.4	6.5	5.3	6	—	16	8.7	0.4	0.0	5.0	162	30	25	90	5.2	270
3	Lake Drummond	10/02/70	22	0.3	0.48	5.4	1.1	6.0	1.1	2	—	13	9.5	0.1	0.8	0.37	95	18	16	81	4.6	180
4	Jericho Ditch	4/12/73	—	4.1	0.70	1.3	0.7	4.2	1.3	0	0	—	6.0	0.6	3.0	0.20	175	6	6	110	3.5	1000
4	Jericho Ditch	9/28/73	—	6.7	0.90	3.3	1.1	9.5	1.4	0	0	12	17	0.4	4.0	0.21	232	12	12	146	3.7	1000

probably flows through the interconnected desiccation cracks. As the water table is lowered 1 to 2 feet below the peat surface, the flow probably decreases drastically. Horizontal groundwater movement through the lower parts of the sapric peat is probably very slow. Except near the ditches, most of the movement is probably in a vertical direction by capillary action.

Groundwater Outflow

Groundwater discharge in Dismal Swamp is from the Norfolk aquifer and from the peat and muck. Discharge from the Norfolk aquifer is by three routes: (1) by upward seepage into Lake Drummond through the overlying peat, where the confining beds of the Sand Bridge Formation are permeable or absent, (2) by direct seepage into canals and ditches that intersect the aquifer, and (3) by pumping along the Suffolk Scarp. The amount of water discharged is probably large, but no direct measurements have been made.

Discharge from the peat is by evapotranspiration and by seepage into ditches, canals, and streams. A detailed analysis of the seepage has not been made, but evapotranspiration withdraws by far the larger quantity of water from the peat.

Pumpage along the scarp is estimated to be 100,000 gallons per day. This withdrawal has apparently reversed the gradient in the Norfolk aquifer for a portion of the year in parts of the Suffolk Scarp (Fig. 4).

Groundwater Quality

Samples of groundwater were collected from a shallow flowing well in the Feeder Ditch near the Dismal Swamp Canal, a deep flowing well at the abandoned Canal Bank Motel, a shallow domestic well on the Suffolk Scarp, and shallow auger holes near Washington Ditch. The analyses are shown in Table 5. The concentrations of the various chemical constituents vary considerably from well to well.

The color was high (80–350 units) in water from the auger holes on Washington Ditch because the water was contaminated by the overlying peat. The chloride content of the Canal Bank Motel well water was slightly above the U.S. Public Health limit of 250 milligrams per liter (U.S. Public Health Service, 1962), but it is not harmful.

Table 5. Chemical quality of groundwater from Dismal Swamp area (results in milligrams per liter except as indicated)

No. used on Fig. 1	Location of sampling site	Date of collection	Temperature (°C)	Dissolved silica (SiO₂)	Iron (Fe)	Dissolved calcium (Ca)	Dissolved magnesium (Mg)	Dissolved sodium (Na)	Dissolved potassium (K)	Bicarbonate (HCO₃)	Carbonate (CO₃)	Dissolved sulfate (SO₄)	Dissolved chloride (Cl)	Fluoride (F)	Nitrate (NO₃)	Phosphate (PO₄)	Dissolved solids (residue at 180°C)	Hardness Calcium, magnesium	Hardness Non-carbonate	Specific conductance (micromhos at 25°C)	Laboratory pH	Color (platinum-cobalt units)
5	Flowing well in Feeder Ditch	7/19/73	15	50	0.47	140	5.5	170	28	624	0.0	3.7	170	0.3	0.3	0.16	221	370	0	1490	7.1	30
6	Flowing well at Canal Bank Motel	7/10/73	19	9.8	0.14	3.5	3.4	580	70	1010	0.0	75	260	3.5	0.3	0.22	147	22	0	2500	8.0	10
7	Auger hole near Washington Ditch	7/28/73	—	24	0.41	3.2	1.6	40	3.1	53	0.0	29	30	0.5	1.6	0.13	250	14	0	205	5.9	350
8	Auger hole near Washington Ditch	7/28/73	—	23	0.09	7.9	0.7	26	1.9	19	0.0	33	20	0.2	0.4	0.04	173	22	7	170	5.5	80
9	Shallow domestic well on White Marsh Road	9/27/73	—	6.2	0.01	6.4	2.7	31	4.1	5	0.0	53	15	0.1	34	34	154	27	23	245	5.4	5

FEASIBILITY OF PRESERVING THE DISMAL SWAMP

It is obviously feasible to preserve the Dismal Swamp from direct development by man. This can be done by government acquisition of the land, by legislation governing activities within the Swamp, cooperation of landowners, or any combination of these. A major factor involved in preserving the Swamp and Dismal Swamp Canal is financial support.

The Dismal Swamp has changed since colonial times, and it is likely that American Indians modified the Swamp by burning and other means long before Europeans saw it. Since George Washington's time the drainage canals and ditches and their accompanying spoilbanks have changed surface-water levels and flow patterns. In at least parts of the Swamp, roads built on spoilbanks have provided high ground and sunlit areas. Such changes and repeated lumbering have caused a different flora and fauna to develop. If present trends continue, the Swamp of the future will be more like an upland forest than it is at present (see Levy and Walker, this volume).

Water levels in the Swamp can be raised by sealing the locks or restricting pumping from the Norfolk aquifer. Data are insufficient at present to predict the hydrologic effect of various possible control measures, but if water levels are abruptly raised too high, many trees will be unable to adapt rapidly and will be killed (Mary Keith Garrett, pers. comm.).

Restoring the Swamp to its original condition seems impossible because that condition is not clearly understood. The Swamp has been and is still changing, even without human interference; therefore, perhaps it would be best to manage the Swamp for its best uses within the framework of conservation, rather than try to return it to some ill-defined previous condition. This would probably involve maintaining a variety of ecosystems, which would, in turn, involve a variety of hydrologic conditions.

SUGGESTED FOLLOW-UP ACTIONS

Hydrologic studies needed to provide data to aid in managing the Dismal Swamp include:

1. Defining the present role of the Norfolk aquifer (Scattered borings indicate that some parts of the Swamp remain wet even during droughts because of upward seepage of groundwater. Determining the extent and amount of upward seepage is essential.)

2. Determining how withdrawal of water from the Norfolk aquifer has changed groundwater flow patterns and the effect future withdrawal may have on the Swamp

3. Identifying those parts of the Swamp best suited to wetter types of ecosystems and those best suited to dryer types

4. Determining surface inflow to the Swamp from the Suffolk Scarp

5. Determining surface outflow from the Swamp

6. Determining the number and types of structures necessary to control surface water movement in the Swamp

7. Determining the water budget of the Swamp

8. Monitoring seasonal and long-term changes in the chemical quality of both surface water and groundwater

SUMMARY

The Dismal Swamp, on the border between eastern Virginia and North Carolina, is one of the few remaining large (approximately 210,000 acres) areas of wet wilderness in the eastern United States. There has been much speculation concerning the hydrologic conditions that led to the formation of the Swamp.

Oaks and Coch (1973) recently completed a detailed investigation of the geology and morphology of the area. An analysis of their geology and of the pollen work of Whitehead (1972) has led the authors to the following hypothesis concerning the hydrologic conditions that led to the formation of the peat in the Swamp.

A permeable sand facies of the Norfolk Formation underlies Dismal Swamp. This facies was originally completely covered by the Sand Bridge Formation, which is a confining layer, and underlain by the impermeable Yorktown Formation. Movement of water eastward within the Norfolk Formation from the outcrop area on the top of the Suffolk Scarp was further restricted by a less permeable facies of the Norfolk east of the Swamp, thereby creating an artesian head within the permeable sand facies of the Norfolk Formation.

Erosion during the Pleistocene age breached the Sand Bridge confining layer and allowed upward seepage of water along the shallow stream valleys. This seepage, combined with the abundant rainfall and naturally sluggish surface drainage, may have been sufficient to trigger the formation of peat along stream valleys about 9000 years ago. The peat further inhibited surface drainage, which in turn accelerated the accumulation of peat until the interfluve areas were covered. The present role of the Norfolk Formation in the hydrology of the Swamp is not clear, but it is considered to be one of the most important aspects of the hydrology to be studied in future investigations.

Surface inflow is from small streams draining from the west. The flow of these streams varies widely, being generally less in the summer than in winter. Outflow is primarily through the Feeder Ditch into the Dismal Swamp Canal, which discharges at South Mills and Deep Creek locks.

The rates and direction of surface flow within the Swamp are partly controlled by gates on many of the ditches. Inadequately controlled ditches penetrating the Norfolk Formation, plus withdrawal of water from wells along the Suffolk Scarp, have altered the flow of groundwater under the Swamp. These modifications and the loss of water through the Dismal Swamp Canal have probably resulted in a generally drier swamp as indicated by changes in the vegetation. It is feasible to preserve Dismal Swamp, but more detailed studies of the hydrology are needed to aid in future management.

REFERENCES CITED

Brown, P. M., J. A. Miller, and F. M. Swain. 1972. Structural and stratigraphic framework, and spatial distribution of permeability of the Atlantic Coastal Plain, North Carolina to New York. *U.S. Geol. Survey, Prof. Pap.* 796. 79 pp.

Harrison, W., R. J. Malloy, G. A. Rusnak, and J. Terasmae. 1965. Possible late Pleistocene uplift, Chesapeake Bay entrance. *J. Geol.* 73:201–229.

McLean, J. D., Jr. 1966. Miocene and Pleistocene foraminifers and Ostracoda of southeastern Virginia. *Va. Div. Mineral Resources, Rpt. Inv.* 9. 123 pp.

Main, C. T., Inc. 1971. Dismal Swamp study 1659–25. Charles T. Main Engineers, Inc., 1301 E. Morehead St., Charlotte, N.C. 34 pp.

Oaks, R. Q., Jr., and N. K. Coch. 1973. Post-Miocene stratigraphy and morphology, southeastern Virginia. *Va. Div. Mineral Resources, Bull.* 82. 135 pp.

U.S. Geological Survey. 1972. Water resources data for Virginia, 1971. Richmond. 305 pp.

U.S. Public Health Service. 1962. Drinking water standards, 1962. *U.S. Public Health Serv. Pub.* 956. 61 pp.

U.S. Weather Bureau. 1965. Climatic summary of the U.S., 1951–1960, Virginia. Washington, D.C.

Whitehead, D. R. 1972. Developmental and environmental history of the Dismal Swamp. *Ecol. Monographs* 4:301–315.

LAKE DRUMMOND:
WITH A DISCUSSION REGARDING ITS
PLANKTON COMPOSITION

Harold G. Marshall

The phytoplankton composition of Lake Drummond has been previously discussed by Poore (1971), Marshall and Poore (1972), and Poore and Marshall (1972). The zooplankton composition was reviewed recently by Marshall (1974). In these past studies the major plankton populations have been identified and their seasonal patterns of concentration discussed. The phytoplankton is dominated throughout the year by the diatom *Asterionella formosa.* The seasonal values for this species reflect the growth pattern of the total phytoplankton in the lake. Population growth curves are generally bimodal, with maxima occurring during the fall and spring. Other common phytoplankters in the lake include the desmids, which are found throughout the year but in lesser concentrations than *Asterionella formosa.* Dominant genera of desmids common to Lake Drummond include *Arthrodesmus, Closterium, Cosmarium,* and *Staurastrum.* The zooplankton composition is dominated by cladocerans with *Bosmina* the major genus present, having lowest concentrations during the winter months with numbers increasing during spring and summer before declining in the fall. In addition to the cladocerans, populations of copepods and rotifers are also abundant. A broader perspective of the character and dynamics of Lake Drummond is needed to appreciate fully the floral and faunal plankton components within this body of water.

LAKE DRUMMOND: GENERAL FEATURES

Specific morphometric measurements for the lake were determined using aerial photographs from the Old Dominion University Remote

Sensing Laboratory. Lake Drummond, located approximately in the center of the Dismal Swamp, is almost circular in shape with a north-south dimension of approximately 2.7 miles and a maximum east-west dimension of about 2.4 miles. The shoreline is approximately 9.5 miles in length. The embankments are abrupt with tree growth generally to the margin of the lake. There are numerous bald cypress (*Taxodium distichum*) found within the offshore waters along the eastern lake border and at several other scattered marginal sites. The lake has a surface area of approximately 3180 acres. The maximum water depth is about 6–7 feet (see Marshall and Robinson, this volume) with an estimated storage capacity of 4610 million gallons (Main, Inc., 1971). The total drainage area for the lake is given by the Army Corps of Engineers as 140 square miles. Significant seasonal fluctuations in the lake level are common and have been recorded by the Army Corps over the past 48 years. When Lake Drummond is considered full, lake elevation is 17.15 feet above sea level using U.S. Coast and Geodetic Survey mean sea level datum. If one were to use a Norfolk Harbor data base, the lake level would be given as 18.65 feet above mean zero low water. Over the past 48 years there have been distinct periods when the lake level dropped considerably.

A pattern of decreasing water level is frequently noted during the late summer months into fall, followed by a return to normal levels by midwinter and early spring. Past records have indicated that since 1926 the lake level has dropped over 4 feet seven times, between 2 and 4 feet fifteen times, with lesser fluctuations taking place the other years. Such fluctuations may be attributed to several factors influencing the water entry and exit from Lake Drummond. A major source for water to the lake and surrounding drainage basin is precipitation, and subsequent drainage into the lake. Monthly precipitation records have been taken since 1926 at Wallaceton, located along the eastern margin of the Swamp. The yearly records indicate an annual average precipitation for the area of 49.46 inches. The periods of higher rainfall occur more typically during spring and summer months. Average monthly precipitation records since 1926 indicate that months of greatest precipitation are June, July, August, and September with October and November having the lowest values. During those years where a marked decrease in water level was recorded, a drop in lake elevation would begin about late May or June and continue to lowest values during October and November. Full lake level would be restored usually between December and March.

The apparent paradox of ample spring and summer rains accompanied by a drop in lake water elevation may be explained by two conditions, one a natural phenomenon, the other a product of man's utilization of Lake Drummond. First, the occurrence of large amounts of rain in the watershed does not mean that the water will be retained in the area. The capacity of the shallow lake is limited, and once maximum levels are reached, water drains through natural outlets. The studies of Lake Drummond's watershed by the Charles T. Main Corporation (Main, Inc., 1971) indicate the average annual inflow to the lake to be 25,000 million gallons (MG). This figure was further broken down to indicate that of this total, 800 MG came directly from precipitation (minus evaporation), 11,000 MG as drainage from sections of the Swamp mainly north of the lake, and 13,100 MG from upland sections generally to the west. With a maximum volume of 4610 MG, the lake has a limited storage capacity that results in a major flow of water into and out of the lake with its volume renewed five to six times during the year. This passage of water is further influenced by a network of ditches within the Swamp, many connected directly to Lake Drummond. The ditches have resulted in the other major factor influencing water level in Lake Drummond (see Fig. 1 of Levy and Walker, and of Lichtler and Walker, this volume, for location of ditches).

In 1812 a Feeder Ditch was constructed to connect Lake Drummond to the Dismal Swamp Canal, which represents a portion of the Atlantic Intracoastal Waterway located between the locks of Deep Creek and South Mills. This Feeder Ditch is 3.5 miles in length, about 40 feet wide, and 3 to 4 feet deep. Water from Lake Drummond is controlled by a spillway located on the Feeder Ditch near the lake. Controlled operation of this spillway prevents the lake exceeding 17.15 feet above sea level. Water from the lake is required throughout the year to maintain the water level within the Dismal Swamp Canal, which may drop considerably during dry periods. One such period took place during the phytoplankton study by Poore and Marshall (1972) in 1970. Canal waters were so low between May and December 1970 that approximately 3900 MG (18.1 MG per day) were released from Lake Drummond to restore canal depths. The lake level dropped during this period over 1 meter, exposing numerous marginal stumps and off-shore areas normally covered by lake water. In addition to water from Lake Drummond, other drainage canals coming from the Swamp, precipitation, highway culverts, and seepage are also used as a source for water in the Dismal Swamp Canal. However, whenever dry periods occur, a greater dependency is placed on Lake Drummond to counteract any condition that may reduce the water content of the canal system. Lockages within the canal result in water loss that must be replaced either by natural drainage into the system or directly from Lake Drummond via the Feeder Ditch. The Army Corps of Engineers estimates that it requires 1.25 MG of water for every lockage within the Dismal Swamp Canal. The loss of lockage water is most common in the canal system during the summer months due to increased boat traffic. In addition, water is lost due to leakage through the locks, the passage to groundwater, and evaporation. The combined effects of canal usage and evaporation result in the need for quantities of water from Lake Drummond that frequently are difficult to offset by normal precipitation and drainage into the canal. The combination of heavy canal traffic, little precipitation, and continued evaporation has generally resulted in a marked reduction of the water level in the lake. If conditions are extreme during extended dry periods, the lake level may drop so low that adequate water is not available to maintain normal operations within the Dismal Swamp Canal. Actual closures or restrictions have been placed on boat traffic fourteen times over the past 43 years due to such conditions.

The general drainage pattern for the Dismal Swamp is to the east and south. A gradual slope extends eastward from the Suffolk Scarp, where elevations begin decreasing gradually from 25 feet. A 20-foot contour line circumscribes Lake Drummond on the north, south, and western margins. The surface elevations range from 20 to 15 feet eastward. Thus, Lake Drummond, with a maximum possible elevation of 17.15 feet above sea level, is surrounded on three sides by high ground, with low ground providing natural drainage to the east.

A significant amount of drainage water enters the lake through ditches along the northern margin. These include Jericho and East ditches, which bring in water from the northern sections, and Washington Ditch, which drains the more upland sections to the west. Jericho is much longer than Washington Ditch and dates back to 1810. Washington Ditch was dug in the 1760s. Jericho Ditch passes through extensive peat deposits; hence the waters are highly acidic and stained a dark tea color. The waters of Washington Ditch, draining higher ground to the west, are acidic and stained, but not to the extent of Jericho. Undoubtedly the present character of Lake Drummond water is influenced by such drainage, and changing the present balance of water entering the lake from the western upland and northern peat sections would have a profound effect on water quality in the lake.

The water of Lake Drummond is tea brown in color and acidic throughout the year, owing to drainage through the rich peat deposits. The annual pH range for the lake has been noted as 3.2–6.8, but the majority of readings over a two-year period are 4.2–4.8. These acidic conditions may be attributed to the leeching of various organic acids from the surrounding peat deposits, the formation of H_2SO_4 (Frey 1949), and decomposition products in the lake drainage ditches. The central lake area has a mud or fine silt bottom intermixed with fine sand. A sandy shore and bottom area is found along the northern lake margin that extends from the opening of Jericho Ditch along the northern and eastern lake margins. More peatlike and detrital material and remnants of stumps occur in the marginal section near the Feeder Ditch opening. Similar substrata are also scattered along the southern and western lake border.

The broad, windswept surface and the shallowness of the lake generally result in repeated periods of turnover. There has been no evidence of a seasonal thermocline, although brief periods of thermal stratification have been noted under a winter ice cover and on calm summer days. Water temperatures vary little with depth, and oxygen values frequently reach saturation throughout the water column. Fluctuations in oxygen level occur seasonally and after rains and are influenced by the waters and particulate matter entering the lake from the drainage ditches. The oxygen range within the lake was 3.3–8.6 ml/l in the one-year study by Poore and Marshall (1972). Assorted unpublished field data plus the Charles Main Corporation report indicate adequate nutrient levels for phytoplankton development in the lake, 0.2–0.6 ppm total phosphate and 0.6–1.5 ppm nitrate-nitrogen. Total hardness values have ranged 15–30 ppm (as $CaCO_3$). Turbidity is generally high, Secchi disc readings ranging 8–70 cm, and mostly 30–45 cm. The highest readings have been noted during winter months when total plankton densities were lowest. Net collections generally yield suspended detrital materials as well as plankton.

PLANKTON COMPOSITION

A study of the plankton composition in Lake Drummond was conducted between September 1973 and August 1974. Water samples were taken in Lake Drummond at two stations at about monthly intervals. One station (L-1) was located approximately 100 meters south of the entrance of Jericho Ditch to the lake, with another station (L-2) at a mid-lake position marked by a buoy. Additional sampling was done in Jericho Ditch, Washington Ditch, the Feeder Ditch, and the Dismal Swamp Canal. Water for phytoplankton analysis was collected at the surface in 0.5 liter polyethylene bottles. These samples were preserved immediately with buffered formalin. On several occasions duplicate samples were collected and preserved in a modified Lugol's solution. A settling and siphoning procedure was used to obtain a final 25 ml concentrated sample. The concentrate was placed in a settling chamber and examined with a Zeiss inverted microscope to note the number of phytoplankton cells per liter. Zooplankton samples were taken at the same two open-water stations in the lake using a Clarke-Bumpus apparatus (diameter = 6 inches). At each station 10-minute tows were made over an area approximately 2000 square meters using a net apperture of 70 microns. Collections were also made at the spillways of Jericho and Washington ditches. At each station temperature was taken with a reversing thermometer. The pH values were determined in the field with a model 126A photovolt analyzer.

Phytoplankton

A total of 71 phytoplankters have been identified in Lake Drummond with the diatom *Asterionella formosa* predominating. These phytoplankters included 29 species of diatoms, 29 chlorophyceans (16 were desmids), 1 cyanophycean, 3 euglenophyceans, 5 pyrrhophyceans, and 4 chrysophyceans (Table 1). The dominance of *Asterionella formosa* was evident during each of the samplings. Largest concentrations of this species occurred during the spring and fall months, with peak numbers of approximately 2.9 million cells per liter on 4 June 1974, corresponding to a previous study of Lake Drummond (Poore and Marshall 1972). Concentrations of this species generally reflected the value for the total phytoplankton.

The seasonal pattern of phytoplankton concentrations was bimodal, with maxima taking place during spring and fall, interspaced by minima in winter and summer months. Collections taken during the fall (1973) period indicated a gradual decline in total phytoplankton populations into winter. The flora consisted of mainly diatoms and desmids with *Asterionella formosa* the most abundant. Counts for this species were frequently over 150,000 cells per liter. Other common diatoms included *Melosira granulata, Fragilaria crotonensis, Surirella* spp., and *Navicula* spp. There was a variety of desmids, which included *Arthrodesmus incus extensus, Closterum* spp., and *Staurastrum paradoxum*. Other species included *Scenedesmus quadricauda, S. opoliensis,* and several pyrrhophyceans, including *Peridinium limbatum* and *P. westii.*

The winter phytoplankton consisted predominantly of *Asterionella formosa* and *Melosira granulata*. Minimal numbers for the study were recorded during the winter months with a low count of 56,000 cells per liter noted on 12 February 1974. The desmids were represented by *Arthrodesmus incus extensus, Closterium gracile, C. lineatum,* and *Staurastrum paradoxum*. Other species included *Scenedesmus quadricauda, S.* was a rise in the population densities with *A. formosa, M. granulata,* and *Straurastrum* spp. the spring dominants. During both winter and spring the desmid forms were common but with lower population densities than the diatoms mentioned above. The spring peak was mainly the product of increased numbers of *A. formosa*. Highest values during the study occurred on 4 June 1974 when 3.1 million cells per liter were recorded, of which 2.9 million were *A. formosa*. During this spring pulse the desmids also reached their highest concentrations and were represented by *Staurastrum* spp., *Closterium* spp., and *Triplocerus gracile*.

The summer plankton exhibited little change in the dominant forms from those of late spring. *A. formosa* was still the most numerous species, followed by a variety of desmids. Collections taken in July and August indicated a population drop which continued into mid-summer but which was less severe than the winter low.

Summer collections in Jericho and Washington ditches also showed differences in the phytoplankton composition, as well as in the characteristics of the water entering the lake. Diatoms, such as *Asterionella formosa*, *Pinnularia* spp., *Tabellaria fenestrata*, *Frustulia rhomboides*, and *Fragilaria crotonensis*, were common in Washington Ditch, with desmids becoming more numerous at sections nearer the lake. Desmids most common in Washington Ditch included *Closterium* spp., *Cosmarium* spp., and *Euastrum bidentatum*. Jericho Ditch generally contained a higher diatom concentration. The desmids were common, but not abundant, and there were significant concentrations of *Eunotia pectinalis* and the green alga *Oedogonium* (spp.). Waters from Jericho Ditch were generally more acidic and stained than in Washington Ditch. The phytoplankton composition at stations in the Feeder Ditch and the Dismal Swamp Canal was similar to that in Lake Drummond. However, collections in the Dismal Swamp Canal were limited to the central sections near the entrance of the Feeder Ditch.

Observations over several seasons have indicated considerable variability in the forms of characteristic species found in the lake. This is most obvious in the genus *Melosira*, where distinct variations were found in the shape and structure of this genus over the study period. Distinct forms noted during one season or year were not found at a later period. Such variability suggests a rapid response of large populations of phytoplankton to a particular stimulus or change within the water. This type of reaction is more understandable when one considers the yearly water exchange that occurs within this lake. As stated previously, the lake storage capacity is approximately 4610 MG. Yet the average annual inflow of water to the lake is 25,000 MG. Such a flow of water into this shallow lake could result in its volume being renewed five to six times each year. As water quality affecting phytoplankton growth changes, so should the growth response of the phytoplankton be modified. It is suggested that many of the various *Melosira* found in Lake Drummond are different forms of *Melosira granulata* and should be included under that listing. The apical

Table 1. Phytoplankton recorded from stations in Lake Drummond

Chrysophyta

    Bacillariophyceae

        Asterionella formosa Hassal
        Cyclotella sp. Kutz
        Cymatopleura solea (Breb.) W. Smith
        Cymbella ehrenbergii Kutz
        Epithemia turgida (Ehr.) Kutz
        Eunotia curvata (Kutz) Lagerheim
        Eunotia pectinalis (Kutz) Rabenhorst
        Fragilaria capucina Desmarziers
        Fragilaria crotonensis Kitton
        Frustulia rhomboides (Ehr.) DeToni
        Gyrosigma sp. Hassal
        Melosira granulata (Ehr.) Ralfs
        Melosira granulata augustissima O. Muller
        Melosira Herzogii Lemin
        Meridion circulare (Grev.) Agardh
        Navicula spp. Bory
        Neidium iridis vernalis Reichelt
        Pinnularia sp. Ehrenberg
        Pinnularia acuminata W. Smith
        Pinnularia biceps Gregory
        Pinnularia gibba Ehrenberg
        Pinnularia lata (Breb.) Rabenhorst
        Pinnularia latevittata Cleve
        Surirella sp. Turpin
        Surirella biseriata constricta Grunow
        Synedra sp. Ehrenberg
        Synedra acus Kutz
        Synedra radians Kutz
        Synedra ulna longissima (W. Sm.) Brun
        Tabellaria fenestrata (Lyng) Kutz
        Tabellaria flocculosa (Roth) Kutz

    Chrysophyceae

        Dinobryon divergens Imhof.
        Dinobryon sertularia Ehrenberg
        Mallomonas acaroides Perty
        Synura caroliniana Whitford

Chlorophyta

    Chlorophyceae

        Ankistrodesmus nannoselene Skuja
        Coelastrum cambricum Archer
        Coelastrum microporum Nageli

Table 1. (cont.)

    Geminella minor Nageli
    Microspora pachyderma (Wille) Lagerheim
    Mougeotia sp. Agardh
    Oedogonium spp. Link
    Scenedesmus sp. Meyen
    Scenedesmus denticulatus Lagerheim
    Scenedesmus hystrix Lagerheim
    Scenedesmus opoliensis P. Richter
    Scenedesmus quadricauda (Turp.) Brebisson
    Spirogyra sp. Link
Desmidiaceae
    Arthrodesmus incus extensus Anderson
    Closterium sp. Nitzsch
    Closterium gracile Brebisson
    Closterium lineatum Ehrenberg
    Closterium rostratum Ehrenberg
    Cosmarium sp. Corda
    Cosmarium portianum Archer
    Euastrum bidentatum Nageli
    Gonatozygon kinahani (Arch.) Rabenhorst
    Penium margaritaceum (Ehren.) Brébisson
    Spirotaenia condensata Brébisson
    Staurastrum cingulum var. *floridense* Scott and Gronblad
    Staurastrum leptocladum Nordstedt
    Staurastrum manfeldtii var. *fluminese* Schumacher
    Staurastrum paradoxum Meyen
    Triplocerus gracile Bailey

Pyrrhophyta

    Cryptomonas ovata Ehrenberg
    Peridinium sp. Ehrenberg
    Peridinium limbatum (Stokes) Lemmermann
    Peridinium westii Lemmermann
    Peridinium wisconsinense Eddy

Euglenophyta

    Phacus sp. DuJardin
    Pacus lemmermannii (Swir.) Skvortzow
    Trachelomonas spp. Ehrenberg

Cyanophyta

    Merismopedia elegans A. Br.

cells of these forms have typically contained spines or teeth of varying lengths and a combination of different valvular shapes and sizes.
This grouping may also include *M. Herzogii*, previously reported in
the lake by Marshall and Poore (1972), as an example of *M. granulata*'s morphological variability and local response to specific environmental growth conditions extant in the lake. Bethge (1925) has
noted the wide range of different forms of *Melosira granulata*, other
Melosira species, and their variations. He suggested the placement of
these forms under *Melosira polymorpha*, which would specifically include *M. granulata*, *M. italica*, and *M. distans*.

Another example of such variations is found with *Asterionella formosa*.
Distinct differences have been observed in the shape and size of the
inflated ends of the valves in this species. The basal end usually pos-
sesses a more typical rounded capitate form, whereas the degree of
development of the head end of the valve will differ. The head-end
size will always be less than the basal structure and in some cells may
lack any development. It is feasible that variations of *Asterionella formosa* are present (e.g., *Asterionella formosa* var. *ralfsii*), or these too may
simply represent a morphological response of *A. formosa* to local conditions.

Zooplankton

An effort was made to characterize the major zooplankton constituents for Lake Drummond and to tie seasonal variations in the
zooplankton populations to pulses noted in the phytoplankton. No
attempt was made toward a complete census, which would include
protozoa, meroplankton, and forms having diurnal migratory habitats in the water column. The net sampling indicated three major
faunal categories predominating in the zooplankton: cladocerans,
copepods, and rotifers. Other forms collected included nematodes,
ostracods, insect larvae, protozoa, larval fish, and various planktonic
eggs. *Bosmina longirostris* was the most dominant zooplankter during
the collection period. This species is commonly found in lakes undergoing a period of enrichment and in acidic, brown-water lakes. The
abundance of these smaller cladocerans and the rotifers in a lake generally indicates a heavy fish predation of the larger zooplankters
(Hrbacek et al. 1961). Accompanying this condition would be the
expected dominance of the larger phytoplankters (e.g., *Asterionella
formosa, Melosira granulata*), with an inverse concentration relationship
to the larger herbivorous zooplankton.

There were distinct seasonal changes in the zooplankton concentrations. The fall populations were dominated by the cladocerans,
with *Bosmina longirostris* the most abundant species. The zooplankton

decreased steadily into winter with lowest total numbers occurring in January and February. *Bosmina longirostris* was also the most common species during the winter months. The copepods were present in low concentrations throughout the winter but showed an increase in numbers into spring. However, the cladocerans dominated the spring collections, with the *Bosmina* population beginning to wane in late spring. The summer zooplankton may be characterized as containing the annual peak of the copepods, an increase in the rotifer populations, and the ever present *B. longirostris*. The summer zooplankton development was accompanied by a decrease in phytoplankton values, and also coincided with the time of increased loss of lake water through the Feeder Ditch. The zooplankton noted from seasonal collections in the Feeder Ditch was comparable to that present at the same time in Lake Drummond. Hillard (1974) has also noted *Bosmina longirostris* as the dominant species in the Dismal Swamp Canal, with peak numbers occurring in spring and lowest values in winter.

SUMMARY

Each natural lake system has either a unique combination of characteristics or is so situated in its temporal stage of eutrophication that the lake has its own distinct individuality. Lake Drummond illustrates this position probably moreso than the majority of natural lakes in the region. Its character is to a major extent determined by the drainage received from the local watershed. The large volume of water received annually in relation to basin capacity and the subsequent loss by seasonal outflow patterns have retarded the natural eutrophication patterns expected in a shallow, brown-water lake and greatly influenced the biotic composition.

Lake Drummond may be characterized as a temperate, brown-water lake on the Atlantic Coastal Plain. It is of moderate size (3180 acres) with a maximum depth of about 7 feet, and the water level is subject to seasonal fluctuations. The waters are acidic, stained brown, and are rather turbid. Submerged or emergent vegetation is rare, with the line of tree growth typically extending to the lake margin. The lake bottom is mostly of a mud-sand consistency with sand and more peatlike substrates scattered along marginal areas (see Marshall and Robinson, this volume). Bald cypress trees may be found along the lake's margin and within the lake at several offshore sites. The broad, windswept surface results in frequent turnover conditions in the shallow lake. Seasonal periods of thermal stratification are rare, although a winter ice cover may become established for brief periods. Water level and quality are greatly influenced by the man-made ditch system that brings water into and controls flow out of the lake. Further modification to the present drainage into the lake would have a direct effect on the water quality, biota, and rate of eutrophication.

The pH values of 3.2–6.8 recorded during this study correspond to those in previous investigations. Plankton tows and Secchi disc readings consistently indicated waters of high turbidity with considerable amounts of detrital material held in suspension. The Secchi readings ranged from 8 to 64 cm. The lower values were more common and indicate less light penetration, which would tend to reduce the productivity and eutrofication rates. Water temperature and seasonal rainfall data during the study were considered typical of average values for previous years in which the lake level was not lowered excessively. Nutrient levels were adequate to support phytoplankton blooms that frequently exceeded 1 million cells per liter. Characteristic drainage patterns resulted in a major flow of water through the lake during spring and summer months. Loss of water through the Feeder Ditch spillway was a seasonal phenomenon, with major water flow through the lake occurring between May and November. This was a period of maximum concentrations for the phytoplankton and groups within the zooplankton. Various degrees of relationship between these physical parameters within the lake and the plankton composition were noted.

The plankton populations for Lake Drummond are basically similar to those found in other acidic, brown-water lakes of temperate regions. The phytoplankton exhibited a bimodal pattern of maximum production periods occurring in spring and fall. The winter minimum was more extensive in duration and resulted in lower population levels than the summer minimum. *Asterionella formosa* was the most abundant species throughout the study, with changes in its concentrations generally reflecting the total phytoplankton values. Present in substantial numbers throughout the year were desmids, other chlorophyceans, and additional species of diatoms. There were low concentrations of cyanophyceans, euglenophyceans, pyrrhophyceans, and the chrysophyceans. The zooplankton consisted primarily of a cladoceran-copepod-rotifer expression where *Bosmina longirostris* was the conspicuous species throughout the study. The cladocerans had major population peaks during the fall and spring months, with the copepod concentrations highest in summer. The period of lowest zooplankton concentrations occurred in late winter. The significance of the drainage ditch system into the lake was indicated. These ditches drain diverse areas that impart different qualities to the waters entering the lake, and subsequently influence the plankton composition in Lake Drummond. The plankton composition within Lake Drummond is similar to that found in the Feeder Ditch and adjacent portions of the Dismal Swamp Canal.

ACKNOWLEDGMENTS

I wish to extend my appreciation to the Army Corps of Engineers, Norfolk Division, and representatives from the Dismal Swamp National Wildlife Refuge for their assistance in providing access into the Dismal Swamp, and to Dr. L. A. Whitford for the identification of several species.

REFERENCES CITED

Bethge, H. 1925. *Melosira und ihr Planktonbegleiter.* Pp. 1–85 *in* R. Kolkwitz (ed). *Pflanzenforschung.* Part 3. Jena.

Frey, D. G. 1949. Morphometry and hydrography of some natural lakes of the North Carolina Coastal Plain: the Bay Lake as a morphological type. *J. Elisha Mitchell Sci. Soc.* 65:1–37.

Hillard, O. C. 1974. Observations on the distribution and composition of zooplankton in portions of the Intra-coastal Waterway, Virginia. Master's Thesis Old Dominion Univ. 71 pp.

Hrbacek, J., M. Dvorakova, V. Korinek, and L. Prochazkova. 1961. Demonstration of the effect of the fish stock in the species composition of zooplankton and the intensity of metabolism of the whole plankton association. *Verh. Int. Verein. Limnol.* 14:192–195.

Hustedt, F. 1930. *Die Kiesealgen Deutschlands, Osterreichs und der Schweiz,* v. 7, pts. 1 and 2, *in* L. Rabenhorst. *Kryptogamen-Flora Von Deutschlands, Osterreichs und der Schweiz.* Johnson Reprint Corp., New York.

Main, C. T., Inc. 1971. Dismal Swamp Study 1659-25. Charles T. Main Engineers, Inc., 1301 E. Morehead St., Charlotte, N.C. 34 pp.

Marshall, H. G. 1974. Zooplankton populations in Lake Drummond, Dismal Swamp, Virginia. *Va. J. Sci.* 25:66 (Abs.)

Marshall, H. G., and W. H. Poore. 1972. Phytoplankton composition at Lake Drummond in the Dismal Swamp, Virginia, summer 1970. *Castanea* 37:59–67.

Patrick, Ruth, and C. W. Reimer. 1966. *The diatoms of the United States, exclusive of Alaska and Hawaii,* v. 1. *Acad. Nat. Sci. Phila., Monographs* 13. 688 pp.

Poore, W. H., Jr. 1971. Phytoplankton composition at Lake Drummond in the Dismal Swamp, Virginia. Master's Thesis Old Dominion Univ. 83 pp.

Poore, W. H., Jr., and H. G. Marshall. 1972. Lake Drummond of the Dismal Swamp: I. Phytoplankton composition. *Va. J. Sci.* 23:72–76.

U.S. Army, Corps of Engineers, Norfolk District. 1974. The Dismal Swamp Canal as related to the Great Dismal Swamp study, P.L. 92–478. Norfolk, Va. February. 63 pp. and map.

NOTES ON THE OVERLYING SUBSTRATE AND BOTTOM CONTOURS OF LAKE DRUMMOND

Harold G. Marshall and W. Wright Robinson

During the spring of 1974 observations were made of 155 benthic samples taken within quadrats distributed over a grid system designed for Lake Drummond. In addition, soundings were made by means of a suspended lead weight within each quadrat. The bottom samples were taken from a boat with an Ekman grab attached to a hand-held rod 6 feet in length. The grab samples had an area of 36 in² (231 cm²) with the maximum penetration depth of 6 inches (15.24 cm). The quadrats were approximately 1000 feet square and included the entire lake. Transit observations were made between fixed points along the shoreline, with marker poles placed in the lake to identify the marginal extent of each quadrant and assure accuracy in sampling on successive dates. Samples were taken at the approximate center of each quadrat. Each bottom sample was recorded under one of three categories, as follows:

1. Sandy. A substrate consisting of over 50 per cent light brown or whitish, fine-grained sand. At some locations low concentrations of mud were intermixed with the sand, and this usually represented a transitional margin between categories.

2. Mud. Lake bottom muds were composed of a soft, fine, slippery ooze, typically very dark (black) in color and having a characteristic odor of hydrogen sulfide.

3. Peat. This refers to a substrate consisting of a mixture of detrital material, mud, and, in some areas, small concentrations of sand. This substrate would include parts of plant stems and the typical peaty materials found in terrestrial areas surrounding the lake.

Results

Figure 1 indicates the depth contours and distribution of the three substrate types for Lake Drummond. Due to the seasonal fluctuations in lake level, the depth measurements are all relative to water dynamics at that particular time (see Marshall, this volume). The depths presented for the lake are based on a full lake level of approximately 17 feet above sea level, with 17.15 feet considered as the full lake level using U.S. Coast and Geodetic Survey mean sea level data (Note: if one were to use the Norfolk Harbor data base, this same lake level would be given as 18.65 feet above zero mean low water). At capacity the lake contours have a somewhat symmetrical pattern, shallow marginally and increasing in depth toward the center of the lake. Here the maximum depth is approximately 6 feet, with occasional low pockets 6.5 to 7.0 feet deep. No depth exceeding 7.0 feet was found under conditions of maximum high water.

Although he did not take the measurements himself, Ruffin (1837) reported soundings of 15 feet in the middle of the lake. An early (1879) map of the Lake Drummond area by the Army Corps of Engineers also shows a depth of 11 feet near the center of the lake. However, Kearney (1901) gives the depth in November 1898 as less than 2 meters. He also explains that the greatest depth previously noted for the lake was 4.5 meters (15 ft) due to the "digging of canals and other artificial causes," whereas before that period the depth did not exceed 2 meters. Washington Ditch was constructed in the 1760s, with Jericho Ditch completed about 1810. The Feeder Ditch, draining Lake Drummond eastward into the Dismal Swamp Canal, was constructed in 1812, with Riddick Ditch cut around 1818 to provide passage of water from the south end of the lake into the Corapeake Canal (See Fig. 1 of Levy and Walker, and of Lichtler and Walker, this volume, for orientation). Redredging of the Feeder Ditch took place in 1896. Brown (1970) provides an illustration of a dipper dredge on Lake Drummond in 1898. The dredge was passed through newly constructed locks about 200 yards from the lake and dredged a channel from the Feeder Ditch into the deeper part of the lake. The existing dam and spillway in the Feeder Ditch were constructed in 1935. Subsequent surveys of Lake Drummond by the Army Corps of Engineers in 1935 and 1970 indicate no soundings greater than 6.5 feet. The bottom of Lake Drummond was given as having an elevation of 12.2 feet above the mean low water of the Norfolk Harbor figure with a normal lake level of 8.07 feet. Further information from core-sample analysis within the lake and rates of surrounding peat formation would be necessary to assess more fully the validity of fluctuating depths recorded for Lake Drummond over the past 150 years. However, it is obvious that the previous margin of the

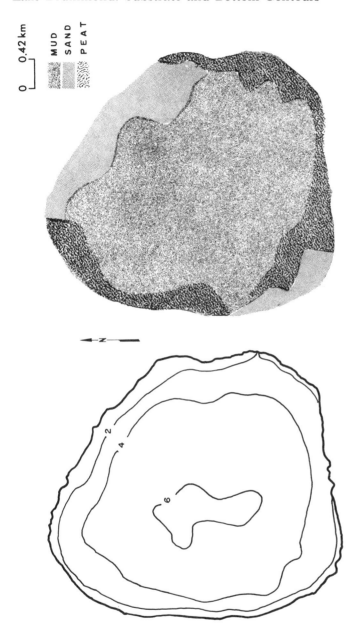

Fig. 1. Bottom topography and substrate composition of Lake Drummond.

lake was much smaller than today and that the lake area has increased over the past several hundred years, with accompanying sedimentation. Although ditches such as Washington, Jericho, and Interior have brought water more quickly into the lake basin, the increased volume of the lake is directly related to the amount of natural drainage to the east and south.

The northern and northeastern margins of the lake possess a sandy bottom that extends into the lake from occasional sand-covered embankments along the northeast shoreline. The sandy deposits are at the entrance of the combined Washington-Jericho ditches and continue east of the openings for East and Portsmouth ditches. A smaller extent of offshore sand deposits also occurs along the southwest margin of the lake off the entrance of Interior Ditch. Due to the compact nature of the bottom sands, deep penetration with the grab was not possible, it usually entering the substrate only 2–3 inches (5.0–7.6 cm). Deeper grab entry was common along the more central marginal areas of sand where higher concentrations of mud provided a less compact substrate. These were transition areas to the mud region.

The lake muds were found covering the largest and most central extent of the lake bottom. The thickness of the mud (ooze) varied with the samples. Peat and sand deposits were often found covered by several cm of ooze. Such samples were noted along sections bordering the sand and peat bottoms. In the more central lake locations, narrow streaks of sand deposits were frequently found in the ooze samples, forming a distinct sediment stratum. In the deeper lake sections the bottom grab would obtain a full 6-inch (15 cm) mud sample. No samples below this depth were taken at this time. The stratal evidence of sand transport into the lake sediment may be associated with the high volume of water that enters the lake seasonally from the northern drainage ditches. Exposed sandy bottoms and embankments are common in Washington Ditch, which may be a source for such sediment along the northeastern margin.

The peat substrate, which often includes scattered stumps, roots, fallen trees, and various detrital materials represents the composition of the marginal area along the northwest and eastern sections of the lake. Live bald cypress trees (*Taxodium distichum*) commonly extend into the water beyond the eastern shoreline, with the scattered submerged stumps a hazard to boat operation. Noting the distribution of the peat substrate in Figure 1, it is conceivable that the peat originally encircled the lake. The recent sand deposits entering the lake have covered portions of the peat. This ring of peat has possibly been included in the present lake system in recent times following raised lake levels after construction of the previously mentioned ditches and spillway on the Feeder Ditch. This marginal area is shallow and can be navigated with a power boat safely only during high water. It is through this eastern portion of the lake that a small boat channel leads into the Feeder Ditch. The Feeder Ditch channel approaching the lake margin is shallower than the central part of the lake, so complete drainage of the lake could not take place through the open spillway gates on the Feeder Ditch.

ACKNOWLEDGMENTS

Appreciation is extended to the Dismal Swamp National Wildlife Refuge staff and to the U.S. Army Corps of Engineers, Norfolk Division, for their assistance in this study.

REFERENCES CITED

Brown, A. C. 1970. *The Dismal Swamp Canal.* Norfolk Co. Hist. Soc. Chesapeake, Va. 234 pp.

Kearney, T. H. 1901. Report on a botanical survey of the Dismal Swamp region. *Contrib. U.S. Natl. Herbarium* 5:321–585.

Ruffin, E. 1837. Observations made during an excursion to the Dismal Swamp. *Petersburg (Va.) Farmers' Register* 4(1 Jan.):513–521.

HYDROCARBON BACKGROUND LEVELS AT TWO RURAL SITES IN TIDEWATER VIRGINIA

R. S. Davis, P. J. Maroulis, Robert B. Denyszyn, and A. R. Bandy

INTRODUCTION

Present strategies for controlling atmospheric photochemically generated oxidants concentrate on regulating anthropogenically produced hydrocarbons (U.S. Dept. HEW 1970; Code of Federal Regulations 1971; Federal Register 1971, 1974). The reasons for this approach are explained in great detail in the literature and will not be discussed here (U.S. Dept. HEW 1970). Recently, however, the oxidant-control strategies prescribed by the Environmental Protection Agency have come under attack by various industries and state air pollution control boards (Stasink and Coffey 1974; U.S. Fifth Circuit Court of Appeals 1974; Virginia State Air Pollution Control Board, pers. comm.). These conflicts have arisen because ozone levels greater than the National Standard have been found in relatively rural areas (Miller et al. 1972; Ripperton and Worth 1974; A. R. Bandy et al., unpublished data.) The origin of this high ozone level is being intensely debated in scientific circles, and no definite resolution of the problem is at hand.

Our interests centered on the hypothesis that NO and NO_2 are transported from urban areas to the rural areas. These anthropogenically produced concentrations of NO and NO_2 then react with the naturally generated active hydrocarbons to produce the high ozone sometimes observed in rural areas.

The hydrocarbon requirement can be seen by inspecting the basic mechanism by which ozone is formed in the troposphere:

(1) $NO_2 + h\upsilon \ (\lambda < 4100 \text{Å}) \longrightarrow NO + O\cdot$

(2) $O\cdot + O_2 \longrightarrow O_3$

(3) $NO + O_3 \longrightarrow NO_2 + O_2$

Reaction 1 leads to both a precursor for ozone (O· through reaction 2) and a savenger of ozone (NO through reaction 3). Thus, as NO builds up from Reaction 1, the destruction rate of ozone from Reaction 3 increases. In a system of NO, NO_2, and sunlight, little O_3 exists at photochemical equilibrium.

When hydrocarbons are added to the system, peroxides are formed. In urban atmospheres these peroxides oxidize NO to NO_2 at a rate considerably faster than the rate of oxidation of NO by ozone. Thus, the rate of destruction of O_3 is relatively smaller in a system containing hydrocarbons, NO and NO_2 than in a system of NO and NO_2 alone. Consequently the steady-state ozone concentration is higher in the system containing ozone.

The opposite question of transport of naturally generated hydro-carbons into urban areas was also considered. It was concluded that this transport was less important because NO and NO_2 are effective in much lower concentrations than active hydrocarbons; thus, the activity of NO and NO_2 is affected much less by dilution during trans-port. Therefore our research concentrated on a study of naturally gen-erated hydrocarbons.

Two sites were sampled (Fig. 1). Site 1 was designated the Dismal Swamp site as it is located on the northeast edge of the Dismal Swamp, just north of the Northwest River and east of Rt. 17. We anticipated that winds from the south and west bear high concentrations of nat-ural hydrocarbons due to the heavily forested areas located in these directions from the site. Additionally, winds from the north and east would bear lower fractions of natural materials since heavily urban and industrialized areas lie in these directions from the site (see end-papers and Carter, this volume).

Site 2 was designated the Nansemond County site and was located east of the mouth of the Nansemond River and north of Rt. 17 (Fig. 1). This is agricultural land with forested areas several miles to the south and west. Heavily populated areas lie to the north (Newport News) and east (Norfolk). An oil refinery is being planned for this vicinity in the near future.

MATERIALS AND METHODS

Ambient air hydrocarbons were sampled using the stainless steel traps shown in Figure 2. The traps were cleaned by heating them to 250°C followed by a purge cycle with hydrocarbon-free air. The traps were readied for field use by evacuation to 10^{-6} torr.

Samples in the field were taken by immersing the trap in liquid ni-

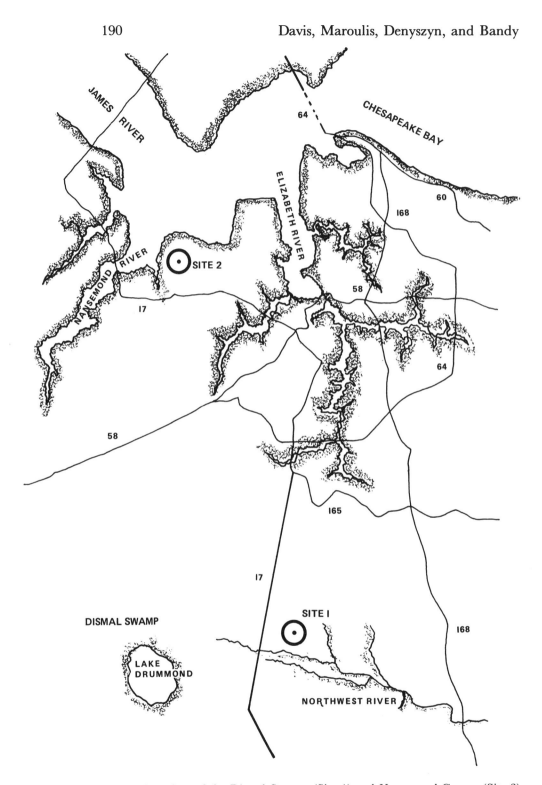

Fig. 1. Locations of the Dismal Swamp (Site 1) and Nansemond County (Site 2) sites sampled during this study of ambient air hydrocarbons.

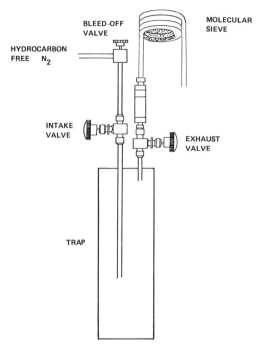

Fig. 2. Stainless steel traps used in obtaining ambient air samples of hydrocarbons; sonic capillaries (50 ml/min) were used for flow control.

trogen and opening a metal filling valve on the trap. The flow rate (50 ml/minute) was regulated with a sonic capillary so that the volume of the air sampled could be calculated from the length of the sampling period (7 minutes). To prevent formation of liquid oxygen, the sample pressure in the trap was not allowed to exceed 0.5 atm.

A schematic diagram of our laboratory apparatus for gas chromatographic analysis of the hydrocarbons sampled using the stainless steel traps is shown in Figure 3. The stainless steel traps were connected to the injection system of the gas chromatograph by 0.25-inch Swagelok® connectors. All-stainless-steel bakeable high vacuum valves were used throughout the system and were heated to 100°C after each use to insure complete transfer of the hydrocarbons to the column.

The sample was transferred from the trap to the column by cooling the trap and column to –190° and –70°C, respectively, and then diverting carrier gas (nitrogen) so that it flowed through the trap and column. The temperature of the trap was then raised and the contents of the trap transferred to the head of the capillary column (250 ft OV101–CO880 Scott column). The temperature of the column was then programmed from –70°C to 170°C to release the hydrocarbons. A flame ionization detector was used, providing a detectivity after the concentration step of about 10 parts per trillion.

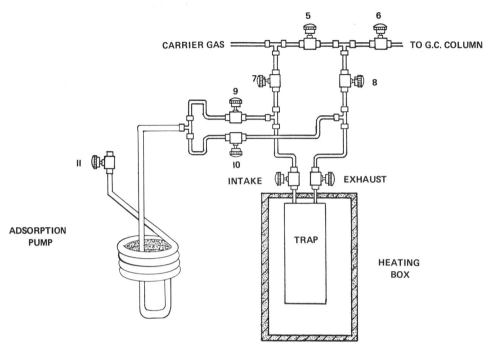

Fig. 3. Manifold for transfer of hydrocarbon sample from the stainless steel trap to the column of the gas chromatograph.

A typical chromatogram is shown in Figure 4. The C_1 and C_2 hydrocarbons are not retained by the column. Hydrocarbons in the C_3 to C_8 range elute between 10° and 70°C. Hydrocarbons in the C_{15} range elute at about 130°C. All calibrations were carried out with a 10 ppm methane-in-nitrogen standard. All data reported here are relative to methane (ppm carbon).

RESULTS AND DISCUSSION

Samples were taken at the Dismal Swamp site (Site 1) approximately weekly during the period 15 April to 1 July 1974. Samples were taken on Wednesdays at 1200 EDT.

A plot of nonmethane hydrocarbon concentration for the sampling period is shown in Figure 5. There appears to be no large dependence of the nonmethane hydrocarbon concentration on wind direction, although it seems to be slightly higher with southwest winds. A summary of the findings is shown in Table 1. Note that the low value for nonmethane hydrocarbons was 145 ppb (parts per billion) and the high value 692 ppb. These data suggest that the nonmethane hydro-

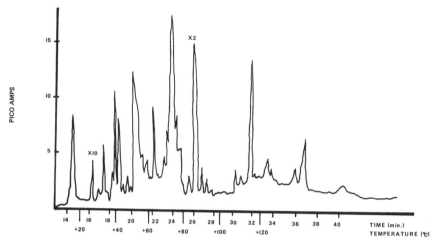

Fig. 4. Typical gas chromatogram of an ambient air hydrocarbon sample obtained in this study.

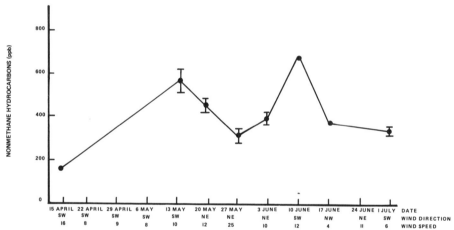

Fig. 5. Plot of nonmethane hydrocarbon concentration for the Dismal Swamp site (Site 1) during the sampling period 15 April to 1 July 1974.

carbon level during this period may have exceeded the National Primary Standard of 240 ppb (6–9 AM average) during most of the sampling period.

Figure 6 is a plot of α-pinene concentration during the sampling period. The α-pinene maxima are clearly higher with southwest winds than with northeast winds. The correlation of the α-pinene concentration with nonmethane hydrocarbon concentration is very good (Fig. 5). This result suggests that naturally generated hydrocarbons are a significant contribution to the nonmethane hydrocarbon level. Relatively low values for the nonmethane hydrocarbons, α-pinene

Table 1. Data summary for Dismal Swamp site (Site 1)

Compound	Number of samples	Concentration range (ppb carbon)
Nonmethane hydrocarbons	16	145.00–692.00
α-pinene	17	0.44– 14.00
Limonene	17	0.00– 9.02

(Fig. 6), and limonene (Fig. 7), at the beginning and end of the sampling period, also support this idea. Apparently the peak in emission rates of natural hydrocarbons occurs during the spring with lower rates during winter and summer. It would seem reasonable that natural emission rates might also peak in the fall at the end of the growing season, but this was not investigated.

The α-pinene concentration with northeast winds is greater than expected relative to that found with southwest winds because the area to the southwest of the sampling site is very heavily wooded. This observation may arise from a shielding effect by the tree canopy. Much slower wind speeds were observed inside the canopy.

The α-pinene is a useful tracer for naturally generated hydrocarbons although it is somewhat nonconservative. The nonconservative nature of this tracer leads to an underestimation of the contribution of natural hydrocarbons to the hydrocarbon loading. This underestimation should be minimized in this case since the natural sources are presumed to be only a short distance from the site.

Samples were taken each Sunday and Thursday (1200 EDT) at the Nansemond County site (Fig. 1, Site 2) during the period 20 June to 7 July 1974. A plot of α-pinene concentration for this period is given in Figure 8. The data are too few to deduce a correlation with wind direction. The high concentration of α-pinene in late spring and its rapid decay in summer, however, are clearly indicated. A similar variation is observed for limonene (Fig. 9).

The nonmethane hydrocarbon concentration (Fig. 10) is not correlated with the α-pinene or limonene concentrations. This observation suggests that naturally generated hydrocarbons are much less important contributors to the nonmethane hydrocarbon loading than at the Dismal Swamp site. Inspection of Figure 10 reveals that the nonmethane hydrocarbon level exceeds 240 ppb in every case but one, and suggests that the nonmethane hydrocarbon level exceeds the National Standard during most of the sampling period. Table 2 summarizes data for Site 2.

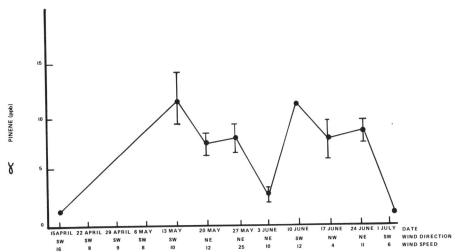

Fig. 6. Plot of α-pinene concentration at the Dismal Swamp site (Site 1) during the
period 15 April to 1 July 1974.

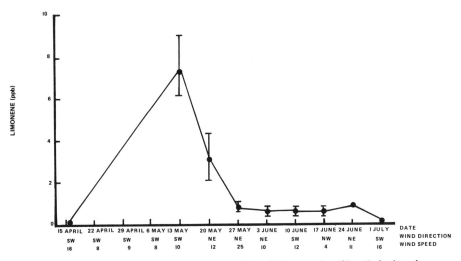

Fig. 7. Plot of limonene concentration at the Dismal Swamp site (Site 1) during the
period 15 April to 1 July 1974.

Table 2. Data summary for Nansemond County site (Site 2)

Compound	Number of samples	Concentration range (ppb carbon)
Nonmethane hydrocarbons	10	236.00–629.00
α-pinene	10	0.00– 11.90
Limonene	10	0.00– 1.46

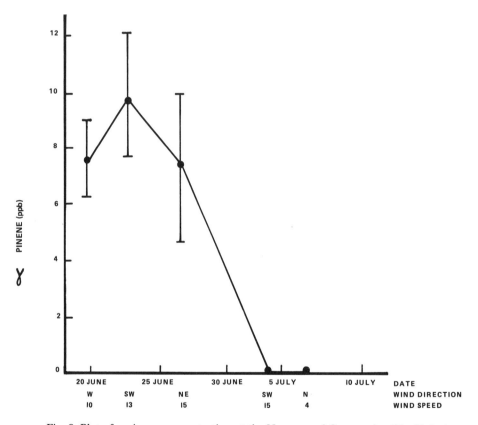

Fig. 8. Plot of α-pinene concentration at the Nansemond County site (Site 2) during the period 20 June to 7 July 1974.

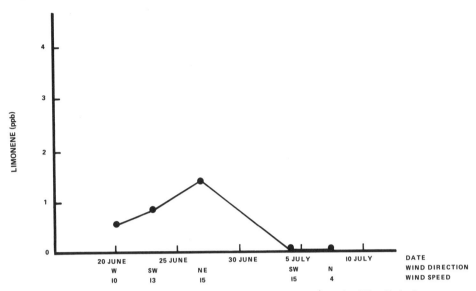

Fig. 9. Plot of limonene concentration at the Nansemond County site (Site 2) during the period 20 June to 7 July 1974.

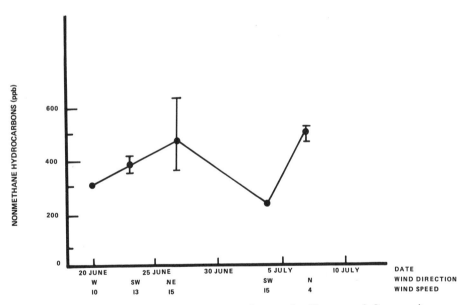

Fig. 10. Variation of nonmethane concentration at the Nansemond County site (Site 2) during the period 20 June to 7 July 1974.

SUMMARY

Atmospheric hydrocarbons were determined by gas chromatography at a rural site along the northeastern margin of the Dismal Swamp (Site 1) and another, more urban site well to the north of the Swamp (Site 2). Naturally generated hydrocarbons appear to contribute more to the nonmethane hydrocarbon levels at Site 1 than at Site 2, although nonmethane hydrocarbon levels at both sites exceeded 240 ppb for all but one reading at each site.

At the Dismal Swamp site (Site 1), naturally generated compounds including α-pinene and limonene reached peak levels in spring. Presumably these levels are lower in winter due to the relative inactivity of trees and lower in summer because of a decrease in emission rates by the trees or through scavenging by ozone, whose concentration is higher during the summer months.

It is clear that the concentrations of active hydrocarbons in both areas studied are sufficient to produce levels of ozone exceeding the National Standard of 240 ppb. Nitrogen oxides and intense solar radiation are the remaining ingredients necessary to produce a highly reactive photochemical system. Apparently NO and NO_2 can be very effective in low concentrations and could be supplied by transport from urban areas.

REFERENCES CITED

Code of Federal Regulations (CFR), 40. 1971. paragraph 51.16 (17 Dec.) 36FR24002.

Federal Register. 1971. 36:8195 and 15491.

————. 1974. 39:9671.

Miller, P. R., M. H. McCutchan, and H. P. Milligan. 1972. Oxidant air pollution in the Central Valley, Sierra Nevada foothills, and Mineral King Valley of California. *Atmos. Environ.* 6:623–633.

Ripperton, L. A., and J. J. B. Worth. 1974. Interstate ozone studies. Paper presented at 2nd joint conferences on sensing of environmental pollutants, Washington, D.C.

Stasink, W. N., Jr., and P. E. Coffey. 1974. Rural and urban ozone relationships in New York State. *J. Air Polln. Contr. Assn.* 24:564–568.

U.S. Dept. Health, Education, and Welfare (HEW). 1970. Air quality criteria of photochemical oxidants. *Natl. Air Polln. Contr. Admin. Publ.* AP-63.
U.S. Govt. Print Off., Washington. (10 chapters, pp. not numbered con-
secutively.)

U.S. Fifth Circuit Court of Appeals. 1974. Petition for review of orders and
regulations of Environmental Protection Agency, No. 73–3540, State
of Texas et al. vs. EPA.

AQUATIC INSECTS OF THE DISMAL SWAMP

James F. Matta

INTRODUCTION

Until the 1960s knowledge of the insects of the Dismal Swamp was limited to Banks's information (1904) on the yellow fly, records by Clark and Clark (1939) on butterflies of the Swamp, and casual comments by workers in other fields concerning the more noxious insect species. Gurney (1963) discussed the Orthoptera of the Swamp and recorded two species of Trichoptera, *Cernotina truncona* Ross and *Molanna uniophila* Varhies. Baldwin (1969) discussed the insects of the Swamp, giving many records of butterflies and skippers and repeating Gurney's observations on the Orthoptera and Trichoptera. Battle and Turner (1971) gave several records for *Culicoides,* and Pechuman (1973) listed many of the Tabanidae occurring in the Dismal Swamp. Matta (1973) reviewed the aquatic Coleoptera from the Swamp and listed 53 species with notes on habitat preferences and distribution within the Swamp. [Most recent detailed information on Coleoptera from the Dismal Swamp is included in the series "Insects of Virginia," Matta treating the Hydrophilidae (1974) and Haliplidae (1976), and Michael and Matta (1977) the Dytiscidae—ed.]

This paper gives an annotated list of the known species of aquatic insects in the Dismal Swamp. The information presented is based on literature records and over 100 individual collections made by the author over a four-year period. Collections were generally made by dip netting; however, light-trap and black-light collections, aerial netting, and Echman dredge samples were also taken.

Many of the habitat types mentioned in the species list were discussed by Matta (1973) and Poore and Marshall (1972) for Lake Drummond only. The major aquatic habitats including several not discussed in the above publications are briefly described below, but the reader is referred to Matta (1973) for a review of minor habitats. The characteristic species mentioned for each habitat type should not be interpreted as a complete list of all aquatic insects, as those encountered occasionally are not listed.

DESCRIPTION OF AQUATIC HABITATS AND THEIR INSECT FAUNA

Woodland Pools

The most important aquatic habitat in the Swamp in terms of area is the series of shallow woodland pools located in the interior. These pools fluctuate greatly in size and depth with the season, rarely exceeding 2–3 feet in depth and often becoming quite shallow or dry. The water is amber to fuscus in color, and the pH varies from 4.0 to 6.0. The density of the insect fauna in these pools varies but is rarely high. Characteristic species include *Hydroporus lobatus, Copelatus glyphicus,* and *Pachydiplax longipennis.*

The woodland pools located near the western margin of the Swamp are usually shallow, occasionally supporting rooted aquatic vegetation. The water is usually amber colored, and the pH ranges between 6.0 and 7.0. These pools support a more diverse fauna including *Chauliodes pectinicornis, Notonecta irrorta, Ranatra buenoi, Pachydiplax longipennis, Tetragoneuria cynosura, Hydrochara obtusatus, Agabetes accuductus, Bidessonotus inconspicuus, Acilius mediatus, Thermonectus basillaris, Dytiscus fasciventris,* and *Hoparius planata.*

Most roads in the Swamp are bordered by a ditch on one side and woodland on the other, often with a series of pools between the road and the woodland. These pools—interconnected during wetter portions of the year—support a dense growth of algae and many rooted aquatic vascular plants. The aquatic insect fauna is quite diverse and includes *Epiaeshna heros, Erythemis simplicicollis, Pachydiplax longipennis, Tetragoneuria cynosura, Ranatra buenoi, Notonecta uhleri, N. irrorta, Platycentropus* sp.*, Fabria inornata, Peltodytes dunavani, Hydroporus carolinus, Laccornis difformis, Enochrus ochraceus, Tropisternus blatchleyi blatchleyi, T. collaris striolatis,* and *Aedes canadensis.*

A large roadside pool along Jericho Ditch Lane is unusual in that it has developed into a willow swamp and supports a unique fauna. In addition to most of the above species, the following are characteristic of this area: *Hesperocorixa nitida, Pelocoris femoratus, Hydrometra hungerfordi,* and *Belostoma testaceum.*

Ditches

The network of ditches that drain the Swamp (see Levy and Walker, Fig. 1, this volume, for orientation) may be classified as acid and nonacid. Those draining large areas of the Swamp are quite acid (pH 4.0–5.0) and support little rooted vegetation. Characteristic species include *Epiaeshna heros, Enallagma* sp.*, Chauliodes pectinicornis, Coptotomus i. interrogatus,* and *Hydroporus venustrus.*

The ditches having primary drainage areas outside of the Swamp are much less acidic (pH 6.0–7.0 in some areas) and support a variety of rooted aquatic vegetation. The upper end of Washington Ditch is a good example. Characteristic aquatic insect species include *Dineutus carolinus, D. discolor, Nononecta irrorta, Gerris nebularis,* and *Pelocoris femoratus.*

Marshes

Several marshy areas within the Dismal Swamp are mostly the result of old peat burns or agricultural disturbance. One of particular interest is a large marsh (approximately 60 acres) located near Hamburg Ditch in Gates County, North Carolina.

To date only winter collections have been made at this site and the characteristic aquatic species present were *Hydrobius tumidus, Cymbiodyta blanchardi,* and *Hydroporus* sp.

Another marshy area (approximately 2 acres) occurs beside Railroad Road. This small, shallow pond has sparser aquatic vegetation. The water is usually clear with a thick layer of detritus in some portions. Characteristic species include *Libellula semifaciata, Notonecta irrorta, Agabus aeruginoeus,* and *Berosus infuscatus.*

Lake Drummond

Chemical and physical characteristics of Lake Drummond are given by Marshall in this volume. Characteristic aquatic insects include *Chaoborus punctipennis, Ablabesmyia* sp., and *Chironomus* sp.

GENERAL CONSIDERATIONS

There are 155 aquatic and semiaquatic insect species recorded from the Swamp at the present time. These represent seven orders including 34 families and 86 genera. The orders Coleoptera and Diptera form the major components of the aquatic insect fauna with 67.5 percent of the species present.

Table 1 presents a summary of the aquatic insects of the Dismal Swamp. To save space, the following designations and abbreviations have been used:

Abundance: number of specimens collected; number of separate instances in which adults or larvae have been collected is given in parentheses; numbers followed by a plus sign are conservative minima.

Distribution: geographic distribution for the North American Continent, with these abbreviations: NA = North America, E = Eastern, S = Southern, N = Northern, C = Central, SE = Southeastern, NE = Northeastern; when the known distribution is limited to three or fewer states, these are named.

Season: first and last month in which material has been collected in the Dismal Swamp; first and last months collected in southeastern Virginia if different from the above are given in parentheses; flight season of adult if different from the above is given in brackets.

Typical habitats of aquatic stage:
    1 woodland pools
    2 roadside pools
    3 willow swamp
    4 ditches
    5 marsh
    6 Lake Drummond
    7 *Juncus* marsh
    8 stream
    9 only light trap records available
    10 tire track
    11 temporary pools
    12 recorded from biting collections
    13 no habitat data available from Dismal Swamp
    14 sweep net collections

Reference: literature citations for distribution records are included in References Cited.

Unless otherwise indicated, voucher specimens are in the Old Dominion University Aquatic Insect Collection.

Table 1. Summary of aquatic insects of the Dismal Swamp

Species	Abundance	Distribution	Reference	Season	Typical habitats
Order Ephemeroptera					
1. *Leptophlebia austrinus*	20 (4)	VA, NC	Needham et al. 1935	2–5 [5]	8
Order Odonata					
2. *Anax junius*	1	NA	Needham & Westfall 1955	7	13
3. *Epiaeshna heros*	25+ (15)	E	Needham & Westfall 1955	1–12 [6–9]	1, 2, 4

Table 1. (cont.)

Species	Abundance	Distribution	Reference	Season	Typical habitats
4. *Gomphaeschna antilope*	2 (2)	E	Needham & Westfall 1955	5	13
5. *G. furcillata*	3 (2)	E	Needham & Westfall 1955	5	13
6. *Gomphus exilus*	2 (2)	E	Needham & Westfall 1955	5	13
7. *Erythemis simplicicollis*	25 + (10)	NA	Needham & Westfall 1955	6–7 (4–9)	2
8. *Libellula cyaenea*	1	E	Needham & Westfall 1955	7	13
9. *L. incesta*	10 (3)	E	Needham & Westfall 1955	7	2
10. *L. semifasciata*	7 (4)	E	Needham & Westfall 1955	4–5 (4–7)	13
11. *L. flavida*	3 (2)	E	Needham & Westfall 1955	7–8 (6–8)	13
12. *Pachydiplax longipennis*	25 + (10)	NA	Needham & Westfall 1955	4–5 (4–10)	13
13. *Plathemis lydia*	11 (3)	NA	Needham & Westfall 1955	4–5 (4–10)	4
14. *Tetragoneuria cynosura*	25 + (10)	E	Needham & Westfall 1955	1–12 [4–5]	4
15. *Calopteryx maculatum*	25 +	NA	Johnson 1974	1–12 [7–8]	4
16. *Lestes disjunctus*	1	NA	Walker 1952	5	13
17. *Anomalagrion hastatum*	2 (1)	E	Johnson & Westfall 1970	4	13
18. *Enallagma duram*	3 (2)	E	Johnson & Westfall 1970	4	13
19. *Enallagma* sp.	15 (5)	—	—	5–7	4

Table 1. (cont.)

Species	Abundance	Distribution	Reference	Season	Typical habitats
Order Hemiptera					
20. *Hesperocorixa brimleyi*	25 + (7)	E	Hungerford 1948	2–8	2, 4
21. *H. interruptus*	1	E	Hungerford 1948	8 (8–10)	4
22. *H. nitida*	25 + (8)	E	Hungerford 1948	3–10	3
23. *Sigara* sp.	25 + (7)	—	—	5–11	3, 4, 5, 6
24. *Hydrometra hungerfordi*	1	E	Bobb 1974	8 (5–8)	3
25. *Pelocoris femoratus*	25 + (7)	E	Bobb 1974	3–8 (1–12)	2, 3, 4
26. *Ranatra australis*	1	E	Bobb 1974	6 (6–11)	7
27. *R. buenoi*	5 (5)	E	Bobb 1974	6–7 (3–10)	1, 4
28. *R. drakai*	1	E	Bobb 1974	6 (6–7)	2
29. *R. kirkaldyi*	5 (4)	E	Bobb 1974	2–6 (2–10)	4
30. *Notonecta irrorta*	25 + (10)	E	Bobb 1974	5–8 (5–10)	2, 4
31. *N. raleighi*	2 (1)	E	Bobb 1974	12 (5–12)	4
32. *N. uhleri*	25 + (11)	E	Bobb 1974	7–12	2, 3, 5
33. *Belostoma testaceum*	10 (3)	E	Bobb 1974	5–9	3, 4
34. *B. flumineum*	1	E	Bobb 1974	9 (5–9)	4
35. *Gerris nebularis*	25 + (10)	SE	Bobb 1974	5–7	4
36. *G. canaliculatus*	25 + (6)	E	Bobb 1974	7–9 (7–10)	2, 4
37. *G. marginatus*	25 + (9)	NA	Bobb 1974	6–8 (2–9)	4
38. *Gelastocoris oculatus*	1	NA	Bobb 1974	6 (4–10)	4
39. *Hebrus burmeisteri*	25 + (10)	E	Bobb 1974	5–9	3, 4, 5
Order Neuroptera					
40. *Chauliodes pectinicornis*	5 (4)	E	—	5–11 (6–8)	1, 4
41. *Sialis americana*	2 (2)	Washington, D.C., Dismal Swamp	Flint 1964	5	9

Table 1. (cont.)

Species	Abundance	Distribution	Reference	Season	Typical habitats
Order Trichoptera					
42. *Leptocella pavida*	25+ (3)	E	Ross 1944	6–8	9
43. *Oecetis cinerascens*	25+ (3)	E	Ross 1944	5–8	9
44. *O. inconspicua*	5 (2)	NA	Ross 1944	6–8	9
45 *Athripsodes tranversus*	2 (1)	E	Ross 1944	8	9
46. *Cernotina truncona*	25+ (3)	FL, NC, VA	Gurney 1963	6–8	9
47. *Platycentropus* sp.	7 (3)	–	–	4–5	1, 2
48. *Limnephilus* sp.	9 (3)	–	–	4–5	1
49. *Caborius* sp.	2 (1)	–	–	5	4
50. *Fabria inornata*(?)	11 (4)	MN, IL, VA	–	3–6	4
51. *Molanna uniophila*	1	NE	Ross 1944	4	9
Order Coleoptera					
52. *Peltodytes oppositus*	25+(5)	SE	Matta 1976	6–8	2, 3
53. *P. dunavani*	25+ (9)	SE	Matta 1976	5–8	1, 2, 3, 4
54. *P. muticus*	20 (8)	E	Matta 1976	6–8 (2–10)	2, 3, 4
55. *Haliplus leopardus*	7 (3)	NE	Matta 1976	6–9	4
56. *H. fasciatus*	1	E	Matta 1976	7	1
57. *Laccophilus fasciatus rufus*	25+ (7)	E	Zimmerman 1970	5–8 (4–10)	11
58. *L. m. maculosus*	10 (5)	E	Zimmerman 1970	5–7 (5–10)	11
59. *Bidessonotus inconspicuus*	36 (7)	E	Young 1954	7–8	1
60. *B. pulicaris*	8 (4)	FL, GA, VA	Matta 1973	7–8 (6–8)	1
61. *Uvarus lacustris*	4 (2)	E	Young 1954	8 (6–10)	4
62. *Hydroporus lobatus*	25+ (15)	E	Fall 1923	3–12	1, 4
63. *H. carolinus*	25+ (9)	E	Fall 1923	4–12	1
64. *H. clypealis*	25+ (7)	E	Fall 1923	5–8	1
65. *H. niger*	1	NA	Fall 1923	6	11

Table 1. (cont.)

Species	Abundance	Distribution	Reference	Season	Typical habitats
66. *H. venustrus*	18 (5)	E	Fall 1923	5–12	1
67. *Laccornis difformis*	15 (4)	E	Fall 1923	6–12	1, 2
68. *Agabetes accuductus*	25 + (10)	E	Young 1954	6–7 (3–7)	1
69. *Agabus stagninus*	1	NE	Fall 1922*a*	7	1
70. *A. aeruginosus*	9 (1)	E	Fall 1922*a*	4	1
71. *A. gagates*	25 + (9)	NE	Fall 1922*a*	7–8	1
72. *Copelatus caelati- pennis princeps*	5 (3)	SE	Young 1963	7	1
73. *C. glyphicus*	20 (6)	NA	Young 1963	2–7	1, 2, 11
74. *Coptotomus i. interrogatus*	25 + (15)	E	Young 1954	5–12	1, 2, 4
75. *Rhantus calidus*	5 (5)	E	Young 1954	6–12	1
76. *Hoparius planata*	11 (7)	SE	Spangler 1973	5–9 (3–9)	1
77. *Dytiscus fasciventris*	7 (4)	NE	Hatch 1928	6–10	1, 4
78. *Hydacticus bimarginatus*	25 + (15)	SE	Young 1954	7–8 (4–8)	1, 4
79. *Acilius mediatus*	25 + (12)	E	Hilsenhoff 1975	6–8 (6–10)	1
80. *A. fraternus dismalus*	25 + (11)	SE	Matta and Michael 1976	6–12	1
81. *Thermonectus basillaris*	25 + (9)	E	Young 1954	6–8 (1–11)	1, 11
82. *Hydrocanthus iricolor*	2 (2)	E	Young 1954	6 (5–10)	2, 3
83. *Suphisellus* sp.	1	—	—	5	5
84. *Gyrinus borealis*(?)	1	NE	Fall 1922*b*	5 (5–10)	4
85. *G. elevatus*	1	E	Fall 1922*b*	5	4
86. *G. frosti*	3 (3)	NE, LA	Fall 1922*b*	5–9	4
87. *Dineutus carolinus*	25 + (15)	SE	Roberts 1895	5–9	4
88. *D. discolor*	25 + (11)	E	Roberts 1895	5–9	4

Table 1. (cont.)

Species	Abundance	Distribution	Reference	Season	Typical habitats
89. *Hydrochus* sp.	14 (3)	—	—	7	11
90. *Tropisternus b. blatchleyi*	21 (3)	SE	Matta 1973	6–7 (2–12)	3, 10
91. *T. collaris striolatis*	12 (5)	E	Matta 1973	6–8 (2–12)	4, 11
92. *T. lateralis nimbatus*	9 (4)	E	Matta 1973	6–7 (3–12)	3, 4, 10
93. *T. natator*	1	E	Matta 1973	6 (6–10)	11
94. *Hydrophilus triangularis*	1	NA	Matta 1973	10	6
95. *Hydrochara obtusatus*	25 + (10)	E	Matta 1973	5–9 (3–9)	1
96. *Berosus aculeatus*	19 (6)	E	Matta 1973	7–8	4, 11
97. *B. exiguus*	10 (2)	E	Matta 1973	7 (7–10)	11
98. *B. infuscatus*	25 +	S	Matta 1973	6–8 (5–11)	2, 4, 11
99. *B. peregrinus*	3 (2)	NA	Matta 1973	5 (5–8)	1, 4
100. *Paracymus subcupreus*	14 (2)	NA	Matta 1973	7 (7–8)	1, 11
101. *Enochrus cinctus*	1	E	Matta 1973	6 (5–8)	11
102. *E. consortus*	7 (3)	NA	Matta 1973	7 (2–11)	4
103. *E. ochraceus*	3 (1)	E	Matta 1973	7 (2–11)	11
104. *E. sublongus*	1	SE	Matta 1973	8 (6–8)	4
105. *Hydrobius tumidus*	12 (2)	E	Matta 1973	3–4	5
106. *Helocombus bifidus*	3 (2)	E	Matta 1973	7	1
107. *Cymbiodyta blanchardi*	5 (3)	E	Matta 1973	6–7 (3–12)	1
108. *C. vindicata*	1	E	Matta 1973	7 (7–8)	1
109. *Hydraena* sp.	3	—	—	7	10
Order Diptera					
110. *Ablabesmyia* sp.	25 + (3)	—	—	6–8	9
111. *Chironomus* sp.	25 + (4)	—	—	4–8	9
112. *Paratendipes* sp.	25 + (4)	—	—	4–8	9
113. *Forcipomyia* sp.	25 + (2)	—	—	7–8	9

Table 1. (cont.)

Species	Abundance	Distribution	Reference	Season	Typical habitats
114. *Dasyhelea* sp.	4 (1)	—	—	8	9
115. *Culicoides debilipalpis*	—	SE	Battle & Turner 1971	—	—
116. *C. furens*	—	E	Battle & Turner 1971	—	—
117. *C. stellifer*	—	NA	Battle & Turner 1971	—	—
118. *Simulium* sp.	15 (4)	—	—	4	4
119. *Chaoborus punctipennis*	25+ (5)	E	Stone et al. 1965	6–8	6
120. *Eucorethra underwoodi*	25+ (3)	N	Stone et al. 1965	4–8	1
121. *Corethrella* sp.	25+ (1)	—	—	8	9
122. *Aedes canadensis*	25+ (12)	NA	Stone et al. 1965	4–7	1, 12
123. *A. vexans*	4 (1)	NA	Stone et al. 1965	4	2
124. *Psorophora ferox*	10 (1)	NA	Stone et al. 1965	4	2,12
125. *Culiseta melanura*	7 (1)	E, C	Stone et al. 1965	8	9
126. *Mansonia perturbans*	15 (1)	NA	Stone, et al. 1965	8	9
127 *Chrysops brimleyi*	6 (2)	SE	Pechuman 1973	4–5	12
128. *C. cintincornis*	4 (2)	E	Pechuman 1973	5	12
129. *C. flavidus*	10 (4)	E	Pechuman 1973	6–8	12
130. *C. hinei*	5 (2)	E	Pechuman 1973	9	12
131. *C. macquarti*	16 (4)	E	Pechuman 1973	5–6	12
132. *C. niger*	1	E	Pechuman 1973	5	12
133. *C. pikei*	8 (3)	E	Pechuman 1973	5–6 (5–8)	12
134. *C. reicherti*	15 (3)	E	Pechuman 1973	6–7 (5–9)	12
135. *C. univittatus*	3 (2)	E	Pechuman 1973	6–7	12
136. *C. upsilon*	5 (2)	E	Pechuman 1973	6–7	12
137. *C. vittatus vittatus*	25+ (7)	E	Pechuman 1973	6–8	12
138. *C. v. floridanus*	6 (3)	SE	Pechuman 1973	6–7	12

Table 1. (cont.)

Species	Abundance	Distribution	Reference	Season	Typical habitats
139. *Diachlorus ferrugatus*	25+ (15)	E	Pechuman 1973	6–8	12
140. *Chlorotabanus cre-puscularis*	1	E	Pechuman 1973	7 (6–8)	14
141. *Hybomitra hinei*	9 (2)	NE	Pechuman 1973	5–6	12
142. *H. lasiophthalma*	25+ (10)	E	Pechuman 1973	5 (4–6)	12
143. *Tabanus aar*	1	SE	Pechuman 1973	–	–
144. *T. americanus*	12 (4)	E	Pechuman 1973	6–8	12
145. *T. atratus atratus*	2 (2)	E	Pechuman 1973	5 (5–6)	12
146. *T. fulvulus*	1	E	Pechuman 1973	6 (6–8)	13
147. *T. fusconervosus*	2 (2)	E	Pechuman 1973	6	13
148. *T. lineola*	25+ (10)	E	Pechuman 1973	5–7	12
149. *T. melanocerus*	1	E	Pechuman 1973	7 (6–7)	13
150. *T. nigrovittatus*	1	E	Pechuman 1973	7 (6–8)	12
151. *T. petiolatus*	25+ (10)	E	Pechuman 1973	6–7	12
152. *T. pumilus*	5 (3)	E	Pechuman 1973	5–6	12
153. *T. sparus milleri*	2 (2)	E	Pechuman 1973	5–6	12
154. *T. trimaculatus*	4 (4)	E	Pechuman 1973	6 (5–6)	12
155. *T. zythicolor*	1	SE	Pechuman 1973	8	13

ANNOTATED LIST OF AQUATIC
AND SEMIAQUATIC INSECTS OF THE
DISMAL SWAMP

Order Ephemeroptera

A single species of Ephemeroptera (Family Leptophlebiidae) has been recorded from the Dismal Swamp and is rather restricted in distribution, *Leptophlebia austrinus* (Traver). This species has been collected in abundance only in a small stream crossing Desert Road. The nymphs were found associated with the spleenwort hepatic (*Plagiochila* sp.) in slow-moving water; adults were found flitting about beside the stream in early May. A single nymph of this species has been collected from a pool beside Railroad Road.

Order Odonata

Eighteen species of Odonata are presently recorded from the Swamp. It is possible that several additional species could be added to this list by intensive collecting during the spring season.
Aeshnidae
   Anax junius (Drury). A single adult of this species has been taken on Jericho Ditch. No nymphs have been collected.
   Epiaeshna heros Fabr. This large species is quite abundant during the late summer and fall. The nymphs have been collected in open pools beside Washington Ditch Road, from several of the ditches, and from woodland pools.
   Gomphaeschna antilope Hagen. Adults of this species have been collected only during the spring. Nymphs have not yet been collected.
   G. furcillata (Say). Adults of this species are most frequently encountered on Jericho Ditch Lane. No nymphs have been collected.
Gomphidae
   Gomphus exilus Selys. Two adults of this species were collected on Washington Ditch Road in May of 1970. Nymphs have not been collected.
Libellulidae
   Erythemis simplicicollis (Say). Adults of this species are abundant throughout the summer and fall. Nymphs are found in the open pools which border many of the roads in the Swamp.
   Libellula cyaenea Fabr. Adults of this species are found during the summer months. Nymphs have not been collected.
   L. incesta Hagen. Adults are common during the summer months. Nymphs have been collected from roadside pools along Washington Ditch Road.

L. semifasciata Burmeister. Adults of this species have been collected during April and May, but no nymphs have been collected.

L. flavida (Rumbur). The adults of this species are found during the summer and fall, but no nymphs have been collected to date.

Pachydiplax longipennis Burmeister. The adults are quite abundant during the summer and fall months. Nymphs have been collected from roadside pools and woodland pools.

Plathemis lydia Drury. Adults of this species have been collected during April and May; however, it should be found throughout the summer and fall also. No nymphs have been collected.

Tetragoneuria cynosura (Say). Adults of this species have been collected during the early spring; nymphs were quite abundant in woodland pools.

Calopterygidae

Calopteryx maculatum Beauvois. This beautiful damselfly appears to be most abundant along Washington Ditch. The nymphs are found in aquatic vegetation at the margins of the ditches.

Lestidae

Lestes sp. probably *disjunctus* Selys. A single specimen of this species was collected in May of 1970 beside Washington Ditch.

Anomalagrion hastatum (Say). This distinctive species is represented in the Dismal Swamp collection by two specimens collected in April of 1970 on Jericho Ditch Road.

Enallagma durum Hagen. This distinctive blue species has been collected in April and May along many of the roads in the Swamp.

Order Hemiptera

Hesperocorixa brimleyi (Kirkald). This species is common in the open pools and ditches of the southern part of the Swamp. It is only occasionally collected in those areas north of Lake Drummond.

H. interruptus (Say). A single specimen of this species has been collected from Washington Ditch. It is common in other areas of Tidewater.

H. nitida (Fieb.). This species is abundant in the willow swamp on Jericho Ditch Lane. It is only rarely collected in other areas of the Swamp.

Sigara sp. Members of this genus are found in scattered locations throughout the Swamp, most notably at the mouth of Jericho Ditch, in the willow swamp on Jericho Ditch Lane, and in an open marsh on Railroad Road. More than one species may be involved, but the genus is a large and complex one and positive identification to the species level has not been possible.

Naucoridae

Pelocoris femoratus (Beauvois). This species is abundant in the Tidewater area and is commonly found in the Swamp in most of the open pools and ditches. It becomes very abundant in any water which supports a dense stand of submerged aquatic vegetation.
Hydrometridae

Hydrometra hungerfordi Bueno. This species is found at the margins of ditches and open pools in the Swamp. It is relatively common but shows a distinctive preference for backwater and marshy margins.
Nepidae

Ranatra australis Hungerford. This species is represented by a single specimen taken in a *Juncus* marsh at the edge of the Swamp.

R. buenoi Hungerford. This, the largest and most abundant species of *Ranatra* in Tidewater, is found in deep pools and at the margins of ditches throughout the Swamp.

R. drakai Hungerford. A single specimen of this species has been collected from a roadside temporary pool which was exposed to direct sunlight.

R. kirkaldyi Bueno. Several specimens of this species have been collected from Washington Ditch, where it is generally found associated with dense growths of *Myriophyllum*.
Notonectidae

Notonecta irrorta Uhler. This species is abundant throughout the state and it can be found in most ditches and open pools throughout the Swamp. It is found year-round.

N. raleighi Bueno. This species is not common in Virginia and is represented in the Swamp collection by 2 specimens collected on December 31, 1972, in Washington Ditch.

N. uhleri Kirkald. This species is abundant in the Swamp and exhibits a marked preference for standing water. While it is infrequently found in the ditches, it is quite common in the open pools and marshes in the Swamp. The adults appear to be most common during the late summer and fall.

Belostomatidae

Belostoma testaceum (Leidy). This is the only commonly encountered belostomatid in the Dismal Swamp. It is frequently collected from the willow swamp on Jericho Ditch Lane and the upstream portion of Washington Ditch. It has been collected during May, June, and September.

B. flumineum (Say). A single specimen of this species has been collected from Washington Ditch on 30 September 1972.
Gerridae

Gerris nebularis Drake and Hottes. This species is rare in Virginia except in the Dismal Swamp. It is abundant in Washington Ditch and is occasionally found in other ditches. It has been collected in May, June, and July.

G. canaliculatus Say. This widely distributed species in the eastern United States is abundant in the Swamp. It occurs at the margins of most ditches and on open pools throughout the year and is most abundant during the summer months.

G. marginatus Say. This species is found over much of North and South America. It is widespread in the Swamp, occurring primarily at the margins of ditches. It has been collected from February through September in the Tidewater area but only during June through August in the Dismal Swamp.

Gelastocoridae

Gelastocoris oculatus (Fab.). This species is most commonly encountered at the margins of Washington Ditch in those sections which have a gradually sloping shore.

Hebridae

Hebrus burmeisteri Lethierry and Severin. This little species is found at the margins of most ditches and pools in the Swamp. It appears to be most abundant in areas where *Lemna* forms a mat on the water surface. It is very abundant in the willow swamp on Jericho Ditch Lane.

Order Neuroptera

Corydalidae

Chauliodes pectinicornis L. This is the only species of Dobsonfly found in the coastal plain in Virginia, and it is much more abundant in the Swamp than in other areas of Tidewater. The larvae are common at the margins of the more acid ditches and in woodland pools. Adults are occasionally collected resting on tree trunks during the day and often come to light at night.

Sialidae

Sialis americana (Ramb.). This species is represented in the Dismal Swamp collection by 2 specimens, both collected by sweeping the vegetation beside Washington Ditch in May. No larvae have been collected.

Order Trichoptera

The Caddisfly records presented below are based primarily on light-trap collections made in August 1973 and in April, May, and June 1974 near Lake Drummond and numerous larval collections made throughout the year in all regions of the Swamp.

Leptoceridae

Leptocella pavida (Hagen). Recorded from light-trap collections only.

Oecetis cinerascens (Hagen). Recorded from light-trap collections only.

O. inconspicua (Walker). This species is recorded only from light-trap collections.

Athripsodes transversus (Hagen). Recorded from light-trap collection only.

Psychomyiidae

Cerotina truncona Ross. This species was first recorded from the Swamp by Gurney (1963). It has also been collected in light-trap collections by the author.

Limnephilidae

Platycentropus sp. Larvae of this species have been collected from woodland pools beside Railroad Road and open pools beside Washington Ditch. No adults have been collected.

Limnephilus sp. This species has been recorded only from larvae collected in woodland pools beside Railroad Road.

Caborius sp. Larvae of this species have been collected at the head of Washington Ditch.

Phryganeidae

Fabria inornata (Banks) (?) Larvae which are tentatively identified as *Fabria inornata* have been collected from open pools beside Washington Ditch.

Molannidae

Molanna uniophila Varhies. This species is recorded from the Swamp by Gurney (1963). The author has collected a single specimen at a black light in April.

Order Coleoptera

The aquatic Coleoptera of the Dismal Swamp having been reviewed recently by Matta (1973), the list below includes only new annotations on habitat or distribution that were not reported earlier. [Also see Matta (1974, 1976) and Michael and Matta (1977)—ed.]

Peltodytes oppositus Roberts. This species reaches the northern limit of its range in the Dismal Swamp. It has not been collected in any other area of the state.

P. dunavani Young. An examination of the male genitalia of a number of *Peltodytes* indicates that this species is more abundant in the Swamp than previously indicated (Matta 1973). It is found in most of the nonacid pools of the Swamp.

P. muticus (LeConte).

Haliplus leopardus Roberts. This species, previously reported as *H.*

puntatus, is most frequently encountered in the ditches of the southern portion of the Swamp.

    H. fasciatus Aube.

Dytiscidae

    Laccophilus fasciatus rufus Melsheimer.

    L. maculosus maculosus (Say).

    Bidessonotus inconspicuus (LeConte).

    B. pulicaris (Aube).

    Uvarus lacustris (Say).

    Hydroporus lobatus Sharp.

    H. carolinus Fall.

    H. clypealis Sharp.

    H. niger Say.

    H. venustrus LeConte.

    Laccornis difformis LeConte.

    Agabetes accuductus (Harris).

Agabus stagninus Say. A single specimen of this species was collected in July 1970 from a woodland pool.

    A. aeruginosus Say. An interesting series of this species has been collected from an open marsh on Railroad Road. It has not been collected from other areas in the Swamp and this is the first record of the species in Virginia.

    Agabus gagates Aube. A comparison of Dismal Swamp material with specimens in the fall collection at the Museum of Comparative Zoology, Harvard University, indicates that this previously unidentified species (Matta 1973) is *Agabus gagates* Aube. This is the first Virginia record for the species, but it has been recorded as far south as North Carolina (Fall 1922) and collected in other areas of Virginia by the author.

    Copelatus caelatipennis princeps Young.

    C. glyphicus (Say).

    Coptotomus interrogatus interrogatus (Fabricius).

    Rhantus calidus (Fabricius).

    Hoparius planata (Fall).

    Dytiscus fasciventris (Say).

    Hydacticus bimarginatus (Say).

    Acilius fraternus dismalus Matta and Michael.

    A. mediatus (Say).

    Thermonectus basillaris (Harris).

T. ornaticollis Aube. This species was reported in error by Matta (1973) and has not been collected in the Swamp.

Noteridae

Hydrocanthus iricolor Say. Two specimens have been collected, one from a pool beside Washington Ditch and another from the willow swamp.

Suphisellus sp. A single specimen of *Suphisellus* has been collected from the open marsh on Railroad Road.

Gyrinidae

Gyrinus borealis Aube.

G. elevatus LeConte.

G. frosti Fall.

Dineutus carolinus LeConte.

D. discolor Aube.

Hydrochidae

Hydrochus sp.

Hydrophilidae

Tropisternus blatchleyi blatchleyi D'Orchymont.

T. collaris striolatis (LeConte).

T. lateralis nimbatus (Say).

T. natator D'Orchymont.

Hydrophilus triangularis Say.

Hydrochara obtusatus (Say).

Berosus aculeatus LeConte.

B. exiguus Say.

B. infuscatus LeConte.

B. peregrinus Herbst.

Paracymus subcupreus (Say).

Enochrus cinctus (Say).

E. consortus Green.

E. ochraceus (Melsheimer).

E. sublongus (Fall).

Hydrobius tumidus LeConte. A single specimen of this species was collected from a flooded tire track near Jericho Ditch Lane, and other specimens were collected from the open marsh area of the Dismal Swamp in Gates County, North Carolina. This is the first record of the species from North Carolina. It is quite rare in the Tidewater area and the number of specimens encountered in the North Carolina collection was remarkable for this species.

Helocombus bifidus (LeConte).

Cymbiodyta blanchardi Horn.

C. vindicata Fall.

Hydraenidae

Hydraena sp.

Order Diptera

A total of 46 species of aquatic Diptera has been recorded from the Dismal Swamp and it is probable that this represents only a small fraction of the actual number present.

Chironomidae

Ablabesmyia sp. This genus is often encountered swarming at the margins of Lake Drummond.

Chironomus sp. Large swarms of *Chironomus* are encountered beside the ditches and at the margins of Lake Drummond. There are probably several species of this genus present in collections, but none have been identified.

Paratendipes sp. Members of this genus are less frequently encountered than of *Chironomus*. They have been collected from the margins of Lake Drummond.

Ceratopogonidae

Forcipomyia sp.

Dasyhelea sp.

Culicoides. The following three species of *Culicoides* are recorded from the Dismal Swamp by Battle and Turner (1971).

Culicoides debilipalpis Lutz.

C. furens (Poey).

C. stellifer (Coquillett).

Simulidae

Simulium sp. The larvae of an unidentified species of *Simulium* have been collected in several of the faster-moving ditches (Washington, Hamburg, and Jericho). No adults have been collected.

Chaoboridae

Chaoborus punctipennis (Say). Adults of this species have been collected from the margin of Lake Drummond in August, and larvae have been collected from bottom samples taken in the lake in February.

Eucorethra underwoodi Underwood. Larvae of this species are frequently collected in woodland pools. Adults have been obtained in light-trap collections made during August.

Culicidae

Aedes canadensis (Theobald). This species is very abundant during the spring. Larvae are found in many woodland pools and in roadside pools.

Aedes vexans (Meigen). Larvae of this species have been collected from pools beside Railroad Road.

Psorophora ferox (Humboldt). Larvae of this species have also been collected from pools beside Railroad Road.

Culiseta melanura (Coquillett). This and the following species were collected in light traps at the margin of Lake Drummond in August.

Mansonia perturbans (Walker).

Tabanidae

Work on the family Tabanidae has been much more complete than that on any other aquatic dipteran family in the Swamp. Many large collections taken by the author have been identified by L. L. Pechu-

man, and these records are included in Pechuman (1973). Because
of this recent review, the species from the Swamp are listed with only
those of special significance having annotation.

Chrysops brimleyi Hine.

C. cinticornis Walker.

C. flavidus Wiedemann.

C. hinei Daecke.

C. macquarti Philip.

C. niger Macquart.

C. pikei Whitney.

C. reicherti Fairchild

C. univittatus Wiedemann.

C. upsilon Philip. The only Virginia records for this species are from
the Dismal Swamp. They were collected in June and July.

C. vittatus vittatus Wiedemann.

C. vittatus floridanus Johnson. The only Virginia records for this
species are from the Dismal Swamp and from Hickory, Virginia, which
is near the edge of the Swamp.

Diachlorus ferrugatus (Fabricius). This species is very abundant in
the Swamp and was the subject of the first published paper dealing
with the insects of the Swamp (Banks 1904).

Chlorotabanus crepuscularis (Bequaert).

Hybomitra hinei (Johnson). All Virginia records for this species are
from the Dismal Swamp or nearby localities in the City of Nansemond.

H. lasiophthalma (Macquart). This is the first species of Tabanidae
to appear during the spring in the Swamp.

Tabanus aar Philip. Two specimens of this species were collected by
Wills Flowers in August 1968. The Dismal Swamp records represent
the northern limit of the range.

T. americanus Foster.

T. atratus atratus Fabricius.

T. fulvulus Wiedemann.

T. fusconervosus Macquart. The only Virginia records of this species
are from the Dismal Swamp. They were collected in June 1970.

T. lineola Fabricius.

T. melanocerus Wiedemann.

T. nigrovittatus Macquart

T. petiolatus Hine.

T. pumilus Macquart

T. sparus milleri Whitney.

T. trimaculatus Beauvois.

T. zythicolor Philip.

SUMMARY

A total of 155 species of aquatic and semiaquatic insects is recorded from the Dismal Swamp. The orders included are 1 species of Ephemeroptera, 18 Odonata, 22 Hemiptera, 2 Neuroptera, 10 Trichoptera, 58 Coleoptera, and 46 Diptera. Many more species of aquatic insects, especially in the Odonata, Trichoptera and Diptera could be added by increased collecting of these groups.

[Editors' note: Since receipt of this manuscript, the author has recorded 27 more species of insects in the Swamp, including many Odonata.]

REFERENCES CITED

Banks, N. 1904. The "Yellow-fly" of the Dismal Swamp. *Entomol. News* 15:290–291.

Baldwin, J. T., Jr. 1969. Insects—mostly butterflies—of Dismal Swamp. *Va. Wildlife* 30:11–16.

Battle, F. V., and E. C. Turner, Jr. 1971. A systematic review of the genus *Culicoides* (Diptera: Ceratopogonidae) of Virginia. *Va. Polytech. Inst. and State Univ. Res. Bull.* 44. 129 pp.

Bobb, M. 1974. The aquatic and semi-aquatic Hemiptera of Virginia. *Va. Polytech. Inst. and State Univ. Res. Bull.* 87. 195 pp.

Clark, A. H., and Leila F. Clark. 1939. Butterflies of a wood road at Suffolk, Virginia. *Entomol. News* 50:1–5.

Fall, H. C. 1922a. A review of the North American species of *Agabus* together with a description of a new genus and species of the tribe Agabini. John H. Sherman, Jr., Mt. Vernon, N.Y. 36 pp.

_____. 1922b. The North American species of *Gyrinus* (Coleoptera). *Trans. Amer. Entomol. Soc.* 47:269–306.

_____. 1923. A revision of the North American species of *Hydroporus* and *Agaporus*. John D. Sherman, Jr., Mt. Vernon, N.Y. 129 pp.

Flint, O. S. 1964. New species and new state records of *Sialis* (Neuroptera: Sialidae). *Entomol. News* 25: 9–13.

Gurney, A. B. 1963. A brief look at the Dismal Swamp and its natural history, especially the insects. *J. Wash. Acad. Sci.* 53:57–63.

Hatch, M. H. 1928. Studies on Dytiscidae. *Bull. Brooklyn Entomol. Soc.* 23:217–229.

Hilsenhoff, W. L. 1975. Notes on Nearctic *Acilius* (Dytiscidae) with the description of a new species. *Ann. Entomol. Soc. Amer.* 68:271–274.

Hungerford, H. B. 1948. The Corixidae of the Western Hemisphere. *Univ. Kansas Sci. Bull.* 32:1–827.

Johnson, C. 1974. Taxonomic Keys and distributional patterns for Nearctic species of *Calopteryx* damselflies. *Fla. Entomol.* 57:231–248.

Johnson, C., and M. J. Westfall, Jr. 1970. Diagnostic keys and notes on the damselflies (Zygoptera) of Florida. *Bull. Fla. State Mus.* 15(2):45–89.

Matta, J. F. 1973. The aquatic Coleoptera of the Dismal Swamp. *Va. J. Sci.* 24:199–205.

———. 1974. The aquatic Hydrophilidae of Virginia (Coleoptera: Polyphaga). *Va. Polytech. Inst. and State Univ. Res. Bull.* 94. 44 pp.

———. 1976. The Haliplidae of Virginia (Coleoptera: Adephaga). *Va. Polytech. Inst. and State Univ. Res. Bull.* 109. 26 pp.

Matta, F. F., and A. G. Michael. 1976. A new subspecies of *Acilius* from the southeastern United States. *Entomol. News.* 87:11–16.

Michael, A. G., and J. F. Matta. 1977. The Dytiscidae of Virginia (Coleoptera: Adephaga) (subfamilies: Laccophilinae, Colymbetinae, Dytiscinae, Hydaticinae and Cybistrinae). *Va. Polytechn. Inst. and State Univ. Res. Bull.* 124. 53 pp.

Needham, J. G., J. R. Traver, and Y. Hsu. 1935. *The biology of mayflies.* Comstock Publishing Co., New York. 759 pp.

Needham, J. G., and M. J. Westfall, Jr. 1955. A manual of the dragonflies of North America. Univ. Calif. Press, Berkeley. 615 pp.

Pechuman, L. L. 1973. Horse flies and deer flies of Virginia (Diptera: Tabanidae). *Va. Polytech. Inst. and State Univ. Res. Bull.* 81. 92 pp.

Poore, W. H., Jr., and H. G. Marshall. 1972. Lake Drummond of the Dismal Swamp: I. phytoplankton composition. *Va. J. Sci.* 23:72–76.

Roberts, C. H. 1895. The species of *Dineutes* of America north of Mexico. *Trans. Amer. Entomol. Soc.* 22:279–288.

Ross, H. H. 1944. The caddisflies or Trichoptera of Illinois. *Ill. Nat. Hist. Surv. Bull.* 23:1–326.

Spangler, P. J. 1973. The bionomics, immature stages and distribution of rare predacious water beetle, *Hoperics planatus. Proc. Biol. Soc. Washington* 86:423–434.

Stone, A., C. W. Sabrosky, W. W. Wirth, R. H. Foote, and J. R. Coulson. 1965. A catalog of the Diptera of America north of Mexico. *U.S. Dept. Agri. Handbook* 276. 1696 pp.

Walker, E. M. 1952. The *Lestes disjunctus* and *forcipatus* complex (Odonata: Lestidae). *Trans. Amer. Entomol. Soc.* 78:59–74.

Young, F. N. 1954. The water beetles of Florida. *Univ. Florida Stud. Biol. Sci. Ser.* 5(1):1–238.

———. 1963. The Nearctic species of *Copelatus* Erichson (col. *Dytisc). Quart. J. Fla. Acad. Sci.* 26:56–77.

Zimmerman, J. R. 1970. A taxonomic revision of the aquatic beetle genus *Laccophilus* (Dytiscidae) of North America. *Mem. Amer. Entomol. Soc.* 26:1–275.

THE ECOLOGY OF THE TWO DOMINANT TICK SPECIES IN RELATION TO THE DISMAL SWAMP NATIONAL WILDLIFE REFUGE IN VIRGINIA

Mary Keith Garrett and Daniel F. Sonenshine

INTRODUCTION

Little is known about the natural mechanisms that restrict the spread of the American dog tick, *Dermacentor variabilis* (Say) or the lone star tick, *Amblyomma americanum* (L.). The presence of standing water for extended periods, as in a swamp, might be considered a natural limiting factor rendering a habitat unsuitable for these ticks. Consequently, reports of the frequent presence of the American Dog tick and the lone star tick in the Dismal Swamp of eastern Virginia and North Carolina challenged our understanding of their ecology. Study of this unexpected association provided an opportunity to assess some of the natural factors facilitating or limiting the spread and survival of these disease vector ticks. The studies were also important as a basis for formulating management plans for the Dismal Swamp National Wildlife Refuge.

This paper reports results of studies to determine (1) the species composition of the ticks in the Dismal Swamp, (2) comparative densities and variations in distribution of the two most abundant species, *D. variabilis* and *A. americanum*, (3) survival of laboratory-reared, translocated, and native ticks, and (4) the relative importance of specific biotic and abiotic factors that may affect the survival and abundance of these ticks. Population dynamics of the ticks were not studied.

MATERIALS AND METHODS

Species Composition, Abundance, and Distribution

All work was conducted in two natural areas, accessible solely by unimproved roads or tracks, in the northwestern section of the Dismal

Swamp National Wildlife Refuge and a part of the Newport News City Park. The relative locations of these protected areas in eastern Virginia are shown in Figure 1. The area in the Newport News City Park was the same as that described by Sonenshine and Levy (1972).

Tick species in the Swamp were surveyed by flagging and host examination. Comparative densities and distribution of *D. variabilis* and *A. americanum* in the Swamp were determined by selective flagging at regular intervals. The flag was a standard 1 m^2 unbleached muslin cloth mounted on a 1.5 m rod. One worker flagged the vegetation while another followed approximately 5 m behind and flagged the same vegetation. The flags were checked for ticks at regular intervals and ticks captured were recorded for each 20 m. In 1971 the study area encompassed 21,800 m^2 of forest-road ecotone and 2500 m^2 of forest interior (Fig. 2). During the period 5 June through 22 July, 1900 m^2 of west Washington Ditch Road were sampled four times; 2150 m^2 of east Washington Ditch Road were sampled twice; 4400 m^2 of Lynn Ditch Road were sampled twice; 5200 m^2 of Jericho Ditch Road were sampled twice; 3300 m^2 of Badger Ditch Road were sampled once, and 4850 m^2 of Williamson Ditch Road were sampled once. The 2500 m^2 of forest interior were also sampled during this period. In 1972 sampling in the Dismal Swamp was restricted to precisely defined study areas of forest-road ecotone (13,600 m^2) and forest interior (3500 m^2), and each sample was collected during a precise period of time. The 13,600 m^2 of forest-road ecotone sampled included the entire lengths of Washington and Lynn Ditch roads. Each sampling collection represented the total number of individuals found in this area within a 7-day period; samples were obtained during the period 1 July to 31 July, representing most of the tick-activity season. The 13,600 m^2 of Washington Ditch and Lynn Ditch forest-road ecotone were divided into seventeen segments, each 800 m^2. These were designated as WA through WI on Washington Ditch Road and LA through LH on Lynn Ditch Road (Table 1). The 800-m^2 segments were divided into 40 sections each 20 m long and numbered 1–40. The 3500 m^2 forest-interior study area comprised (1) 150 randomly located 1-m by 10-m plots, 100 in the 4 hectares of forest at Dismal Town, 50 in the 2 hectares of forest adjacent to Lake Drummond, and (2) 20 random transects, each 1 m by 100 m, projected into the forest at right angles from the two roads. Sample collections in the forest interior were also completed in 7 days, but only 4 samples were obtained during the season of tick activity. The Newport News City Park study area comprised of 1600 m^2 of forest-road ecotone, and 200 m^2 of forest interior divided into 2 transects 1 m by 100 m. This study area was sampled in the same manner as in the Dismal Swamp, and five samples were obtained during the tick-activity season.

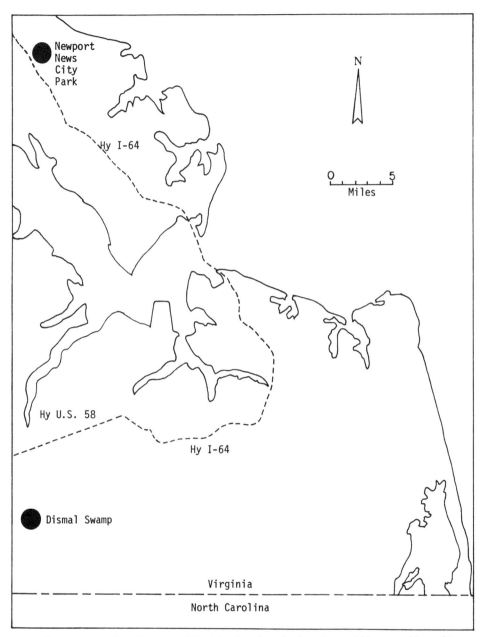

Fig. 1. Map of southeastern Virginia showing the locations of Newport News City Park and Dismal Swamp National Wildlife Refuge.

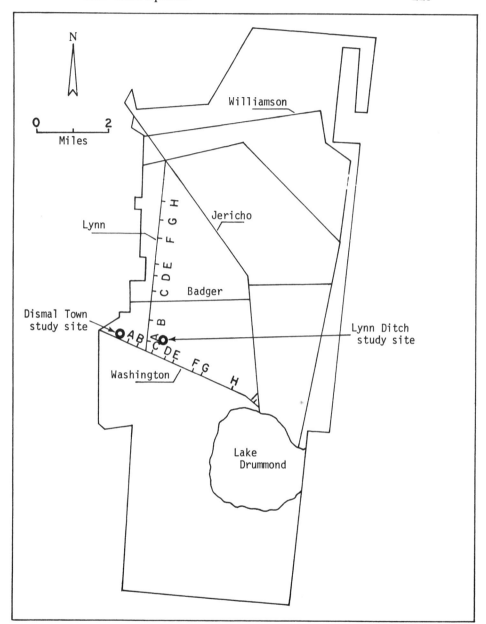

Fig. 2. Map of the Dismal Swamp National Wildlife Refuge showing all roads flagged during the 1971 and 1972 tick-activity season, the random transects flagged in 1972, and Dismal Town and Lynn Ditch study sites.

The species, life stage, sex, and exact location were recorded for ticks captured by flagging. Ticks in the Swamp were immediately released at the point of capture; ticks captured in the Newport News study area were taken to the laboratory. The flagging locations in the Newport News study area were changed at each new sample period so that tick removal would not result in biased data due to tick removal.

Survival Studies

Survival of ticks in the Dismal Swamp and the Newport News City Park was determined through release of laboratory-reared and translocated ticks into environmental containers. Additional ticks from these same sources were marked and released at the random sites described above. Containers were 15.2 cm in diameter by 12.7 cm high, of 24-gauge galvanized sheet metal, with galvanized strips supporting a chiffon cloth and wire covering. Elastic rope with a foam rubber gasket was used to seal the containers. The containers were set 12.7 cm into the leaf litter and upper soil profile, leaving only the cover above ground so as to allow as much air circulation as possible. The survival containers were placed at three sites. Two sites located within the Swamp were at the Dismal Town (DT) study area and at the intersection of Washington Ditch Road and Lynn Ditch Road (LD). The third site was located in the Newport News study area (NN).

Flat adults and nymphs of both species of ticks from laboratory colonies and flat wild *A. americanum* ticks were released into the three sites. The ticks were divided by life stage and origin (laboratory-reared and wild *A. americanum* adults and nymphs and laboratory-reared *D. variabilis* adults and nymphs). Each group was placed into 12 containers at each site within a 48-hour period. These containers were sampled four times during the tick-activity season. During each sampling interval, three of the survival containers (consisting of 25 per cent of the total life stage of released ticks) were taken to the laboratory with all contents. Viability of ticks present was recorded.

Engorged ticks of each species (larvae and nymphs) were placed in three containers at each site within a 24-hour period after their drop from laboratory hosts. Control groups were held in the laboratory for each of the two trials. These containers were removed from the field 14 days after the laboratory controls had molted in Trial I and 42 days after molting in Trial II. The numbers of emerged ticks from the three containers at each site were counted and the percent survival was calculated from the totals.

Overwinter survival of the flat, laboratory-reared ticks was studied in the same manner as the summer-survival studies. The same containers and the same sites were used. Due to inundation, the LD site was sampled within a shorter period of time.

In order to determine the expected percent of tick recovery as a function of the apparatus and the extraction methods, three containers with ticks of each species and life stage were kept for 24 hours in the laboratory to allow dispersal throughout the leaf litter. These ticks were subsequently removed and counted, and a correction factor was computed to be used in conjunction with field extractions.

Laboratory-reared and translocated ticks were released free in the natural habitat at the two Dismal Swamp sites. Comparison of activity and survival with native ticks was attempted. One hundred and fifty groups, each comprising 5 laboratory-reared and 4 wild-caught *A. americanum* adults, 10 laboratory-reared and 4 wild-caught *A. americanum* nymphs, and 3 laboratory-reared *D. variabilis* adults, were marked with Testor® brand enamel paint and released to each of the 150 random sites. Flagging of these sites was conducted according to the methods previously described.

Environmental Studies

Continuous recordings of ground-level temperature and relative humidity were made at three Dismal Swamp sites with a Bacharach hygrothermograph during the months of May, June, July, and part of August 1971. The instruments were shielded in a standard U.S. Weather Bureau shelter placed on the ground without legs. A single instrument was maintained in 1972 at the DT site to record extremes.

It was hypothesized that standing water affected tick overwinter survival. The percentage of forest floor inundated and the duration of inundation were sampled in the Swamp. For the purpose of this study, inundation was defined as standing water up to or above the base of the most recently fallen leaf-litter layer. The top layer was excluded because of its frequent tendency to float in mass, obscuring the submergence of the litter layers below. One hundred and twenty markers were placed at 20-m intervals along the 20 random transects previously described. The water levels were measured at each of the 120 points four times during the late fall. The relative percentage of submerged versus exposed forest floor was determined for a 1-m radius around each marker.

Host availability was determined by several methods. Systematic live trapping of small mammal hosts was conducted in the 4-hectare DT area during all seasons. Medium-sized mammal hosts such as raccoons and opossums were trapped sporadically in the DT area. Rabbits and squirrels were observed by checking bags of local hunters.

The availability of large mammal hosts was surveyed by examination of official hunting records for the area.

The pH of the soil was measured three times within the tick-activity season. Five samples each from the LD and DT sites were prepared on three different dates.

RESULTS

Species Composition in the Dismal Swamp

Four species of ixodid ticks were collected by the flagging technique: *A. americanum*, *D. variabilis*, *Ixodes scapularis* (Say), and *Haemaphysalsis leporispalustris* (Packard). *D. variabilis* was most abundant and was the only species found in all areas sampled throughout the Swamp. *A. americanum* collections were concentrated near Lake Drummond and the north end of Lynn Ditch, with only isolated specimens in other locations. No captures were made at station WI adjacent to Lake Drummond. Only 3 *I. scapularis* and 1 *H. leporispalustris* were collected during the 2-year effort.

All species were found on hosts examined for ectoparasites. *D. variabilis* larvae and nymphs were found infesting the white-footed mouse (*Peromyscus leucopus leucopus* Raf.) and the golden mouse (*Ochrotomys nuttalli nuttalli* Harlan). *D. variabilis* adults were found on five raccoons (*Procyon lotor lotor* L.). *A. americanum* larvae were found on two hunting dogs (*Canis familaris* L.) and two white-tailed deer (*Odocoileus virginianus virginianus* Zimmermann), and *H. leporispalustris* were found on cotton-tail rabbits (*Sylvilagus floridanus mallurus* Thomas) in November.

Abundance and Distribution of Ticks in the Dismal Swamp and Newport News

Table 1 summarizes the seasonal roadside flagging effort in the Dismal Swamp for 2 years. A total of 596 *D. variabilis* and 17 *A. americanum* was captured in 1971. The total flagging effort in the 21,800 m^2 ecotonal area resulted in an average catch of 13.7 *D. variabilis*/1000 m^2/sample and 0.4 *A. americanum*/1000 m^2/sample. Only three *D. variabilis* were captured in the total flagging effort made in the 2500 m^2 forest interior, representing a catch percentage only 1.2 ticks/1000 m^2/sample.

A total of 2710 *D. variabilis* adults, 140 *A. americanum* adults and 25 nymphs was collected during the 1972 season along the Dismal Swamp roadsides. This represented a density of 33.2 *D. variabilis* adults/ 1000 m^2/sample, 1.7 *A. americanum* adults/1000 m^2/sample

Table 1. Seasonal totals of flagged tick capture for 1971 and 1972 from the road-forest ecotone in the Dismal Swamp National Wildlife Refuge

1971

	W. Washington Ditch Road		E. Washington Ditch Road		Lynn Ditch Road		Jericho Ditch Road		Badger Ditch Road		Williamson Ditch Road	
	Total Ticks	Ticks/ 1000 m²	Total Ticks	Ticks/ 1000 m²	Total Ticks	Ticks/ 1000 m²	Total Ticks	Ticks/ 1000 m²	Total Ticks	Ticks/ 1000 m²	Total Ticks	Ticks/ 1000 m²
DV[1] Adult	225	29	70	16	139	15	53	5	34	10	75	15
AA[2] Adult	0	0	6	1.4	0	0	0	0	0	0	11	2

Washington Ditch Road—1972[3]

	WA		WB		WC		WD		WE		WF		WG		WH		WI	
	Total Ticks	Ticks/ 1000 m²	Total Ticks	Ticks/ 1000 m²	Total Ticks	Ticks/ 1000 m²	Total Ticks	Ticks/ 1000 m²	Total Ticks	Ticks/ 1000 m²	Total Ticks	Ticks/ 1000 m²	Total Ticks	Ticks/ 1000 m²	Total Ticks	Ticks/ 1000 m²	Total Ticks	Ticks/ 1000 m²
DV Adult	128	32	101	21	54	11	223	46	104	22	74	15	161	34	154	32	0	0
AA Adult	1	0.3	0	0	0	0	2	0.4	4	0.8	5	1	14	3	57	12	0	0
AA Nymph	3	0.8	0	0	0	0	0	0	0	0	0	0	0	0	0	0	0	0

Lynn Ditch roadside—1972[3]

	LA		LB		LC		LD		LE		LF		LG		LH	
	Total Ticks	Ticks/ 1000 m²	Total Ticks	Ticks/ 1000 m²	Total Ticks	Ticks/ 1000 m²	Total Ticks	Ticks/ 1000 m²	Total Ticks	Ticks/ 1000 m²	Total Ticks	Ticks/ 1000 m²	Total Ticks	Ticks/ 1000 m²	Total Ticks	Ticks/ 1000 m²
DV Adult	79	16	218	45	247	51	251	52	265	66	296	62	225	47	130	41
AA Adult	7	1	1	0.2	0	0	2	0.4	0	0	7	1	12	3	28	9
AA Nymph	0	0	0	0	0	0	2	0.4	0	0	3	0.6	10	2	7	2

[1] D. variabilis.   [2] A. americanum.   [3] See text for explanation of abbreviations.

and 0.3 *A. americanum* nymphs/1000 m^2/sample. *A. americanum* made up a total of 6 percent of the seasonal roadside flagging effort. The seasonal totals of ticks collected in the samples taken in the forest transects and random sites were 25 *D. variabilis* adults and 1 *A. americanum* adult. The forest habitat, representing 18.3 percent of the total area sampled, contributed only 0.9 percent of all *D. variabilis* (24 adults) and 0.6 percent of all *A. americanum* collected during the 1972 season.

In Newport News City Park, the total number of ticks collected from the roadside samples was 10 *D. variabilis* adults, 909 *A. americanum* adults, 1623 *A. americanum* nymphs, and approximately 6500 *A. americanum* larvae. The density was 1.3 *D variabilis* adults/1000 m^2/sample, 113 *A. americanum* adults/1000 m^2/sample, 202 *A. americanum* nymphs/1000 m^2/ sample, and 813 *A. americanum* larvae/1000 m^2/ sample in a sampling area comprising 17,800 m^2. In the forest transects at Newport News, 107 *A. americanum* adults and 183 *A. americanum* nymphs were captured representing a relative density of 119 *A. americanum* adults/1000 m^2/sample and 203 *A. americanum* nymphs/1000 m^2/ sample. No significant difference was found in the relative densities between the roadside and forest sampling areas during flagging efforts in the Newport News study area.

Variations in the density of ticks within the Dismal Swamp were noted in the 1972 season (Table 1). Lynn Ditch Road had consistently higher densities of adult *D. variabilis* (39.6 ticks/1000 m^2/sample) than Washington Ditch Road (26.6 ticks/1000 m^2/sample). Washington Ditch Road had four high density pockets, namely, WA, WD, WG and WH (Table 1). The tick density on Lynn Ditch Road remained relatively constant with the exception of the Washington Ditch Road intersection (site LA) where the density was far below average. *A. americanum* was concentrated in two locations, near Lake Dummond (WH) and the northern end of Lynn Ditch Road (LH). The densities at both locations exceeded 10 ticks/1000 m^2 compared to the average of only 2.0 ticks/1000 m^2 throughout the entire sampling area. The 1971 data show a higher density of *D. variabilis* on the western end of Washington Ditch Road and a consistently low density on Lynn Ditch Road. *A. americanum* was concentrated adjacent to Lake Drummond and at the northern periphery of the Dismal Swamp.

Summer Survival: Adult and Nymphal Ticks

Survival of all adult ticks at the three sites was high during the first 77 days (Tables 2 and 3). A significant loss was not observed in the Dismal Swamp sites until 114 days for wild *A. americanum*, 124 days for laboratory-reared *A. americanum*, and 131 days for laboratory-reared *D. variabilis*. The survival of the laboratory-reared ticks at NN remained

Table 2. Summer survival of adult *A. americanum* and *D. variabilis* held in environmental containers in two sites in the Dismal Swamp and one site in Newport News City Park

Species and source of ticks	Site	Release date	Total released	Extraction I		Extraction II		Extraction III		Extraction IV	
				Total elapsed days	% survivors	Total elapsed days	% survivors	Total elapsed days	% survivors	Total elapsed days	% survivors
AA[1] Lab.	DT	5/2/72	30	37	90	79	93	128	87	150	60
	LD	5/2/72	30	37	97	79	93	128	73	150	30
	NN	5/27/72	30	57	97	105	93	137	87	177	83
AA[2] Wild	DT	5/15/72	27	24	89	66	78	115	48	137	37
	LD	5/15/72	27	24	93	66	100	115	22	137	7
	NN	5/27/72	27	66	96	114	85	146	81	186	78
DV[3] Lab.	DT	4/28/72	60	41	97	94	95	132	85	154	53
	LD	4/28/72	60	41	92	94	95	132	65	154	30
	NN	4/29/72	60	85	100	133	98	165	93	205	90

[1] *A. americanum* laboratory-reared.　　[2] *A. americanum* wild-caught.　　[3] *D. variabilis* laboratory-reared.

Table 3. Summer survival of nymphal *A. americanum* and *D. variabilis* held in environmental containers in two sites in the Dismal Swamp and one site in Newport News City Park

Species and source of ticks	Site	Total released	Release date	Extraction I		Extraction II		Extraction III		Extraction IV	
				Total elapsed days	% survivors	Total elapsed days	% survivors	Total elapsed days	% survivors	Total elapsed days	% survivors
AA[1] Lab.	DT	51	6/8/72	69	100	104	80	123	58	149	40
	LD	51	6/8/72	69	80	104	63	123	43	149	31
	NN	51	6/10/72	81	88	127	84	132	88	165	73
AA[2] Wild	DT	51	6/8/72	69	100	104	72	123	54	149	52
	LD	51	6/8/72	69	67	104	55	123	52	149	35
	NN	51	6/10/72	81	100	127	92	132	82	165	69
DV[3] Lab.	DT	51	6/8/72	69	96	104	90	123	66	149	37
	LD	51	6/8/72	69	67	104	75	123	39	149	22
	NN	51	6/10/72	81	96	127	86	132	76	165	76

[1] *A. americanum* laboratory-reared.   [2] *A. americanum* wild-caught.   [3] *D. variabilis* laboratory-reared.

high for the 175-day duration of the test. The wild-caught *A. americanum* showed the greatest loss of all three sites with an average of 40% survival while the laboratory-reared ticks maintained an average of 58% survival. The lowest survival observed was at the LD site with 30% for the laboratory-reared ticks and 7% for the wild-caught ticks.

The flat nymphs showed a similar decline beginning with the third extraction. Survival was 73% at NN after 161 days, 44% at DT after 147 days, and 29% after 147 days at LD. *A. americanum* wild nymphs exhibited the highest survival of the three groups, namely, 52% compared to 49% for *A. americanum* laboratory-reared nymphs and 45% for *D. variabilis* laboratory-reared nymphs.

Six beetles of the family Carabidae were found in 4 of the 12 adult survival containers at LD and were observed feeding on flat adult ticks on one occasion. The six beetles were returned to the laboratory and ticks offered to them. Five of the predators killed and consumed portions of all ticks offered; the sixth carabid killed the ticks without dismembering them. Sixty-two percent of the dead adult ticks recovered at LD were apparently preyed upon as only fragments were found. At DT, 17% of the dead ticks were found fragmented, but no fragments were observed at NN. No signs of predation upon flat nymphs were observed.

Ticks were observed to be highly active at the LD site during the first two extractions. Ninety percent of the ticks at LD were observed rapidly crawling about their containers, whereas less than 40% were found in a similar state of activity at DT and NN. In the last two extractions the majority of the ticks at all three sites were found within the leaf litter in a quiescent state. Surviving adult ticks were almost always found quiescent in an inverted position within the leaf-litter layer just above the fermentation zone.

Winter Survival: Flat Adults and Flat Nymphs

Adults were found quiescent and inverted in the leaf litter 15 days after their release. The nymphs, though quiescent, were not observed in a specific leaf-litter profile layer.

The LD site was saturated with water by the second extraction and inundated for 2 days before the third extraction. The adults were removed after four days of inundation and the nymphs were removed eight days after inundation. All ticks retrieved from inundation were found dead (Tables 4 and 5).

Molting of Engorged Larvae and Nymphs

Molting of *A. americanum* and *D. variabilis* larvae and nymphs at the three sites is summarized in Tables 6 and 7. The NN site reflected near

Table 4. Winter survival of adult *A. americanum* and *D. variabilis* held in environmental containers in two sites in the Dismal Swamp and one site in Newport News City Park

Species and source of Ticks	Site	Release date	Total released	Extraction I		Extraction II		Extraction III		Extraction IV	
				Total elapsed days	% survivors	Total elapsed days	% survivors	Total elapsed days	% survivors	Total elapsed days	% survivors
AA[1]	DT	10/19/72	60	15	98	22	98	91	83	130	78
Lab.	LD	10/19/72	60	15	97	22	73	29	17	30	2
	NN	10/19/72	60	30	98	65	97	106	95	170	90
DV[2]	DT	10/19/72	60	15	98	22	95	91	87	130	72
Lab.	LD	10/19/72	60	15	97	22	82	29	13	30	5
	NN	10/19/72	60	30	100	65	98	106	95	170	93

[1] *A. americanum* laboratory-reared. [2] *D. variabilis* laboratory-reared.

Table 5. Winter survival of nymphal *A. americanum* and *D. variabilis* held in environmental containers in two sites in the Dismal Swamp and one site in the Newport News City Park

Species and source of ticks	Site	Release date	Total released	Extraction I		Extraction II		Extraction III		Extraction IV	
				Total elapsed days	% survivors	Total elapsed days	% survivors	Total elapsed days	% survivors	Total elapsed days	% survivors
AA[1]	DT	10/14/72	255	21	85	28	70	38	54	97	33
Lab.	LD	10/14/72	255	21	89	28	63	34	9	38	3
	NN	10/12/72	255	33	82	61	85	98	78	125	71
DV[2]	DT	10/14/72	255	21	90	28	71	38	49	97	36
Lab.	LD	10/14/72	255	21	86	28	70	34	15	38	1
	NN	10/12/72	255	33	79	61	88	98	75	125	65

[1] *A. americanum* laboratory-reared. [2] *D. variabilis* laboratory-reared.

Table 6. Molting of engorged *A. americanum* and *D. variabilis* larvae in one laboratory control, the Dismal Town study site, the Lynn Ditch site and the Newport News City Park site

Species	Site	Trial I released 5/28/72			Trial II released 7/10/72		
		Total[1] released	Total elapsed days	% molt[2]	Total released	Total elapsed days	% molt
AA[3]	Control	893	15	100	—	—	—
	DT	738	29	96	738	51	77
	LD	738	29	83	738	51	63
	NN	738	29	100	738	51	93
DV[4]	Control	843	15	100	—	—	—
	DT	249	29	92	249	51	76
	LD	249	29	79	249	51	51
	NN	249	29	94	249	51	86

[1] Totals are corrected to percent successful molt observed in laboratory controls.
[2] Containers extracted before field molt was completed; totals include those ticks completing molt in the laboratory.
[3] *A. americanum,* fed on laboratory hosts.
[4] *D. variabilis* fed on laboratory hosts.

Table 7. Molting of engorged *A. americanum* and *D. variabilis* larvae in one laboratory control, the Dismal Town study site, the Lynn Ditch site and the Newport News City Park site

Species	Site	Trial I Released 6/18/72			Trial II Released 8/20/72		
		Total[1] released	Total elapsed days	% molt	Total released	Total elapsed days	% Molt
AA[2]	Control	96	27	100	83	26	100
	DT	15	45	93	25	59	88
	LD	15	45	20	25	59	36
	NN	15	35	93	25	45	100
DV[3]	Control	94	25	100	90	26	100
	DT	14	45	71	27	59	74
	LD	14	45	14	27	59	41
	NN	14	35	93	27	45	96

[1] Totals are corrected to percent successful molt observed in laboratory controls
[2] *A. americanum* fed on laboratory hosts
[3] *D. variabilis* fed on laboratory hosts

optimal molt success with an average of 94% for engorged larvae and 99% for engorged nymphs. The Swamp sites reflect successively less optimum conditions with averages of 85% for larvae and 84% for nymphs at DT and 69% and 49%, respectively, for these same stages at LD. *A. americanum* larvae and nymphs had slightly higher molting success (averaging 81%) than did *D. variabilis* (averaging 72%).

Molting of the ticks held under natural conditions required much more time than those held as laboratory controls, especially in the Dismal Swamp sites. This was not realized until the larvae in Trial I were extracted from field containers 14 days after laboratory controls had completed molt, and 58% of the larvae from the Swamp sites and 10% from the NN site were found in the unmolted state. These unmolted ticks were held under laboratory conditions for an additional 9 days until all molting was completed. The duration of the period of exposure to natural conditions was increased to 51 days during Trial II. Adults molting from engorged nymphs held in the NN site became active within 2 days after laboratory controls had completed molt, but no activity was observed in the Swamp sites for some 20 days after laboratory controls had molted.

Inundation

The sites evaluated for inundation were totally dry throughout the tick-activity season. Limited inundation began in mid-September and progressed until less than 40 percent of the area remained above water. Table 8 summarizes the mean percent inundation at each of the transects for the four examination dates. Those areas that remained above water were generally associated with hummocks at the base of trees.

DISCUSSION

The results of these studies suggest that the Dismal Swamp, in its present state, is a relatively poor habitat for *D. variabilis* and *A. americanum* as compared to upland forest communities elsewhere in eastern and central Virginia (Sonenshine et al. 1966, Sonenshine 1972, Sonenshine and Levy 1972). Both species appear to be extending their range into unsuitable habitats by colonizing artificial openings (roads and ditches). The virtual restriction of these ticks to the road–forest edge ecotone contrasts markedly when compared with the high abundance of ticks in various forest habitats studied elsewhere in the state. Sonenshine et al. (1966), as a basis for his population estimates, reported actual flag collections of adult *D. variabilis* in a 25 hectare area domi-

Table 8. Percent inundation of 20 random transects in the Dismal Swamp at four sample periods in the winter months

Transect no.		Sample I Oct. 31	Sample II Nov. 13	Sample III Jan. 20	Sample IV Feb. 25
WD	1	2	14	16	28
	2	38	54	72	80
	3	72	76	80	80
	4	62	76	80	80
	5	70	74	74	74
	6	78	8	80	80
	7	72	76	76	76
	8	2	42	50	60
	9	52	70	8	80
LD	1	12	18	34	36
	2	20	32	52	60
	3	42	58	66	68
	4	34	46	54	64
	5	66	68	66	70
	6	0	8	14	24
	7	36	60	74	78
	8	52	72	76	78
	9	62	66	74	78
	10	76	78	78	78
	11	76	76	80	76

nated by mixed evergreen-hardwood upland forest communities at 25/1000 m^2/ sample. Though the density of adult *D. variabilis* in the restricted Dismal Swamp road–forest edge was even greater than the density reported by Sonenshine, a much lower density of only 1.4/1000 m^2/ sample was found in the Dismal Swamp interior.

The magnitude of the density variation of adult *D. variabilis* between the roadside and the interior forest communities suggests the existence of some process or processes restricting uniform colonization by these ticks. The restricting factor is probably not due to a lack of host dispersal, as the invasion of ticks into the forest interior was observed through capture and examination of hosts. Immature *D. variabilis* were found on *Peromyscus leucopus* and *Ochrotomys nuttalli* within the 4 hectare Dismal Town trapping area extending at least as far as 120 m into the forest interior. Clearly, a mechanism for spread of these ticks into the forest interior is present. Consequently, other factors appear to be limiting their survival and development.

Inundation, temperature and humidity variations, soil pH, and predation were considered to be among the more important ecologically limiting factors affecting tick success within the forest. Inundation was found to be the most significant single environmental factor limiting tick survival. Inundation did not occur until host-seeking activity had ceased and ticks had moved into the leaf litter and assumed the quiescent state. Submerged ticks made no effort to move from the leaf litter as inundation progressed; they died within 14 days.

The dropping of engorged immature ticks and impregnated female ticks is associated with the random movement of the hosts. Before flooding in the fall, the entire forest interior can be utilized by these vertebrates. It has been demonstrated that those portions of the Swamp that become inundated in the late fall are lethal to overwintering ticks. If inundation were the only limiting factor, overwinter survival of ticks could be expected in those areas remaining dry. Forty percent of the area sampled was found above water at time of greatest inundation. Assuming that the nonflooded area of the interior was as suitable as the road's edge as a tick habitat, a density of about 13.3 *D. variabilis*/1000 m^2/sample would be expected, based on the 1972 ecotonal density measurements (40% of the roadside density of 33.2 ticks/1000 m^2/sample). Instead, a density of only 1.5/1000 m^2/sample was observed. Therefore, it appears that additional factors are limiting the survival of these ticks. The absence of captures at site WI (Table 1), a site frequently inundated by Lake Drummond, tends to support this.

The extremes of humidity, temperature, and moisture deficit were found to be well within the survival limits of *D. variabilis* as described by Smith et al. (1946). Even though these factors are within the survival ranges, Sonenshine (1965) found a significant difference in molting intervals for *D. variabilis* larvae and nymphs as the mean temperature was reduced from 86°F to 75°F. Approximately 28 percent more time is required for both life stages at 75°F as compared to 86°F. The extended duration of the engorged state due to the relatively low mean weekly temperatures found in the Dismal Swamp (62°–77°) increases the vulnerability of these stages to other environmental factors. Two factors in particular that may further reduce tick survival as development time is extended within the forest canopy are predation and relatively highly acid pH of the substrate. Predation was observed upon flat adult ticks by carabid beetles, and other life stages may also be affected. The tick life expectancy is proportionately reduced the longer they are exposed to predators. The pH of the substrate in which ticks occur during the nonparasitic periods may also limit their survival. The mean pH of 15 soil samples collected at the

LD site between 7 May and 1 July 1972 was 4.41 ± 0.25 (SE). Correspondingly, tick survival was more restricted at LD than DT. The possible effect of soil pH on tick survival and development may merit further study.

The extremely low densities of *A. americanum* found throughout the Dismal Swamp suggest even greater environmental restrictions than those limiting *D. variabilis*. The effects of inundation were observed to be equally limiting to both species. The temperature and humidity were observed to be within survival ranges, but again they were found to be suboptimal. Hooker et al. (1912), Lancaster (1955), and Lancaster and MacMillan (1955) found that ranges such as those observed in the Dismal Swamp extended the time required for ovipostion and egg incubation. The vulnerability of *A. americanum* to predators and adverse pH conditions may be expected to be similar to that of *D. variabilis*.

A. americanum in contrast with *D. variabilis* feeds almost exclusively upon medium-sized or large mammal hosts (Tugwell and Lancaster 1962, Clymer et al. 1970, Bolte et al. 1970). White-tailed deer are especially important as *A. americanum* hosts. Though the population of this animal is known precisely in the Dismal Swamp, estimates by the Virginia Game and Fish Commission indicate that it was approximately 71 percent lower than that observed in the Newport News City Park.

It is interesting to note that the two restricted areas with 11–12 *A. americanum*/1000 m^2 (areas WH and LH, Table 1) are associated directly with the artificial influence of dogs. Kennels for hunting dogs are located at the eastern end of Washington Ditch road and numerous family dogs were observed roaming in the northwestern portion of the Dismal Swamp originating from the adjacent residential section.

The recent changes in ownership of the Dismal Swamp and subsequent emphasis on wildlife management may alter the host support-systems of these two ticks, permitting a change in their populations. This, combined with the refuge plans to increase public use of the area from approximately 2000 annual visits to over 1,000,000, greatly increases the potential for disease transmission to humans. This is especially important in Virginia, which usually has the highest annual U.S. incidence of Rocky Mountain spotted fever. Consequently, it is important to understand the ecology of tick vectors in suboptimal environments such as the Dismal Swamp.

SUMMARY

Aspects of the ecology of the two man-biting ticks, the American dog tick *Dermacentor variabilis* (Say) and the lone star tick *Amblyomma americanum* (L.) in the Dismal Swamp National Wildlife Refuge were investigated during the 2-year period 1971 to 1973. *D. variabilis* was found throughout the area sampled in the Swamp, while *A. americanum* was concentrated in several highly restricted localities. *Ixodes scapularis* (Say) and *Haemaphysalsis leporispalustris* (Packard) were found in rare instances. The frequent occurrence of the two man-biting species, *D. variabilis* and *A. americanum*, in an environment that might be regarded as unsuitable habitat for these ticks raised doubts as to the adequacy of our knowledge of their adaptability. Consequently, the relative density and distribution of these ticks in the Dismal Swamp were studied. The survival of native, laboratory-reared, and translocated ticks in relation to selected abiotic factors was also investigated in the Dismal Swamp. The Newport News City Park, approximately 35 miles north of the Dismal Swamp, provided an area with a very large *A. americanum* population that would be used for comparisons of lone star tick abundance, density, distribution, and survival with the population of this tick in the Dismal Swamp.

The results of these studies suggest that *D. variabilis* has colonized the artificial openings (roadside and ditchside environments) of the Dismal Swamp, but few ticks have survived migration or transport into the natural forest interior. *D. variabilis* adult densities in the 21,800 m^2 of road-forest ecotone sampled in 1971 and 13,600 m^2 sampled in 1972 were 13.7 and 33.2/1000 m^2/sample, respectively. In contrast to this ecotone, the *D. variabilis* adult densities in the 2500 m^2 and 3500 m^2 of forest interior sampled during the 1971 and 1972 seasonal periods, respectively, were 1.2 and 1.4/1000 m^2/sample, respectively. *A. americanum* appeared to have been even less successful in colonizing the Dismal Swamp habitats. With one exception, individuals of this species were taken only in roadside or ditchside areas, in one locality in 1971, but in four localities in 1972. In contrast, *A. americanum* adults were very abundant in the Newport News City in 1972, with no significant difference in densities between the 17,800 m^2 of road-forest ecotone and forest interior sampled (113 adults/1000 m^2/sample and 107 adults/1000 m^2/sample, respectively).

To understand the natural mechanisms limiting more successful colonization of the Dismal Swamp by the dog tick and the lone star tick, study of several biotic and abiotic parameters considered important in their ecology was done. The importance of the host species composition and apparent low densities of certain of these hosts as a factor limiting tick populations were considered. Survival and molting of the two tick species were also studied. Survival and molting were consistently greatest at the Newport News study site; these functions were reduced at one of the Dismal Swamp localities (Dismal Town), while few individuals survived or molted at another Dismal Swamp locality (Lynn Ditch). The time required to complete molting at the two Dismal Swamp study locations was more than twice as long as that of the laboratory controls. The importance of persistent inundation of the forest floor on survival and spread of ticks was also considered. More than 60% of the forest included in the tick-sampling area was continuously submerged for periods exceeding 6 weeks during the winter months, i.e., following the cessation of tick seasonal activity. Quiescent ticks died within 8 days when subjected to continuous submergence without becoming active or attempting to escape from their submerged substrate. The significance of the findings described above in relation to the persistence and spread of the American dog tick and the lone star tick in the Dismal Swamp habitats is discussed.

ACKNOWLEDGMENTS

This study was supported in part by a grant through the Old Dominion University Research Foundation.

The authors also wish to express their sincerest appreciation to Mr. Leighton P. Roper, who facilitated the acquisition of funds which made this research possible, and to the anonymous donors who provided these funds. We wish to thank the many persons who contributed to the performance of the study, namely, Drs. G. F. Levy and R. L. Ake, Ms. Pat Gammon, Emily Whaley, Paul Jones, Susan Miner, Bob McCansland, as well as many others who contributed their weekends or holidays.

REFERENCES CITED

Bolte, J. R., J. A. Hair, and J. Fletcher. 1970. White tailed deer mortality following tissue destruction induced by lone star ticks. *J. Wildlife Mgt.* 34:546–552.

Two Dominant Tick Species

Clymer, B. C., D. E. Howell, and J. A. Hair. 1970. Animal hosts of economically important ticks (*Acarina*) in east-central Oklahoma. *Ann. Entomol. Soc. Amer.* 63:612–614.

Hooker, W. A., F. C. Bishop, and H. P. Wood. 1912. Biology and hosts of some North American ticks. *U.S. Dept. Agric. Bull.* 106. 204 pp.

Lancaster, J. L., Jr. 1955. Biology and seasonal history of the lone star tick in northwest Arkansas. *J. Econ. Entomol.* 48:295–297.

Lancaster, J. L., Jr., and E. L. MacMillan. 1955. The effects of humidity on the lone star tick. *J. Econ. Entomol.* 48:338–339.

Smith, C. N., M. N. Cole, and H. K. Gouck. 1946. Biology and control of the American dog tick. *U.S. Dept. Agric. Tech. Bull.* 905. 74 pp.

Sonenshine, D. E. 1965. The ecology of ticks transmitting Rocky Mountain spotted fever on the eastern U.S. 2d Annual Progress Rpt., U.S. Army Med. Res. and Develop. Command Proj. DA 49 193 MC 2639.

———. 1972. The ecology of the American dog tick, *Dermacentor variabilis*, in a study area in Virginia. Part 1. Studies on population dynamics using radio ecological methods. *Ann. Entomol. Soc. Amer.* 65:1164–1175.

Sonenshine, D. E., and G. F. Levy. 1972. Ecology of the American dog tick, *Dermacentor variabilis* in a study area in Virginia. Part 2. Distribution in relation to vegetative types. *Ann. Entomol. Soc. Amer.* 65:1175–1182.

Sonenshine, D. E., E. L. Atwood, and John T. Lamb, Jr. 1966. The ecology of ticks transmitting Rocky Mountain spotted fever in a study area of Virginia. *Ann. Entomol. Soc. Amer.* 59:1234–1262.

Tugwell, P., and J. L. Lancaster, Jr. 1962. Results of a tick host study in northwest Arkansas. *J. Kans. Entomol. Soc.* 35:202–211.

A PROVISIONAL CHECKLIST OF AMPHIBIANS AND REPTILES IN THE DISMAL SWAMP AREA, WITH COMMENTS ON THEIR RANGE OF DISTRIBUTION

David E. Delzell

This preliminary checklist consists mainly of species found by the author or recorded by others, including Brady (1927), Carroll (1950), Wood (1954), Mitchell (1974a and b), Meanley (1973), and the Virginia Herpetological League (pers. comm.). The explorations by myself and my students have concentrated on relatively accessible areas of the Dismal Swamp National Wildlife Refuge, but have included portions of Gates, Perquimans, Pasquotank, Camden and Currituck counties in North Carolina. Limited collections have also been made north of the Refuge across Rt. 13 in Virginia. It must be emphasized that this investigation is far from complete and that one can only speculate at this time on the occurrence of certain uncommon species within many densely vegetated and interior portions of the Swamp.

Species not yet obtained but thought probably to occur in the Swamp are also mentioned; these are marked with an asterisk (*). Annotations stress the general range of each species, the Swamp being an area where the distributions of many northern and southern forms of the coastal plain tend to overlap and possibly hybridize. Hence, this list includes northern and southern coastal plain species having somewhat restricted ecological relationships and wider-ranging species that are either eurytypic in their choice of habitat or capable of extensive emigration until finding the appropriate conditions.

My thanks go to the numerous students who are helping in the collection of data, to the Virginia Herpetological League (V.H.L.) for their assistance, and particularly the staff of the Dismal Swamp Refuge for permitting this long-term investigation to continue. (The editor wishes to thank Dr. Delzell for kindly preparing these general excerpts from his studies in progress, in response to the many requests from symposium attendees and others for some authoritative observations on this often romanticized aspect of Dismal Swamp wildlife.)

SPECIES LIST

Class Amphibia
  Subclass Lissamphibia
    Superorder Salientia
      Order Anura
        Suborder Neobatrachia
          Family Pelobatidae
            Scaphiopus holbrooki holbrooki
          Family Bufonidae
            Bufo americanus americanus
            Bufo terrestris
            Bufo woodhouse fowleri
            Bufo quercicus
          Family Hylidae
            Hyla crucifer crucifer
            Hyla cinerea cinerea
            Hyla femoralis
            Hyla squirella
            Hyla versicolor versicolor
            Limnaoedus ocularis
            Pseudacris triseriata feriarum
            Pseudacris brimleyi
            Acris gryllus gryllus
          Family Ranidae
            Rana catesbeiana
            Rana virgatipes
            Rana clamitans melanota
            Rana utricularia
          Family Microhylidae
            Gastrophryne carolinensis
    Superorder Caudata
      Order Urodela
        Suborder Sirenoidea
          Family Sirenidae
            Siren lacertina
        Suborder Salamandroidea
          Family Proteidae
            **Necturus punctatus punctatus*
          Family Amphiumidae
            Amphiuma means means
        Suborder Ambystomoidea
          Family Ambystomatidae
            Ambystoma opacum

Family Plethodontidae
Desmognathus fuscus auriculatus
Plethodon cinereus cinereus
Plethodon glutinosis glutinosis
Stereochilus marginatus
Eurycea bislineata cirrigera
Class Reptilia
Subclass Anapsida
Suborder Pleurodira
Family Chelydridae
Subfamily Chelydrinae
Chelydra serpentina serpentina
Subfamily Kinosterninae
Sternothaerus odoratus
Kinosternon subrubrum subrubrum
Family Testudinidae
Subfamily Emydinae
Clemmys guttata
Terrepene carolina carolina
Chrysemys picta picta
Chrysemys scripta scripta
Chrysemys concinna concinna
Chrysemys floridana floridana
Chrysemys rubriventris rubriventris
Subclass Lepidosauria
Order Squamata
Suborder Lacertilia
Infraorder Iguania
Family Iguanidae
Anolis carolinensis carolinensis
Sceloporus undulatus hyacinthinus
Infraorder Scincomorpha
Family Scincidae
Lygosoma laterale
Eumeces fasciatus
Eumeces laticeps
Eumeces inexpectatus
Infraorder Anguinomorpha
Superfamily Anguoidea
Family Anguidae
Ophisaurus ventralis
Ophisaurus attenatus longicaudus

Suborder Ophidia
Superfamily Coenophidia
Family Colubridae
Subfamily Colubrinae
Natrix taxispilota
Natrix erythrogaster erythrogaster
Natrix sipedon sipedon
*Natrix rigida
Storeria dekayi dekayi
Storeria occipitomaculata occipitomaculata
Thamnophis sauritus sauritus
Thamnophis sirtalis sirtalis
Virginia valeriae valeriae
Heterodon platyrhinos platyrhinos
Diadophis punctatus punctatus
Carphophis amoenus amoenus
*Farancia erythrogramma erythrogramma
Farancia abacura abacura
Coluber constrictor constrictor
Opheodrys aestivus
Elaphe obsoleta obsoleta
Lampropeltis getulus getulus
Lampropeltis triangulum elapsoides
Family Viperidae
Subfamily Crotalinae
Agkistrodon contortrix contortrix
Agkistrodon piscivorus piscivorus
Crotalus horridus atricaudatus

NOTES ON THE DISTRIBUTION OF AMPHIBIANS

Toads and Frogs

Scaphiopus holbrooki holbrooki (Harlan)
Eastern spadefoot

This species is widely distributed along the east coast of North America, from New England west to southern Illinois and south to the Gulf of Mexico and Florida, avoiding highlands. It has been found most often at the periphery of the Dismal Swamp in the more sandy soils.

Bufo americanus americanus Holbrook
American toad

Reported in the Swamp by Brady (1927) and Meanley (1973, p. 43), but I have not observed toads that I would place in this taxon. The Swamp is near the southern extremity of the range. Blair (1972, p. 98) states that *B. terris* (*sic*) replaces *B. americanus* in the southeastern coastal plain, including southeast Virginia, but that the relation between the two toads is unclear where their ranges approach one another. Martof (1956, p. 72) treats these as subspecies, i.e., *B. terrestris terrestris* (Bonnaterre) and *B. terrestris americanus* (Holbrook).

Bufo terrestris (Bonnaterre)
Southern toad

Found principally in coastal plain regions, this species ranges from southeastern Virginia to the Mississippi River. In the Swamp it has been found in the drainage canals and adjacent roadbeds.

Bufo woodhousii fowleri Hinckley
Fowler's toad

This toad is similar in appearance to *B. terrestris*. It occupies much of eastern North America but is not found on coastal plains of southern North Carolina to Florida. The toad's apparent preference for sandy soils results in a spotty distribution, with occurrence primarily on the periphery of the Swamp.

Bufo quercicus Holbrook
Oak toad

The oak toad is another coastal-plains form occupying essentially the same range as *B. terrestris*. While the northern limit generally is in North Carolina, it has been recorded from the Dismal Swamp, although I have not observed it there.

Hyla crucifer crucifer Wied
Spring peeper

The peeper is widespread, its range encompassing essentially all of the eastern states except the Florida peninsula. In Canada it occurs from Quebec to eastern Manitoba. This deep-forest to open-scrubland form is common in the Dismal Swamp area.

Hyla cinerea cinerea (Schneider)
Green treefrog

A coastal plains species with an extension of its range into the Mississippi Valley and westward into Texas, the green treefrog is common in the Swamp region.

Hyla femoralis Latreille
Pinewoods treefrog

Except for the southern tip of Florida, this is another coastal-plains frog, with its range ending in eastern Louisiana. It is found in pine-woods and cypress swamps.

Hyla squirella Sonnini and Latreille
Squirrel treefrog

This is another coastal-plains hylid occupying essentially the same range as *H. femoralis,* but extending to the tip of Florida and west into eastern Texas. Except during actual breeding, it is found in shrubby and open weedy areas in the Swamp.

Hyla versicolor versicolor (Le Conte)
Gray treefrog

This frog occurs in basically the same range as does *H. crucifer* except that it does not extend into Texas to the west and not quite so far north into Canada. It may be heard vocalizing in vegetation in many parts of the Swamp.

Limnaoedus ocularis (Holbrook)
Little grass frog

This smallest North American frog is another coastal-plains species, but it does not extend westward much beyond the middle of the Flor-ida panhandle. It has been recorded from the Swamp by the V.H.L., but I have observed it only in the cypress gum swamplands of nearby Seashore State Park in Virginia Beach.

Pseudacris triseriata feriarum (Baird)
Upland chorus frog

This subspecies of *P. triseriata* ranges from southeastern Pennsyl-vania and eastern West Virginia into Kentucky, across to southeast-ern Oklahoma and Texas. It is generally absent from the coastal plain north of Louisiana but does enter in Virginia. Also reported from the Swamp by the V.H.L., I have not seen it there. The frog should be found both in woodlands and in moist grassy spots.

Pseudacris brimleyi Brandt and Walker
Brimley's chorus frog

This frog occupies a portion of the coastal plain from southeastern Virginia down to the extreme eastern section of Georgia. In the Swamp it has been collected in moist grassy areas but should occur commonly in other habitats as well.

Acris gryllus gryllus (Le Conte)
Southern cricket frog

The cricket frog occurs from southeastern Virginia along the coastal plain to western Mississippi (excluding the Florida peninsula). In the Swamp it is found often around the moist edges of woodland pools.

Rana catesbeiana Shaw
Bullfrog

This, our largest frog, has a range extending from west of New England and Nova Scotia to South Dakota and south through Texas with the exception of southern Florida. In the Swamp it is widespread, laying its eggs in woodland and open pools.

Rana virgatipes Cope
Carpenter frog

The carpenter frog is a coastal-plains species ranging from New Jersey south to southeastern Georgia. It has been collected in the Swamp in grassy as well as swampy areas.

Rana clamitans melanota Rafinesque
Green frog

The occurrence is from Quebec to western Ontario, south into Oklahoma, and east through the northern parts of the gulf states to southern North Carolina. Large groups of this frog in breeding congresses have been heard in the Swamp, particularly at the northern end.

Rana utricularia Harlan
= *R. pipens sphenocephala* Cope
Southern leopard frog

This species tends to avoid uplands and is found in the coastal plain from Long Island south to Florida, west into the Mississippi drainage pattern to about Arkansas, and south to the Gulf of Mexico. Individuals are commonly found throughout the Swamp.

Gastrophyrne carolinensis (Holbrook)
Eastern narrow-mouthed toad

This species is confined principally to the southeastern part of the United States, extending into eastern Oklahoma and Texas. This is a rather secretive form, usually found under plant debris, logs, and boards or similar cover.

Salamanders

Siren lacertina L.
Greater siren

This aquatic salamander is found in the coastal plain states from southern Maryland to western Florida. It usually occupies ditches, ponds, and lakes and has been found in the Swamp.

*Necturus punctatus punctatus (Gibbes)
Dwarf waterdog

Another large aquatic salamander located on the coastal plain from southeastern Virginia to about south-central Georgia, this species has not been reported from the Swamp but should be in the area.

Amphiuma means means Garden
Two-toed amphiuma

The amphiuma is found along the coastal plain and into the piedmont from southeastern Virginia to the eastern tip of Louisiana. It is essentially an aquatic form found in canals, ditches, and swamps. I have found it in Jericho Ditch in the Dismal Swamp.

Ambystoma opacum (Gravenhorst)
Marbled salamander

The range of this species extends from the lower New England states westerly and southwesterly to eastern Texas and east to the upper portion of Florida. We have collected it along the western edge of the Dismal Swamp, where it is apparently a peripheral form.

Desmognathus fuscus auriculatus (Holbrook)
Southern dusky salamander

This subspecies of the dusky salamander is confined to the coastal plain from southeastern Virginia to eastern Louisiana, excluding the Florida peninsula. Being found in springs along the Swamp border at the Suffolk escarpment, it is suspected to exist within and around pools throughout the Swamp.

Plethodon cinereus cinereus (Green)
Red-backed salamander

This salamander is principally a northeastern North American form with its range extending from north of the Gaspé Peninsula to North Carolina, west and north to Indiana, Minnesota, and Ontario. It is the most commonly sighted salamander in the Dismal Swamp and is found under leaf litter, logs, or almost any cover over moist soil.

Plethodon glutinosis glutinosis (Green)
Slimy salamander

The slimy salamander has a wide range, extending from southern New York southwesterly into Texas and into the southeastern states except the Florida peninsula. It is found rather commonly in the Swamp area under logs where the soil is continually moist but not inundated.

Stereochilus marginatus (Hallowell)
Many-lined salamander

This species is confined to the coastal plain from southeastern Virginia to the southern portion of South Carolina. In the Swamp it is found primarily in woodland pools.

Eurycea bislineata cirrigera (Green)
Southern two-lined salamander

This salamander ranges from the Virginia–North Carolina line through South Carolina, Georgia, and Alabama to the Mississippi River and south to the Gulf of Mexico excluding peninsular Florida. One specimen was taken in a spring along the Suffolk escarpment in the North Carolina portion of the Swamp.

NOTES ON THE DISTRIBUTION OF REPTILES

Turtles

Chelydra serpentina serpentina (L.)
Common snapping turtle

This wide-ranging turtle occupies all of the United States west to the Rocky Mountains. Although not observed as commonly as other turtles, they live in most bodies of water in the Swamp.

Sternothaerus odoratus (Latreille)
Stinkpot

This turtle occupies most of the eastern United States, extending into eastern Iowa and Texas. The species has been recorded from the Swamp area (V.H.L.), but I have not yet found it. In all probability it is confined to the periphery, owing to its preference for clearer water.

Kinosternon subrubrum subrubrum (Lacépède)
Eastern mud turtle

The turtle is found at lower elevations from New England south to Georgia and Florida and west to Indiana. This species has been recorded from the Swamp, but since it prefers shallow, open, marshy areas, it probably is not common.

Clemmys guttata (Schneider)
Spotted turtle

This species occurs from Maine, west across the Great Lakes area to eastern Illinois, and southward along the coastal plain into eastern Georgia. The spotted turtle is commonly found in the ditches traversing the Swamp. It is seldom seen away from water.

Terrepene carolina carolina (L.)
Eastern box turtle

Basically a dry land species, it occupies a range from New England westward (including Michigan) to Illinois and southeasterly from Tennessee through Georgia. It is common on the Swamp's periphery and possibly occurs in drier areas within the Swamp.

Chrysemys picta picta (Schneider)
Eastern painted turtle

The painted turtle occurs in a band of eastern states and Canada from Nova Scotia south into Alabama. It is often seen basking along the ditches in the Dismal Swamp.

Chrysemys scripta scripta (Schoepff)
Yellow-bellied turtle

The Dismal Swamp is the most northern portion of this turtle's range. Its range extends as a broad band along the east coast to eastern Louisiana, but not including peninsular Florida. It is common in ditches in the Swamp.

Chrysemys concinna concinna (Le Conte)
River cooter

Cooters occur in the eastern states from middle Virginia into eastern Alabama. While this is principally a river-oriented species, it has been reported from the Swamp area. It tends to follow streams down to coastal areas and seems to have penetrated into the ditch systems of swampy regions.

Chrysemys floridana floridana (Le Conte)
Florida cooter

Chrysemys rubriventris rubriventris (Le Conte)
Red-bellied turtle

These two species have not been reported or collected by my group in the Swamp. However, on the basis of their preference for southern swampy, marsh, or lake habitats, they could easily be present in the Swamp. Both are extremely wary and thus difficult to catch.

The Florida cooter has the greater range, extending along the coastal plain into Alabama, while the red-bellied turtle is restricted to the coastal plain from Delaware to northeastern North Carolina.

Lizards

Anolis carolinensis carolinensis (Voigt)
Green anole

This lizard ranges from southeastern Virginia along the southern tier of states to eastern Texas. It is an iguanid lizard which is basically arboreal and it has been recorded from the Swamp by the V.H.L.

Sceloporus undulatus hyacinthinus (Green)
Northern fence lizard

The fence lizard's range extends from southeastern New York westward to eastern Kansas and Texas and then north to central South Carolina. It is often seen associated with pine trees but may be found on stumps and logs. The northern form has been collected from the Swamp.

Lygosoma laterale (Say)
= *Leiolopisma laterale* (Say)
Ground skink

A widely distributed skink with a range from New Jersey west to Kansas and Texas and south to Florida, this species is ubiquitous in the Swamp, especially in drier areas.

Eumeces fasciatus (L.)
Five-lined skink

This skink is found in most of eastern United States except Florida and extends into eastern Kansas and Texas. I have found it only on the dry roads in the Swamp, but it probably occurs throughout drier portions of the Swamp. It is seldom located in vegetation above ground.

Eumeces laticeps Schneider
Broad-headed skink

A moist woodlands skink that is sometimes arboreal, this species is found from southern Pennsylvania to eastern Kansas and south into Texas and northern Florida. It is found along Washington Ditch in the Swamp but is more difficult to find than *E. fasciatus*.

Eumeces inexpectatus Taylor
Southeastern five-lined skink

This skink occurs from southern Virginia west to southeastern Arkansas and east to the Florida Keys. In the Swamp it is most commonly observed in drier areas.

Ophisaurus ventralis (L.)
Eastern glass lizard

This lizard has been recorded from the Swamp by the V. H. L.; however, the literature indicates that the northernmost limit is some distance to the south in North Carolina. From there, it occupies the southern states to Louisiana.

*Ophisaurus attenatus longicaudus McConkey
Eastern slender glass lizard

The glass lizard has been found, though not by myself, near the periphery of the Swamp in or on drier soil. Its range extends from eastern Virginia to the Mississippi River in the lower tier of southern states.

Snakes

Natrix taxispilota (Holbrook)
Brown water snake

Basically, as with so many reptiles and amphibians in the Swamp, this is a coastal-plains species. In the Swamp it occurs commonly in or near bodies of water. Its range is from southeastern Virginia in a southwesterly direction to Alabama and in Florida.

Natrix erythrogaster erythrogaster (Forster)
Red-bellied water snake

Another coastal-plains type, this snake is found from Delaware to Alabama. It enters the piedmont region as it occurs farther south and seems to be rather common in the Swamp.

Natrix sipedon sipedon (L.)
Northern water snake

The widespread species consisting of several subspecies occurs from New England west to Colorado, and east through North Carolina and into Virginia. This subspecies is found throughout the Swamp along ditches and in pools. In this part of Virginia specimens show the influence of the fasciata subspecies to the south in North Carolina.

*Natrix rigida (Say)
Glossy water snake

A rather remote possibility exists that this species of water snake will be found in the Dismal Swamp. Its northern limit in the coastal plains of Virginia and North Carolina shows a spotty distribution. It occurs from South Carolina west to Oklahoma and southward to the Gulf excepting peninsular Florida.

Storeria dekayi dekayi (Holbrook)
Northern brown snake

The northeastern part of the United States is the usual range of this species, southward to North Carolina and west into Michigan and Ohio. It is seen in the drier portions of the Swamp.

Storeria occipitomaculata occipitomaculata (Storer)
Northern red-bellied snake

This widely distributed snake is found in Canada from the maritime provinces westward to Manitoba and in the eastern United States except portions of Georgia and most of Florida. The red-bellied snake is found in a variety of habitats, including swampy and boggy areas.

Thamnophis sauritus sauritus (L.)
Eastern ribbon snake

This semiaquatic garter snake occurs in most of eastern United States except the gulf coastal plain. It is usually associated with swampy areas and shallow pools within the Swamp.

Thamnophis sirtalis sirtalis (L.)
Eastern garter snake

This snake may be found in the drier as well as wetter parts of the Swamp. It ranges from eastern Canada to eastern Manitoba and south to Texas and Florida.

Virginia valeriae valeriae Baird and Girard
Eastern earth snake

   This rather secretive, small, dun-colored snake is found in wooded portions of the Swamp, usually under debris. Its range is from New Jersey to northern Florida, west to Mississippi and north to Ohio.

Heterodon platyrhinos platyrhinos Latreille
Eastern hognose snake

   While recorded from the Swamp by the V.H.L., I have found it occupying only the drier sandy periphery of the area. The species is found from southern New England, west to South Dakota and southern Texas, and east to Florida.

Diadophis punctatus punctatus (L.)
Southern ringneck snake

   A small, rather secretive snake that is invariably found under logs or similar debris, it occurs throughout the Swamp in the somewhat drier parts. The range is from New Jersey diagonally south to southwestern Alabama, including all of Florida.

Carphophis amoenus amoenus Say
Eastern worm snake

   Another secretive species, it too is always found under logs or boards in the Swamp during the daylight hours. It ranges from southern New England in a broad band from western Pennsylvania, southwesterly to northern Alabama, and east into South Carolina.

*Farancia erythrogramma erythrogramma Palisot de Beauvois
 = *Abastor erythrogrammus* (Latrielle)
Rainbow snake

   The rainbow snake has not yet been recorded from the Swamp, but it is very likely to occur there. It tends to burrow in swampy areas from southern Maryland down the coastal plains and piedmont into central Mississippi and eastern Louisiana and the central portion of Florida.

Farancia abacura abacura (Holbrook)
Eastern mud snake

   The range of the eastern mud snake along the coastal plain from southeastern Virginia to eastern Alabama and south through Florida. It is a burrower and an occupant of low marshy or swampy areas where it feeds on aquatic vertebrates. In the Swamp it is fairly common in the ditches and pools.

Coluber constrictor constrictor (L.)
Northern black racer

The black racer is one of the most common snakes in the Swamp, occurring in shrubby vegetation in the drier portions. The snake ranges from the maritime provinces of Canada southwesterly into northeastern Mississippi and central Alabama and South Carolina.

Opheodrys aestivus (L.)
Rough green snake

This slender green snake occurs in many types of vegetation in the Swamp. It is often arboreal but also enters water. It ranges from New Jersey, westward to eastern Kansas, and southward into west Texas, Mexico, and Florida.

Elaphe obsoleta obsoleta (Say)
Black rat snake

This snake is probably the most common reptile in the Dismal Swamp, even moreso than the black racer. It has broad environmental tolerances, ranging from the northern coastal plains to highlands. Geographically it occupies the eastern United States from about the middle of New England west to Nebraska, south to Oklahoma, and east into Georgia. It generally avoids the southern coastal plain and the delta region south of Illinois.

Lampropeltis getulus getulus (L.)
Eastern kingsnake

The kingsnake, which feeds on other snakes, occurs in the Swamp near water, but not because it is an aquatic species. It feeds on snakes that are aquatic. Its range is in a broad band extending south of New Jersey to Mississippi, and east to about central Florida.

Lampropeltis triangulum elapsoides (Holbrook)
= *L. doliata doliata* (L.)
Scarlet kingsnake

This is a woodland form often found under logs and loose bark. It is quite secretive throughout its entire range, which is from extreme southeastern Virginia to parts of Tennessee, south to Louisiana, and east to the tip of the Florida Keys.

Agkistrodon contortrix contortrix (L.)
Southern copperhead

This species is easily the most common poisonous snake in the Swamp. It is most often seen on the roads and ditch banks, but it probably occupies almost all low-lying areas adjacent to water. The southern copperhead ranges along the coastal plain from extreme southeastern Virginia to the Florida panhandle, west to Texas, and north to the southern tip of Illinois in the Mississippi drainage.

Agkistrodon piscivorus piscivorus (Lacépède)
Eastern cottonmouth

Another lowlands poisonous snake, generally occupying about the same range as the southern copperhead, except that its western limit is in eastern Mississippi, and it extends to the Florida Keys. Surprisingly enough, I have not found it in great numbers in the Swamp. Perhaps its food preference is not well satisfied in this particular region. (Editor's note: Perhaps the most frequent reports by laymen of snakes presumed to be cottonmouths have been in the Portsmouth Ditch region of the Swamp, but this requires confirmation owing to the superficial similarity of this species to common nonpoisonous snakes, e.g., *Natrix* spp.)

Crotalus horridus atricaudatus (Latreille)
Canebrake rattlesnake

This subspecies of the timber rattler has almost the same range as the southern copperhead, extending from southeastern Virginia to the northern portion of Florida, into the eastern section of Texas and north to southern Illinois in the Mississippi River basin. They have been seen in widely separated parts of the Swamp along ditch banks, roads, and edges of aquatic habitats. The species may be increasing in numbers as the Swamp vegetation becomes more mesic.

SUMMARY

According to the published reports and observations by the Virginia Herpetological League and the author, the Dismal Swamp area includes 62 reptiles as follows: 19 toads and frogs, 8 salamanders, 8 turtles, 7 lizards, and 20 snakes. Six additional species thought possibly to occur in the area include 1 salamander, 2 turtles, 1 lizard and 2 snakes. Of the three poisonous snakes present, the copperhead is most abundand, followed by the canebrake rattlesnake. The eastern cottonmouth is less abundant throughout most of the Swamp than is generally believed. Comments are included on the general distributional range of species, their habitat preferences and relative abundance in the Swamp.

REFERENCES CITED AND SUPPLEMENTAL BIBLIOGRAPHY

Barbour, R. W. 1971. *Amphibians & reptiles of Kentucky.* Univ. Kentucky Press, Lexington. 334 pp.

Blair, W. F. 1972. *Bufo* of North and Central America. Pp. 93–101 *in* W. F. Blair (ed). *Evolution in the genus Bufo.* Univ. Texas Press, Austin.

Brady, M. 1927. Notes on the reptiles and amphibians of the Dismal Swamp. *Copeia* 162:26–29.

Carroll, R. P. 1950. Amphibia and reptiles. Pp. 195–211 in *The James River Basin: past, present and future.* Va. Acad. Sci., Richmond.

Catalogue of American amphibians and reptiles. 1963–. Catalogue Committee, Amer. Soc. for the Study of Amphibians and Reptiles, New York. Pp. 75.1–138.3. (Available from Miami Univ., Oxford, Ohio.)

Conant, R. 1975. *A field guide to reptiles and amphibians of eastern and central North America,* 2d ed. Houghton Mifflin, Boston. 429 pp.

Martof, B. S. 1956. *Amphibians and reptiles of Georgia, a guide.* Univ. Georgia Press, Athens. 94 pp.

Meanley, B. 1973. *The Great Dismal Swamp.* Audubon Nat. Soc. Cent. Atlantic States, Washington, D.C. 48 pp. (checklist p. 48).

Mitchell, J. C. 1974 *a.* The snakes of Virginia. Part I. Poisonous snakes and their look-alikes. *Va. Wildlife* 35(2):16–18 and back cover.

———. 1974 *b.* The snakes of Virginia. Part II. Harmless snakes that benefit man. *Va. Wildlife* 35(4): 12–15.

———. 1976. Turtles of Virginia. *Va. Wildlife* 37(6):17–21.

———. 1977. Salamanders in Virginia. *Va. Wildlife* 38(6):16–19.

Mount, R. H. 1975. *The reptiles and amphibians of Alabama.* Auburn Univ. Agric. Expt. Station, Auburn. 347 pp.

Schmidt, K. P. 1953. *A checklist of North American amphibians and reptiles,* 6th ed. *Amer. Soc. Ichth. Herpt.,* Chicago. 280 pp.

Taylor, E. A. 1952. Virginia's poisonous snakes. *Va. Wildlife* 13(5):18–19, 22 (does not concern the Swamp but provides useful descriptive details for the layman).

U.S. Army, Corps of Engineers, Norfolk District. 1975. Albemarle and Chesapeake Canal and the Dismal Swamp Canal routes of the Atlantic Intracoastal Waterway, Virginia and North Carolina (maintenance dredging): final environmental impact statement. September. Norfolk, Va. 140 pp. (suggests there are about 45 herptile species in the Swamp, pp. 2–24).

Wood, J. T. 1954. The distribution of poisonous snakes in Virginia. *Va. J. Sci.* 5:152–167.

Wood, J. T., F. G. Carey, and R. H. de Rageot. 1955. The nesting and ovarian eggs of the dusky salamander, *Desmognathus f. fuscus* Rad., in southeastern Virginia. *Va. J. Sci.* 6:149–153.

AN ANALYSIS OF THE BIRDLIFE
OF THE DISMAL SWAMP

Brooke Meanley

Although there have been few formal studies made of birdlife in the Dismal Swamp, the accumulated information gathered by J. J. Murray, Paul Sykes, Jr., W. F. Rountrey, and others is enough to reveal some significant patterns.

As far as I can ascertain, the first observations in the Swamp by ornithologists were made in the latter part of the last century and early part of the present one. Four names are prominent in this regard, although other persons accompanied these men. Such well-known scientists of that period as A. K. Fisher of the U.S. Biological Survey, William Palmer and Paul Bartsch of the U.S. National Museum, and T. Gilbert Pearson, later to become director of the National Audubon society, made significant contributions. Fisher (1895) reported the first Swainson's Warbler, then a little-known North American bird; and Pearson (1893) is known for his unsuccessful search for the Ivory-billed Woodpecker, *Campephilus principalis.*

J. J. Murray, dean of Virginia ornithologists, made numerous trips to the Swamp, reporting several new species for the area. Perhaps his outstanding discovery, made with an associate, W. B. McIlwain, was evidence that Wayne's Warbler is a breeding bird in the Swamp (1932, pp. 487–488).

I began studies in the fall of 1957. During four nesting seasons (1966–69) I spent a total of 40 days making observations of Swainson's Warbler as part of my work in writing a monograph on that species (1971).

THE SWAMP FOREST

J. J. Murray (1965) characterized the Swamp in a single sentence: "The Dismal is a finger of the palustrine forest of the Coastal Plain, extended north yet oriented south because of high temperatures, high humidity, and a long growing season."

Apparently much of the original forest was composed of bald cypress (*Taxodium distichum*), tupelo gum (*Nyssa aquatica*), and swamp black gum (*Nyssa biflora*). Even in pristine times there probably were several other major plant communities besides the cypress-gum type. Due to natural causes, such as fire started by lightning during dry periods, and drought, plant communities such as the evergreen shrub-bog (mainly Ericaceae and *Ilex glabra*) and Atlantic white cedar (*Chamaecyparis thyoides*) also existed. Man's disturbance has changed the complexion of the Swamp so that today it probably is more diverse.

Although small stands and individual trees of bald cypress and tupelo gum (Fig. 1) occur today in the wetter sections of the Swamp, the predominant type is a mixed-swamp hardwoods composed largely of swamp black gum, sweet gum (*Liquidambar styraciflua*), water oak (*Quercus nigra*), swamp chestnut oak (*Quercus michauxii*), red maple (*Acer rubrum*), swamp magnolia (*Magnolia virginiana*), red bay (*Persea borbonia*), and American holly (*Ilex opaca*). Pure stands of red maple also share in this predominance; and the evergreen shrub-bog and Atlantic white cedar types cover extensive areas (see Carter, and Levy and Walker, this volume).

NUMBER OF SPECIES OF BIRDS

A total of 179 species of birds has been reported as occurring in the Dismal Swamp (see checklist). Several species are not true swamp birds but are included as they occur within the area of interest. For example, the Bobwhite, an upland bird, has followed roads deep into the Swamp and spends the year within its confines; and the Indigo Bunting, a field border species, occurs along rights-of-way and in cutover areas. There are undoubtedly 25 or more species that occur in the Swamp but have not yet been reported, namely, several ducks, flycatchers, warblers, etc.

There are approximately 85 species of breeding birds. Several that formerly nested in the Swamp have not been noted during the breeding season in recent years. The Bald Eagle is an example.

AN ANALYSIS OF THE BIRD FAUNA

Logging and drainage operations during the past 200 years have resulted in a denser ground cover and in a drier substrate in the Swamp. Such conditions are favorable to ground- and shrub-inhabiting spe-

Fig. 1. Tupelo gum *(Nyssa aquatica)* community type; a habitat of the Prothonotary Warbler.

cies. Therefore, in its pristine condition the Swamp was wetter and thus had a sparser ground fauna.

The ditches in the Swamp are used by coots, Wood Ducks, Mallards, Black Ducks, Blue-winged and Green-winged Teal, Hooded Mergansers, Ring-necked Ducks, herons, and egrets. The large waders are not as common in the Dismal as in some of the more open southern swamps, such as Okefenokee.

Lake Drummond is rather sterile, producing very little waterfowl food; thus it is mainly used as a rest area by loons, grebes, swans, geese, ducks, coots, and cormorants. Shorebirds feed along the margin of the lake when the water is low. Herring, Ring-billed, and occasionally Great Black-backed Gulls feed in the lake.

Great Blue, Little Blue and Black-crowned Night Herons, Wood Ducks, Red-shouldered and Red-tailed Hawks, Barred Owls, Black and Turkey Vultures, Common and Fish Crows, and Pileated Woodpeckers are among the larger birds that breed in the Swamp. There appear to be no records of native Turkeys occurring in the Swamp in the last 30 years.

There have never been any reliable reports of the Ivory-billed Woodpecker in the Swamp. The original range, according to the American Ornithologists' Union Check-List (1957), indicated that it was to be found as far north along the Atlantic coast as southeastern North Carolina. However, it is highly probable that Ivory-billed Woodpeckers formerly inhabited the Dismal, as they were known to occur as far north in the Central States as southern Illinois and southern Indiana, a northern outpost of their range not as suitable for them as the Dismal Swamp. But ornithological surveys in the Swamp in the late 1800s by biologists of the Smithsonian Institution and the U.S. Biological Survey and by T. Gilbert Pearson did not reveal the presence of this species. They probably had been extirpated in that area by that time.

Bachman's Warbler, the rarest songbird in North America, was reported to have been seen in the Dismal Swamp in the 1920s by J. A. Weber and Ludlow Griscom (pers. comm.).

While most of the breeding songbirds of the Dismal Swamp can be found in smaller swamps in nearby southeastern Virginia and northeastern North Carolina, probably nowhere can they be seen in such abundance, and seldom in as high densities. Also, the Swamp's two southern specialties, Swainson's Warbler and Wayne's Warbler (Fig. 2), occur there in greater numbers than in many parts of the coastal plain. Over 100 Wayne's Warbler and 50 Swainson's Warbler have been counted in a single day in the Virginia section of the Swamp.

The student of geographic distribution of birds will be impressed by the absence or rarity of species expected in the Dismal Swamp. In eight breeding seasons (1966–73) I have seen only three Kentucky Warblers in sections of the Swamp where I have concentrated my investigations. Murray (1952) presents no breeding record for this section of Virginia. Apparently there is a partial hiatus in the breeding range of this species along much of the south Atlantic coast.

It seems strange that the Parula Warbler is absent from most hardwood sections of the Swamp during the breeding season. In the forest along the north section of Jericho Ditch, I have not seen one in the last eight breeding seasons; but they are common there during the spring migration. Where it occurs as a nesting bird, it is usually associated with small stands of cypress, no longer a dominant forest type in the Swamp. The Worm-eating Warbler and the Black-and-White Warbler also are conspicuous by their rarity as breeding birds, although they too are common migrants.

The status of the Brown-headed Cowbird in the Swamp has changed

Fig. 2. Wayne's Warbler (*Dendroica virens waynei*) nest with two eggs of the warbler and one of the Brown-headed Cowbird. Pasquotank County, North Carolina, section of the Dismal Swamp, 29 April 1970.

in recent years, as indicated by W. F. Rountrey (letter of 5 June 1958 to F. R. Scott): "I am concerned over the great increase of these birds. In 1951, I did not record them in the nesting season. By 1953, a few were observed. This spring (1958) they are very common." Considering its abundance 100 miles west and north of the Swamp, I would believe the cowbird still not to be an abundant breeding bird in the Dismal. None of the eleven Swainson's Warbler nests that I found (in May and June) were parasitized by cowbirds; yet the Swainson's is an important host species in other sections of the cowbird's breeding range. An increasing breeding cowbird population in the Dismal Swamp might have a deleterious effect on the local Wayne's Warbler breeding population, as this warbler is an early nester (mostly in April) and therefore one of the few host species available in the early part of the breeding season (Fig. 2).

The Red-cockaded Woodpecker is the rarest breeding bird of the Swamp. A few have been observed in pines in the evergreen shrub-bog community. I saw several Red-cockaded Woodpeckers in pond pines (*Pinus serotina*) along the Virginia–North Carolina border in the eastern part of the Swamp in the late 1950s and on February 10 and 13, 1961. In 1973 I saw 2 pairs 5 miles northwest of the Swamp in a mixture of pond and loblolly pines.

From earlier reports the Bald Eagle was often seen about Lake Drummond until about the 1950s. The last reported nest for the Swamp was in March 1961 (by Mr. and Mrs. Jack P. Hailman).

Of the approximately 85 species of breeding birds (Meanley 1973, pp. 44–45), the warbler family is represented by the greatest number. Seventeen species nest in the Swamp (see checklist).

The Red-eyed Vireo, Hooded Warbler, Prothonotary Warbler, Ovenbird and Carolina Wren probably were the five most abundant breeding birds in the Swamp in the late 1960s and early 1970s (see Table 1).

The Prairie Warbler, a species usually found in an open shrub habitat, was found in the same hardwood swamp forest as the Swainson's and Prothonotary Warblers. I have never found the Prairie Warbler elsewhere in the understory of a dense forest.

The White-breasted Nuthatch and Scarlet Tanager are two species that are generally uncommon on the Virginia Coastal Plain during the breeding season, but they are to be found in the Dismal Swamp.

The Whip-poor-will and Chuck-will's-widow occur around the edge of the Swamp and in drier sections of the interior.

THE MIGRATION PERIOD

Birds are moving through and over the Swamp during every month of the year. While the principal migration periods are in the spring and fall, the major movements of birds through the area should more appropriately be referred to as northward and southward rather than spring and fall migration.

By late February some waterfowl, blackbirds, American Robins, Eastern Bluebirds, American Woodcock, Killdeer, and several other species are leaving, arriving, or moving through the Dismal Swamp region. The northward migration is well under way in March, and in the first half of the month among those species arriving are the Common Snipe, Eastern Phoebe (some winter in the Swamp), Purple Martin, Tree Swallow, and some of the sparrows. By late March the Blue-gray Gnatcatcher and the vanguard of breeding warblers are

Table 1. Composition and relative abundance of breeding birds

2 May 1975 8–10 A.M.		3 June 1971 10–12 noon	
Red-eyed Vireo	11	Carolina Wren	9
Hooded Warbler	10	Ovenbird	9
Ovenbird	8	Prothonotary Warbler	8
Prothonotary Warbler	7	Acadian Flycatcher	7
Carolina Wren	6	Tufted Titmouse	7
Cardinal	5	Red-eyed Vireo	7
White-eyed Vireo	5	Wayne's Warbler	6
Swainson's Warbler	4	Hooded Warbler	6
Wood Thrush	4	Eastern Wood Pewee	4
Yellowthroat	4	Swainson's Warbler	4
Red-bellied Woodpecker	4	Carolina Chickadee	4
Louisiana Waterthrush	3	Red-bellied Woodpecker	4
Prairie Warbler	3	Yellow-billed Cuckoo	3
Pileated Woodpecker	2	Blue-gray Gnatcatcher	3
Carolina Chickadee	2	Downy Woodpecker	2
Great Crested Flycatcher	2	Brown-headed Cowbird	2
Tufted Titmouse	2	American Redstart	2
Barred Owl	2	Ruby-throated Hummingbird	2
Blue Jay	1	Prairie Warbler	2
Belted Kingfisher	1	Pine Warbler	2
Scarlet Tanager	1	Scarlet Tanager	1
Blue-gray Gnatcatcher	1	Cardinal	1
Acadian Flycatcher	1	Yellow-throated Vireo	1
Common Crow	1	Wood Thrush	1
Yellow-throated Warbler	1	White-eyed Vireo	1
Pine Warbler	1	Louisiana Waterthrush	1
Wayne's Warbler	1	White-breasted Nuthatch	1
Rufous-sided Towhee	1	Yellow-throated Warbler	1
Brown-headed Cowbird	1	Red-shouldered Hawk	1
Hairy Woodpecker	1	Great Crested Flycatcher	1
Red-shouldered Hawk	1		

NOTE: Territorial males along one mile transect, Jericho Ditch; lists do not include all species that breed in the Swamp.

arriving in the Swamp. These are the Black-and-White, Yellow-throated, and Wayne's warblers and Louisiana Waterthrush. Parula Warblers have been noted by April 2. All of the resident breeding warblers except Swainson's have arrived by the second week in April. Swainson's Warblers begin to appear by April 15.

The last half of April finds northern transient warblers migrating through the Swamp. Among the earliest of these are the Blue-winged Warbler and the Black-throated Blue Warbler. The transient warbler migration peaks around the last week in April and first week in May. Northward migration continues into early June for a few individuals.

The nesting season is virtually over by July; resident birds are beginning to wander, and the migration of swallows over the Swamp is on.

Southward migration is well under way in August. The Swamp's summer-resident population is noticeably thinned out, and by the latter part of the month early transient warblers such as the Canada Warbler and the Northern Waterthrush appear in the Swamp, while Common Nighthawks and Bobolinks are flying overhead. Most of the summer-resident songbirds have departed from the area by the end of September.

The northern transient-warbler migration reaches a peak in late September and early October. Few winter residents arrive before October 1, and the incursion of mass blackbird flights does not get under way until about mid-October.

During the second half of October the ornithological picture has changed from one of transition to that of winter aspect. By this time most of the winter-resident species have returned (see Table 2 and Fig. 3).

Because of the mild winter climate and the abundance of food, the Swamp is the northern limit along the coast for large numbers of wintering Gray Catbirds, Brown Thrashers, American Robins, Rufous-sided Towhees, Fox Sparrows, Common Flickers, and American Woodcock.

In the 1950's and 1960's, blackbirds, American Robins, Common Crows, and Fish Crows formed huge roosts in the extensive evergreen shrub-bog community that straddles the Virginia–North Carolina line in the eastern section of the Swamp. The blackbird roost contained an estimated 30 million birds, the robin roost, 1 million, and the crow roost, one-half million. These estimates were made by censusing along roost flight lines. The Norfolk Bird Club and the U.S. Fish and Wildlife Service cooperated in the December 1961 census of the roosting blackbird population.

Fig. 3. The Rusty Blackbird (*Euphagus carolinus*); a common winter visitor to the Swamp.

The northern finches are represented in the Swamp during the winter by the Purple Finch, Pine Siskin, Evening Grosbeak, and occasionally the Red Crossbill. On 21 January 1970 I saw what was probably the largest number of Pine Siskins ever reported in a single day, an estimated 10,000 birds. They were feeding on the seed of Atlantic white cedar in the great cedar forest just south of the Virginia–North Carolina border.

The Winter Wren, a common winter resident of the Swamp, is usually the only bird that I see in the understory of the dense stands of Atlantic white cedar. The Hermit Thrush, also a winter resident, occurs in the thinner stands of cedar.

The American Woodcock is a fairly common winter resident. I heard 50 calling on a January evening in the late 1950s.

Now that a part of the Swamp is a wildlife refuge with trails through a variety of plant communities and bird habitats, it presents an extraordinary opportunity for study of a rich bird fauna in a wilderness area under ideal working conditions.

Table 2. Composition and relative abundance of late fall–winter birds

Common Grackle	5540	Ruby-crowned Kinglet	6
Fish Crow	473	Brown Thrasher	5
Red-winged Blackbird	435	Blue Jay	5
Common Crow	320	Swamp Sparrow	5
American Robin	276	Gray Catbird	4
Dark-eyed Junco	170	American Kestrel	3
White-throated Sparrow	159	Black Vulture	3
Brown-headed Cowbird	40	Eastern Bluebird	3
Carolina Chickadee	33	Starling	3
Tufted Titmouse	32	Wood Duck	3
American Goldfinch	32	Belted Kingfisher	3
Cardinal	24	Purple Finch	2
Carolina Wren	20	Song Sparrow	2
Hermit Thrush	20	Eastern Phoebe	2
Golden-crowned Kinglet	16	Brown Creeper	2
Mourning Dove	12	Pine Warbler	2
Pileated Woodpecker	12	Downy Woodpecker	1
Rufous-sided Towhee	11	Red-shouldered Hawk	1
Turkey Vulture	10	Barred Owl	1
Red-bellied Woodpecker	10	White-breasted Nuthatch	1
Yellow-shafted Flicker	9	Black Duck	1
Field Sparrow	9	Yellow-bellied Sapsucker	1
Fox Sparrow	8	Mockingbird	1
Rusty Blackbird	7	Water Pipit	1
Pine Siskin	7	Hairy Woodpecker	1
Winter Wren	6	Brown-headed Nuthatch	1
Myrtle Warbler	6	Red Crossbill	1

NOTE: Data based on count made between 8:15 A.M. and 2:15 P.M. in northwest section of the Swamp, 13 November 1973; list does not include all species that occur in the Swamp at this season.

SUMMARY

There are 179 species of birds reported from the Dismal Swamp. Approximately 85 are breeding birds (see checklist).

Southern birds of particular interest are Swainson's Warbler and Wayne's Warbler. The five most abundant breeding birds in the best forest along Jericho Ditch in the late 1960s were the Prothonotary Warbler, Red-eyed Vireo, the Hooded Warbler, Wayne's Warbler, and the Ovenbird.

Ornithological expeditions in the Swamp in the late 1800s failed to produce evidence of the Ivory-billed Woodpecker. There appears to be no evidence of native Turkeys in the Swamp in the last 30 years. By 1973 a few Red-cockaded Woodpeckers occurred in the general region of the Swamp. Black-and-White, Worm-eating, Parula, and Kentucky Warblers generally are uncommon as breeding brids. A variety of waterbirds use Lake Drummond and several ditches as rest areas.

The largest blackbird roost in North America, containing an estimated 30 million birds, was located in the Swamp in the 1950s and 1960s.

The Dismal Swamp is the northeastern wintering ground of large numbers of American Robins, Gray Catbirds, Brown Thrashers, Rufous-sided Towhees, Fox Sparrows, and American Woodcock.

ACKNOWLEDGMENTS

I wish to thank the following for reviewing the manuscript: Anna G. Meanley, Paul A. Stewart, and Danny Bystrak; and the Audubon Naturalist Society for permission to quote from their publication *The Great Dismal Swamp*.

REFERENCES CITED AND SUPPLEMENTAL BIBLIOGRAPHY

American Ornithologists' Union. 1957. *Check-list of North American birds,* 5th ed. Lord Baltimore Press, Baltimore. 691 pp.

Bartsch, P. 1901. A trip to the Dismal Swamp. *Osprey* 5:35–37, 55–56, 67–69.

Daniel, J. W. 1902. Summer birds of the Great Dismal Swamp. *Auk* 19:15–18.

Fisher, A. K. 1895. Occurrence of *Helinaia swainsoni* in the Dismal Swamp, Virginia. *Auk* 12:307.

Meanley, B. 1969. Notes on Dismal Swamp birds. *Raven* 40:47–49.

———. 1971. Natural history of the Swainson's warbler. *N. Amer. Fauna* 69:1–90.

———. 1973. Additional notes on Dismal Swamp birds. *Raven* 44:3–4.

———. 1973. *The Great Dismal Swamp.* Audubon Nat. Soc. Cent. Atlantic States, Washington, D.C. 48 pp.

Murray, J. J. 1932. Wayne's warbler, an addition to the Virginia avifauna. *Auk* 49:487–488.

———. 1948. The Great Dismal Swamp. *Raven* 19: 14–26.

———. 1952. A Check-list of the birds of Virginia. Va. Soc. Ornithology,

———. 1965. The Great Dismal Swamp. Pp. 249–257 *in* O. S. Pettingill, Jr. (ed). *The bird watcher's America.* 1974. Apollo ed., Thomas Y. Crowell Co., New York, publ. by arrangement with McGraw-Hill, New York.

———. 1969. The birds of the Dismal Swamp. *Va. J. Sci.* 20:158–165.

Pearson, T. G. 1893. In the Great Dismal Swamp. *Ornithologist and Oologist* 18:26.

Stevens, C. E., Jr. 1946. Dismal Swamp notes. *Raven* 17:5–60.

CHECKLIST OF BIRDS REPORTED FROM THE DISMAL SWAMP

Common Loon (*Gavia immer*)
Horned Grebe (*Podiceps auritus*)
Pied-billed Grebe (*Podilymbus podiceps*)
Double-crested Cormorant (*Phalacrocofax auritus*)
Anhinga (*Anhinga anhinga*)
*Great Blue Heron (*Ardea herodias*)
*Green Heron (*Butorides virescens*)
*Little Blue Heron (*Florida caerulea*)
Cattle Egret (*Bubulcus ibis*)
Common Egret (*Casmerodius albus*)
*Black-crowned Night Heron (*Nycticorax nycticorax*)
American Bittern (*Botaurus lentiginosus*)
Whistling Swan (*Olor columbianus*)
Canada Goose (*Branta canadensis*)
Mallard (*Anas platyrhynchos*)
*Black Duck (*Anas rubripes*)
Pintail (*Anas acuta*)
Green-winged Teal (*Anas crecca carolinensis*)
Blue-winged Teal (*Anas discors*)
*Wood Duck (*Aix sponsa*)
Ring-necked Duck (*Aythya collaris*)
Canvasback (*Aythya valisineria*)
Hooded Merganser (*Lophodytes cucullatus*)
*Turkey Vulture (*Cathartes aura*)
*Black Vulture (*Coragyps atratus*)
Sharp-shinned Hawk (*Accipiter striatus*)
*Cooper's Hawk (*Accipiter cooperii*)

* Breeding bird.

*Red-tailed Hawk (*Buteo jamaicensis*)
*Red-shouldered Hawk (*Buteo lineatus*)
 Bald Eagle (*Haliaeetus leucocephalus*)
 Marsh Hawk (*Circus cyaneus*)
 Osprey (*Pandion haliaetus*)
 Pigeon Hawk or Merlin (*Falco columbarius*)
*American Kestrel or Sparrow Hawk (*Falco sparverius*)
*Bobwhite (*Colinus virginianus*)
 Turkey (*Meleagris gallopavo*)
*King Rail (*Rallus elegans*)
 Sora (*Porzana carolina*)
 Common Gallinule (*Gallinula chloropus*)
 American Coot (*Fulica americana*)
 Killdeer (*Charadrius vociferus*)
*American Woodcock (*Philohela minor*)
 Common Snipe (*Capella gallinago*)
 Whimbrel (*Numenius phaeopus*)
 Spotted Sandpiper (*Actitis macularia*)
 Solitary Sandpiper (*Tringa solitaria*)
 Greater Yellowlegs (*Tringa melanoleuca*)
 Semipalmated Sandpiper (*Calidris pusilla*)
 Northern Phalarope (*Lobipes lobatus*)
 Great Black-backed Gull (*Larus marinus*)
 Herring Gull (*Larus argentatus*)
 Ring-billed Gull (*Larus delawarensis*)
 Laughing Gull (*Larus atricilla*)
*Mourning Dove (*Zenaida macroura*)
*Yellow-billed Cuckoo (*Coccyzus americanus*)
 Black-billed Cuckoo (*Coccyzus erythropthalmus*)
*Screech Owl (*Otus asio*)
*Great Horned Owl (*Bubo virginianus*)
*Barred Owl (*Strix varia*)
*Chuck-will's-widow (*Caprimulgus carolinensis*)
*Whip-poor-will (*Caprimulgus vociferus*)
 Common Nighthawk (*Chordeiles minor*)
*Chimney Swift (*Chaetura pelagica*)
*Ruby-throated Hummingbird (*Archilochus colubris*)
*Belted Kingfisher (*Megaceryle alcyon*)
*Yellow-shafted Flicker (*Colaptes auratus*)
*Pileated Woodpecker (*Dryocopus pileatus*)
*Red-bellied Woodpecker (*Centurus carolinus*)
*Red-headed Woodpecker (*Melanerpes erythrocephalus*)
 Yellow-bellied Sapsucker (*Sphyrapicus varius*)
*Hairy Woodpecker (*Dendrocopus villosus*)

*Downy Woodpecker (*Dendrocopus pubescens*)
 Red-cockaded Woodpecker (*Dendrocopus borealis*)
 Eastern Kingbird (*Tyrannus tyrannus*)
*Great Crested Flycatcher (*Myiarchus crinitus*)
*Eastern Phoebe (*Sayornis phoebe*)
*Acadian Flycatcher (*Empidonax virescens*)
*Eastern Wood Pewee (*Contopus virens*)
 Tree Swallow (*Iridoprocne bicolor*)
*Rough-winged Swallow (*Stelgidoptery ruficollis*)
*Barn Swallow (*Hirundo rustica*)
 Purple Martin (*Progne subis*)
*Blue Jay (*Cyanocitta cristata*)
*Common Crow (*Corvus brachyrhynchos*)
*Fish Crow (*Corvus ossifragus*)
 Black-capped Chickadee (*Parus atricapillus*)
*Carolina Chickadee (*Parus carolinensis*)
*Tufted Titmouse (*Parus bicolor*)
*White-breasted Nuthatch (*Sitta carolinensis*)
 Red-breasted Nuthatch (*Sitta canadensis*)
*Brown-headed Nuthatch (*Sitta pusilla*)
 Brown Creeper (*Certhia familiaris*)
*House Wren (*Troglodytes aedon*)
 Winter Wren (*Troglodytes troglodytes*)
*Carolina Wren (*Thryothorus ludovicianus*)
*Mockingbird (*Mimus polyglottos*)
*Gray Catbird (*Dumetella carolinensis*)
*Brown Thrasher (*Toxostoma rufum*)
*American Robin (*Turdus migratorius*)
*Wood Thrush (*Hylocichla mustelina*)
 Hermit Thrush (*Catharus gutlatus*)
 Swainson's Thrush (*Catharus ustulatus*)
 Gray-cheeked Thrush (*Catharus minimus*)
 Veery (*Catharus fuscescens*)
*Eastern Bluebird (*Sialia sialis*)
*Blue-gray Gnatcatcher (*Polioptila caerulea*)
 Golden-crowned Kinglet (*Regulus satrapa*)
 Ruby-crowned Kinglet (*Regulus calendula*)
 Water Pipit (*Anthus spinoletta*)
 Cedar Waxwing (*Bombycilla cedrorum*)
 Loggerhead Shrike (*Lanius ludovicianus*)
 Starling (*Sturnus vulgaris*)
*White-eyed Vireo (*Vireo griseus*)
*Yellow-throated Vireo (*Vireo flavifrons*)
 Solitary Vireo (*Vireo solitarius*)

*Red-eyed Vireo (*Vireo olivaceus*)
  Warbling Vireo (*Vireo gilvus*)
*Black-and-White Warbler (*Mniotilta varia*)
*Prothonotary Warbler (*Protonotaria citrea*)
*Swainson's Warbler (*Limnothlypis swainsonii*)
*Worm-eating Warbler (*Helmitheros vermivorus*)
  Golden-winged Warbler (*Vermivora chrysoptera*)
  Blue-winged Warbler (*Vermivora pinus*)
  Bachman's Warbler (*Vermivora bachmanii*)
  Tennessee Warbler (*Vermivora peregrina*)
  Nashville Warbler (*Vermivora ruficapilla*)
*Parula Warbler (*Parula americana*)
*Yellow Warbler (*Dendroica petchia*)
  Magnolia Warbler (*Dendroica magnolia*)
  Black-throated Blue Warbler (*Dendroica caerulescens*)
  Myrtle Warbler (*Dendroica coronata*)
*Wayne's Warbler (*Dendroica virens waynei*)
  Blackburnian Warbler (*Dendroica fusca*)
*Yellow-throated Warbler (*Dendroica dominica*)
  Chestnut-sided Warbler (*Dendroica pennsylvanica*)
  Blackpoll Warbler (*Dendroica striata*)
*Pine Warbler (*Dendroica pinus*)
*Prairie Warbler (*Dendroica discolor*)
  Palm Warbler (*Dendroica palmarum*)
*Ovenbird (*Seiurus aurocapillus*)
  Northern Waterthrush (*Seiurus noveboracensis*)
*Louisiana Waterthrush (*Seiurus motacilla*)
*Kentucky Warler (*Oporornis formosus*)
*Yellowthroat (*Geothlypis trichas*)
*Yellow-breasted Chat (*Icteria virens*)
*Hooded Warbler (*Wilsonia citrina*)
  Wilson's Warbler (*Wilsonia pusilla*)
  Canada Warbler (*Wilsonia canadensis*)
*American Redstart (*Setophaga ruticilla*)
  Bobolink (*Dolichonyx oryzivorus*)
*Red-winged Blackbird (*Agelaius phoeniceus*)
*Orchard Oriole (*Icterus spurius*)
  Baltimore Oriole (*Icterus galbula galbula*)
  Rusty Blackbird (*Euphagus carolinus*)
  Brewer's Blackbird (*Euphagus cyanocephalus*)
*Common Grackle (*Quiscalus quiscula*)
*Brown-headed Cowbird (*Molothrus ater*)
*Scarlet Tanager (*Piranga olivacea*)
*Summer Tanager (*Piranga rubra*)

*Cardinal (*Richmondena cardinalis*)
Rose-breasted Grosbeak (*Pheucticus ludovicianus*)
*Blue Grosbeak (*Guiraca caerulea*)
*Indigo Bunting (*Passerina cyanea*)
Evening Grosbeak (*Hesperiphona vespertina*)
Purple Finch (*Carpodacus purpureus*)
Pine Siskin (*Spinus pinus*)
*American Goldfinch (*Spinus tristis*)
Red Crossbill (*Loxia curvirostra*)
*Rufous-sided Towhee (*Pipilo erythropthalmus*)
Savannah Sparrow (*Passerculus sandwichensis*)
Dark-eyed Junco (*Junco hyemalis*)
Tree Sparrow (*Spizella arborea*)
*Chipping Sparrow (*Spizella passerina*)
*Field Sparrow (*Spizella pusilla*)
White-crowned Sparrow (*Zonotrichia leucophrys*)
White-throated Sparrow (*Zonotrichia albicollis*)
Fox Sparrow (*Passerella iliaca*)
Swamp Sparrow (*Melospiza georgiana*)
Song Sparrow (*Melospiza melodia*)

A SIMULATION MODEL OF A *PEROMYSCUS LEUCOPUS* POPULATION IN AN AREA OF THE DISMAL SWAMP

James E. Paschal, Jr., Daniel E. Sonenshine, and John H. Richardson

INTRODUCTION

The purpose of this study was to observe a population of white-footed mice (*Peromyscus leucopus leucopus* Rafinesque) in an area of the Dismal Swamp and, based on these observations, to develop a computer model to simulate changes of population structure (density, age, and sex ratios). The basic philosophy underlying this study was that modeling could be a useful tool at all stages of investigation. The model was designed as a guide for further studies of *P. leucopus* in the Swamp.

Preliminary studies had shown two closely related species of mice present in the study area, the white-footed mouse and the golden mouse (*Ochrotomys nuttalli nuttalli* Harlan). *P. leucopus* usually inhabits upland coniferous hardwood forests, particularly oak forests (McCarley 1964, Buell et al. 1966), whereas *O. nuttalli* is restricted to woodland habitats, often near rivers or streams (Golley 1962). Trapping during the summer months of 1971 showed a significant number of both species present in the study area, but it could not be assumed that either species was well established. The status of the two species in the whole of the Dismal Swamp is unknown. The model was designed to explain only the population dynamics of *P. leucopus* in the limited area used in this study. The data pertaining to *O. nuttalli* were used to determine the area unavailable to *P. leucopus.*

The Dismal Swamp of North Carolina and Virginia is one of the largest remaining swamp forests of the southeastern coastal plain (see Levy and Walker, this volume). Due to excessive inundation during several months of the year, the Swamp may be regarded by some workers to be of minimum habitat value to small mammals. It was hoped that these studies would contribute to an understanding of the adaptations which permitted *P. leucopus* to colonize and maintain itself in the Swamp. (See also Handley, this volume, regarding *P. leucopus* and *O. nuttalli*.)

MATERIALS AND METHODS

Description of the Study Area

The study area was a 4-hectare wooded area at the presumed site of former Dismal Town on Washington Ditch near the southwest boundary of the Dismal Swamp (see Garrett and Sonenshine, Fig. 2, this volume, for location). The forest habitat varied in character from west to east, the western portion (nearest to the Swamp boundary) resembling the "upland border community" of Meanley (1968), and the eastern portion his "mixed swamp."

Formulation of the Model

The approach used in the study was that termed "strong inference" by Platt (1964). Simply stated, the approach is to ask precise questions about the study system and then formulate propositions that can be tested. Precise questions limit the number of simultaneous hypotheses the model is required to answer. The model was constructed after the format outlined by Kowal (1971): (1) the selection of variables of interest; (2) construction of flow diagrams; (3) classification of variables, operational definitions of the variables, and specification of the variable units; (4) specification of the equations; and (5) the evaluation of constants.

Initially, factors known to affect small mammal populations were chosen and a generalized flow diagram postulated. When selecting variables of interest, the "ideal" approach was used (Babbel, pers. comm.). This approach involves first determining the goal, next determining the least amount of information needed to explain a study system, and, finally, defining the existing constraints. Only that information required to achieve the goal is sought. An "ideal" state with unlimited resources, time, money, and data was assumed. Each factor was then evaluated and the ideal conditions modified to produce a realistic experiment having attainable goals. Forrester (1968) stated a similar approach: "Formulating a model of a system should start from the question: 'where is the boundary, that encompasses the smallest number of components, within which the dynamic behavior under study is generated?'" During the modeling process, other variables were incorporated and some of the initial variables deleted.

Standing water, nest-site availability (expressed as available habitat sites), food availability, reproduction, and home range (assuming the home ranges were exclusive) were believed to account for the greatest change of population density in the study area. Emigration and competition with *O. nuttali* and habitat selection were also included, even though these factors were believed to be of lesser importance. Finally, flow diagrams were drawn as suggested by Forrester (1968) to indicate paths of cause and effect (Fig. 1).

Although living systems are open, the simulated system is closed because of its defined boundary; i.e., it is not dependent on external input. The simulated system is interlinked by a negative feedback loop; i.e., its state is a function of previous states. The operation of the system was determined by input variables, state variables (variables dependent on previous values), and rate variables (variables not dependent on previous values). Explicit operational definitions were assigned each variable and the units stated (Table 1).

State variables, called "levels" by Forrester (1968) or "dynamic state variables" by Kowal (1971), accumulate material in the system and are conserved unless material flows across the system boundary. Flow rates are more generally termed "decision statements" (Forrester 1968) and include a goal or limiting condition, an actual state condition, an expression of the difference between the goal and the actual condition, and an expression for determining action based upon the difference. Rate variables are also called nondynamic state variables by Kowal (1971). Information variables are unconserved; i.e., they are not exhausted, nor do they accumulate flow; and they are the input to the rate equations.

The model equations expressed the state variables as functions of the input variables and other state variables. The equations were the axioms of the mathematical structure of the model, and the arguments of each function were the causes or controls of system behavior. The set of equations was the complex hypothesis, and each equation was a subhypothesis subject to testing and modification.

The set of equations was programmed in FORTRAN IV and run on the IBM 360 computer. Starting with a set of estimated or observed values for the population structure, the program simulated the population change every two weeks for a period of one year.

As a final step the constants of the equations were evaluated. The constants were: (1) formulated hypotheses, (2) values from the literature, or (3) actual measurements (Table 2). A hierarchy for experimentation in the study area was determined by changing the values one at a time and assessing the effect of this change on the simulated population structure.

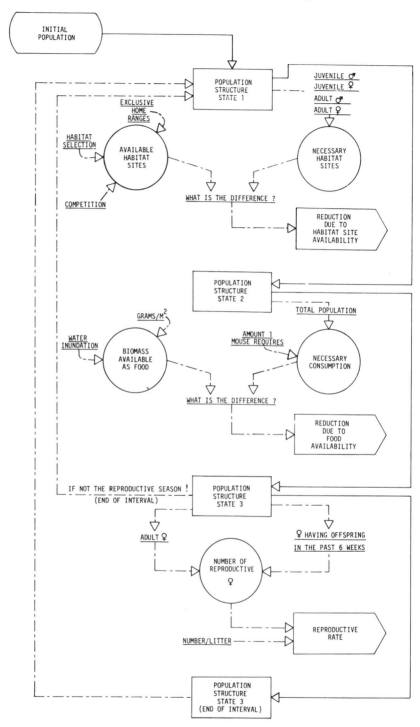

Fig. 1. Detailed systems model indicating data input and the conditions of decision statements.

Table 1. Population model variables

Symbol	Description	Units
Input Variables		
AMNTI (I)	Amount of food one mouse consumes during a two-week period	grams
BIOSM (I)	Amount of food present	grams/m^2
STH20 (I)	Standing water at the surface for the total area (as fraction of the total area)	pure no.
Rate Variables	(the variables utilized in decision statements)	
AMNS	Number of habitat sites available to adult males	pure no.
XJMNS	Number of habitat sites available to juvenile males	pure no.
AFNS	Number of habitat sites available to adult females	pure no.
XJFNS	Number of habitat sites available to juvenile females	pure no.
TBIOA	Total amount of food available to the population	grams
CONSN	Total amount of food required by the population	grams
REPRD	Total reproduction for the time period	pure no.
DYNG	Number of young that die (exclusive of juveniles)	pure no.
State Variables	(the variables that define the condition of the system)	
SPLT (IND, ITIME)	Age-sex structure of population	pure no's.
SPLT (1, ITIME)	Number of juveniles	
SPLT (2, ITIME)	Number of adults	
SPLT (3, ITIME)	Number of females	
SPLT (4, ITIME)	Number of males	
SPLT (5, ITIME)	Number of juvenile males	
SPLT (6, ITIME)	Number of juvenile females	
SPLT (7, ITIME)	Number of adult males	
SPLT (8, ITIME)	Number of adult females	
SPLT (9, ITIME)	Total number of population	
SPLT (10, ITIME)	Number reproduced	
SPLT (11, ITIME)	Number of reproductive females	

NOTE: All variables are for the given simulation period and are based on the total area of 40,000 m^2.

Trapping

White-footed mice and golden mice were trapped live with Sherman traps, 7.6 x 7.6 x 25.4 centimeters. The traps were distributed at 20-meter intervals on an area 100 meters by 400 meters. Two traps were placed at each 20-meter interval except for the line nearest the road, where only one trap was placed per interval. Due to a limited number of traps and the presumption that the road acted as a natural barrier, the arrangement was considered to be the most acceptable. The trapping was done during each of the four seasonal periods from April 1972 through March 1973. Data collected during two nights of one week served as capture data, and data collected during two nights of the following week served as recapture data. The population density was estimated using the Lincoln Index.

Table 2. Population model constants

Symbol	Physical description	Units	Value	Reference
TOTAR	Total area of the study site	m^2	4x10^4	Measured
HRMALE	Mean home-range size of males	m^2	1100	Burt 1940
HRFEM	Mean home-range size of females	m^2	850	Burt 1940
ONUTT	Area inhabited by *O. nuttali*	m^2	6400	Measured
HSELN	Area not inhabited by *P. leucopus* (other than that because of competition)	m^2	4800	Measured
ISSN	Reproductive season (Feb. to Oct.)	pure no.	5–20	Stickel & Warbach 1960
XNL	Modal number of young per litter	pure no.	4	Asdell 1952
BENDL	Fraction of young that die	pure no.	0.96	Bendell 1959
	Mean number of litters born per month per female during the breeding season.*	no./month	0.6	Jackson 1952

* It is assumed that adult females have 1 litter per 6 weeks during the breeding season.

RESULTS

Identification of the System

The comparisons of simulated population structure, observed population structure, and the estimated population structure are outlined in Table 3 and Figure 2.

Chi-square was used to test for significant differences between frequency distributions at each season ($X^2 = 3815$, 3 df., 0.05 *P*). No significant difference between the frequencies of the observed, estimated, and simulated population structures was indicated except for the fall period. The X^2 values for the observed population structure and the simulated population structure based on the observed values of the first trapping period were: 0.36, 0.28, 7.12, and 2.28 for the spring, summer, fall, and winter periods, respectively. The X^2 values for the estimated population structure and the simulated population structure based on the estimated values for the first trapping period were: 0.00, 2.22, 15.00 and 0.31 for the spring, summer, fall, and winter periods, respectively. It was assumed that the discrepancy during the fall period was due to the unexpectedly high number of juvenile males caught. By assuming that three of the juvenile males caught were adult males, the chi-square comparison showed no significant difference between the observed and simulated populations ($X^2 = 2.78$). However, the discrepancy between the estimated and simulated populations was not removed by assuming that three of the juvenile males were adult males ($X^2 = 11.14$). This was probably

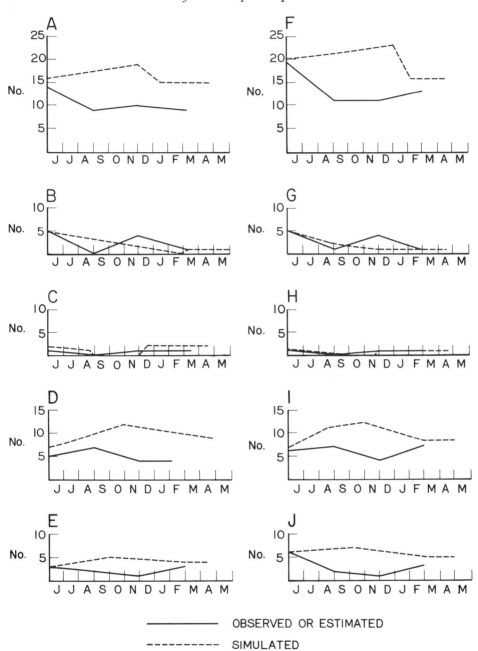

Fig. 2. Comparisons of the simulated population structure and the observed and estimated population structures. The X-axis represents one year (1972–73), the Y-axis the number of animals. Solid lines represent the number of animals, dashed lines the simulated values. Months begin with June. *A* = total observed population; *B* = juvenile males observed; *C* = juvenile females observed; *D* = adult males observed; *E* = adult females observed; *F* = total estimated population; *G* = juvenile males estimated; *H* = juvenile females estimated; *I* = adult males estimated; and *J* = adult females estimated.

Table 3. Comparisons of simulated values to the observed and estimated values

Date[1]	Observed	Simulated[2]	Estimated	Simulated[3]
25 May 1972				
Juvenile males	5	5	5	5
Juvenile females	1	1	1	1
Adult males	5	7	7	7
Adult females	3	3	6	6
Total	14	16	19	19
1 September 1972				
Juvenile males	0	1	0	1
Juvenile females	0	0	0	1
Adult males	7	13	8	14
Adult females	2	4	2	8
Total	9	18	10	24
28 November 1972				
Juvenile males	4	1	4	0
Juvenile females	1	1	1	0
Adult males	4	13	4	12
Adult females	1	5	1	8
Total	10	20	10	20
10 March 1973				
Juvenile males	1	1	1	1
Juvenile females	1	0	1	1
Adult males	4	10	7	9
Adult females	3	4	3	5
Total	9	15	12	16

[1] Last trapping day of the seasonal period.
[2] Based on observed values of the first period as the initial values.
[3] Based on estimated values of the first period as the initial values.

due to the high number of adult females expected from the simulation based on estimated values.

Comparisons of the number of animals in each group indicated that the simulated populations were different from the observed and estimated populations. However, since the frequencies were not significantly different nor the discrepancies of frequency accounted for, and the discrepancies between the totals were expected (see Discussion), the model is assumed to explain the dynamics of the population when it is used as a first approximation.

Incrementation of Constants and Input Variables

The effects of incrementing the model constants and the input variable of food/m^2 are indicated in Figure 3.

The relative importance of each value to the simulation (in decreasing order of importance) was:

1. Mortality rate of the young
2. Food/m^2
3. Area that *P. leucopus* selects against versus the area occupied by *O. nuttali*
4. Home range of males
5. Number of young per litter
6. Breeding season
7. Home range of females

The apparent difference between the area selected against and the area occupied by *O. nuttali* was the result of the different values used for incrementation. The two constants affect the model in the same way.

DISCUSSION

Format of the Model

The state of the system was described by the population-structure variables and indices of the limiting factors. The population was represented as a two-dimensional matrix [SPLT(IND,ITIME)], one dimension representing the age-sex groups of the population (IND) and the other the simulation period (ITIME). The following represents the two-dimensional structure (See Table 1 for the complete structure): SPLT (5, 16), number of juvenile males during the 16th time period; SPLT (6,ITIME), number of juvenile females during a given simulation period; SPLT(7,ITIME), number of adult males during a given simulation period, and SPLT(8,ITIME), number of adult females present during a given simulation period.

The initial values of the population structure were input to the program, and the simulation, based on two-week intervals, was executed for the 26 time periods using a DO–loop based on the statements:

DO 12 ITIME = 2,27 . . . 12 CONTINUE

The two-week simulation interval was chosen because it was one-third of the shortest time-delay in the system (6 weeks). Forrester (1968) found that a simulation interval should be one-half or less of the shortest time-delay in the system in order to reduce fluctuation produced as an artifact of the calculations.

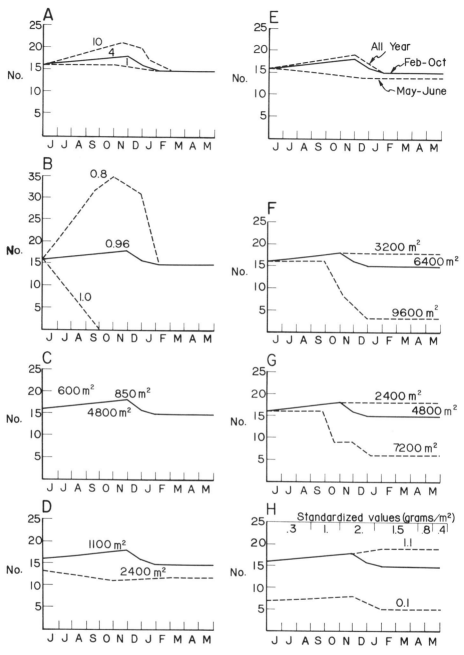

Fig. 3. Effects of incrementing constants and the input variables of food/m². The X-axis represents one year (1972–73), the Y-axis the total number of animals in the population. The solid lines represent the simulated population as standardized in the model. The dashed lines represent the population changes caused by incrementing the values, either the values showing high and low significance, or the extreme high and low values when incrementing. The absence of a dashed line with a number indicates that there was no change from the standardized values. Months begin with June. A = number of young/litter; B = mortality rate of young; C = home range of females; D = home range of males; E = the breeding season; F = the area occupied by $O.$ $nuttalli$; G = selection against habitat area; and H = food/m².

The changes of adult males, juvenile males, adult females, and juvenile females were calculated separately. Initially, the changes due to reproduction and maturation from the previous time period were calculated, then the changes due to habitat and food availability during the existing time period were determined.

The number of juveniles was calculated as those surviving from the previous time period, plus the number produced, minus the number that matured. The number of juvenile males was equal to 0.569 of reproduction, and of juvenile females to 0.431 of reproduction (Rood 1966). Wild mice were considered sexually mature at 75 to 90 days of age (Clark 1938). The number matured was the product of the survival factors from the previous two time periods and the number of juveniles from the period six weeks previous to the present period. The products of maturation of juvenile males and juvenile females were A5 and A6, respectively: A5 = SPLT(5,ITIME-3) × F53 × F52, and A6 = SPLT(6,ITIME-3) × F63 × F62.

The equations for the change of juveniles were: Juvenile males S5 = SPLT(5,ITIME-1) + 0.569 × SPLT(10,ITIME-1) - A5, and juvenile females S6 = SPLT(6,ITIME-1) + 0.431 × SPLT(10, ITIME-1) - A6.

The number of adults was calculated as those surviving from the previous time period, plus the number of mice that matured. The equations for the change of adults were: Adult males S7 = SPLT(7, ITIME-1) + A5, and adult females S8 = SPLT(8,ITIME-1) + A6.

After maturation was considered, the survival of each group was determined for the time period. The factors used were density-dependent; therefore, the number within each age-sex group was compared with the limiting conditions. If the density was greater than the carrying capacity, the population was reduced.

The number of sites available to *P. leucopus* was a function of the total area (calculated as 40,000 m^2), the area *P. leucopus* selected against (HSELN), the area competed for with *O. nuttali* (ONUTT), and the exclusive home ranges (HRMALE and HRFEM). The potential habitat of *P. leucopus* was the total area minus the area selected against, minus the area competed for with *O. nuttali*. Of the potential habitat, each mouse required 1100 m^2 (males) or 850 m^2 (females). A habitat site was operationally defined as the area of potential habitat necessary for one mouse. The number of available habitat sites was compared with the number in the age-sex group present during the time interval. If the number of available habitat sites was insufficient, the number of the age-sex group was reduced to capacity. "Zero" was output if the number of habitat sites was not limiting, and "1" if limiting. The following part of the discussion shows the justification for the factors used to calculate the available habitat site and then indicates how the calculation was performed.

Experiments have shown that members of the genus *Peromyscus* will select specific habitats (Wecker 1964). No mice were captured within a certain portion of the study area during the entire year. It was assumed that this area was unused by *P. leucopus* and was therefore selected against. This calculated area was 4800 m².

P. leucopus and *O. nuttali* were never captured together in the same immediate vicinity; therefore, it was assumed that if *O. nuttali* inhabited an area, it would exclude *P. leucopus*. The area that *O. nuttali* inhabited was 6400 m².

The average size of a male home range of *P. leucopus* is 1100 m², that of a female is 850 m² (Burt 1940). Male and female home ranges overlap, and the female's ranges are minimal during the breeding season (Sheppe 1965). Metzgar (1971) found that mice of the same sex tended to occupy mutually exclusive home ranges. Also, he found that the home-range sizes were stable and that they remained exclusive at high population density. White-footed mice generally spend their entire life within the home range (Nicholson 1941, Snyder 1956). In the model the home ranges were assumed to be exclusive by sex; that is, males excluded other males, and females excluded other females. Home ranges were assumed to remain a constant size throughout the year.

The number of available habitat sites was calculated as the total habitat area, minus the area utilized by the opposite age group (e.g., adult males cannot inhabit areas already inhabited by juvenile males), divided by the home-range size of the sex class. The adults were considered dominant; therefore, the available area for adults was calculated first, thus giving the adults of an increasing population the first opportunity to inhabit available area.

The calculations of the available habitat sites, and the decision statements (rates) were as follows:

Adult males

AMNS = (TOTAR–HSELN–ONUTT–(SPLT(5,ITIME–1)   *×
HRMALE))/HRMALE

If (AMNS–S7) is less than zero, the number of adult males will be reduced;

IF(AMNS–S7) 1122,1,1 (decision statement)
1 SPLT(7,ITIME) = S7 (the adult males are not reduced)
IAM–O (output factor)
GO TO 3
1122 SPLT(7,ITIME) = AMNS (the adult males are reduced)
IAM = 1;

Junvenile males
3 XJMNS = (TOTAR-HSELN-ONUTT-(SPLT(7,ITIME) *×
HRMALE))/HRMALE
4 SPLT(5,ITIME)=S5 (the juvenile males are not reduced)
IJM=O
GO TO 6
5 SPLT(5,ITIME)=XJMNS (the juvenile males are reduced)
IJM=1;

Adult females
6 AFNS=(TOTAR–HSELN–ONUTT–(SPLT(6,ITIME–1) *×
HRFEM))/HRFEM
IF(AFNS–S8) 8, 7, 7
7 SPLT(8,ITIME)=S8 (the adult females are not reduced)
IAF=0
GO TO 9
8 SPLT(8,ITIME)=AFNS (the adult females are reduced)
IAF=1;

Juvenile females
9 XJFNS=(TOTAR–HSELN–ONUTT–(SPLT(6,ITIME–1) ×
*HRFEM))/HRFEM
IF(XJFNS–S6) 11,10,10
10 SPLT (6,ITIME)=S6 (juvenile females are not reduced)
IJF=0
GO TO 112
11 SPLT(6,ITIME)=XJFNS (juvenile females are reduced)
IJF=1.

Inundation was not used as a function of the calculations to determine available habitat sites due to the high trapping success in inundated areas and the observation that mice climbed and nested in the trees.

The next part of the model determined the food availability; if the food was limiting, the population was reduced, to carrying capacity. If food was not limiting, "0" was output, and if limiting, "1." The food requirement was assumed to be the same for adults and juveniles, and for both sexes; therefore, the calculations were based on the total population.

Necessary consumption was calculated as the product of the amount one mouse consumes in a two-week period and the total number of animals of the population. The consumption by one mouse was based on Sealander (1952):

°C	Dry food consumed/ day(gm)	Caloric intake/ gm/day
8.5	6.26–6.85	0.99–1.13
20.5	4.19–4.40	0.67–0.74
30.5	2.79–2.94	0.44–0.49

The food available to the population was calculated as the product of food/m^2 and the ground area available to the population. The food/m^2 was hypothesized as having a seasonal range between 0.3 and 2.0 grams/m^2. The ground area with available food was calculated as the total area, minus the area selected against, minus the area inhabited by *O. nuttali*, minus the area covered with water. Other studies in the Swamp indicated that about 60 percent of the study area was inundated during four months of the year (Garrett and Sonenshine, this volume).

The equations used to determine population change due to food availability were:

Available area with food
AVAIL = TOTAR–HSELN–ONUTT–(STH20(I) × TOTAR):

Total food available
TBIOA = BIOSM(I) × AVAIL;

Determination of the change of the population
IF(CONSN = TBIOA) 13, 13, 14
13 if the difference is less than or equal to 0.,
the population is not reduced
KSURV = 0
14 if the difference is greater than 0.,
the population is reduced
TTPLT = TBIOA/AMNTI(I)
KSURV = 1.

The age-sex groups were recalculated if the population was reduced by limiting food. It was assumed that the age and sex groups were affected alike.

The next portion of the program determined the effect of reproduction during the time period. If the simulated time period occurred during the reproductive season, the reproduction subroutine was called. The reproductive season was based on Stickel and Warbach (1960), who found the reproductive season in Maryland to be from February to October. This corresponds to the two-week periods in the model between 3 and 20. The decision statement used to call the reproduction subroutine was: IF(ISSN.GE.3.ANDISSN.LE.20) call reproduction; ISSN was the variable representing the simulation period.

In southern Michigan adult females averaged 0.6 of a litter per month (Jackson 1952). It was assumed in the model that adult females had a litter every six weeks during the breeding season. The number of reproductive females of the time period was calculated as the number of adult females, minus the number of adult females producing litters in the previous two time periods. The survival of adult females from the previous time periods was calculated by multiplying the number of adult females by factors of survival for the time periods.

The main equation for determining reproductive females was:

RFEML = SPLT(8,ITIME)–SPLT(11,ITIME–1) ×
FACTOR(ITIME)–(SPLT(11,ITIME–2) ×
FACTOR(ITIME) × FACTOR(ITIME–1))
–(SPLT(11,ITIME–3) × FACTOR(ITIME) ×
FACTOR(ITIME–1) × FACTOR(ITIME–2)

The number of young/litter was assumed to be four, the model number/litter calculated by Asdell (1964). The reproduction was calculated as the product of reproductive females and the number of young/litter: REPRD–RFEML × XNL.

Bendell (1959) found the mortality of young on control islands to be 96 percent; therefore, the mortality of young was assumed to be 0.96 of the total produced: DYNG = BENDL × REPRD.

The reproduction for the time period, calculated as a function of the mortality of the young, was: SPLT(10,ITIME)–REPRD–DYNG.

The number of reproductive females was assigned to the population structure: SPLT(11,ITIME) = RFEML, and control was returned to the main program.

If the simulated time period was not within the reproductive season, the reproductive subroutine was not called, and the number of young produced and the number of reproductive females was assigned as 0.

It is suggested that in future studies of *P. leucopus* in the Swamp that a more intensive and varied trapping scheme is used . A full ten-day trapping period would probably be desirable, at least during the summer and fall. Also, studies on control areas might indicate food preferences, and selected baits might increase trapping success. Concurrent use of tracking data (see Sheppe 1965) using smoked paper at bait stations could help determine what other mice are in a given study area.

The International Biological Program (IBP) conducted intensive studies of trapping small mammals and found that a dense-line grid was useful for determining density and immigration (French et al. 1971). It is suggested that a similar scheme be utilized in future studies of *P. leucopus* in the Swamp to determine the significance of immigration and emigration.

The IBP also compared several methods of estimating small mammal populations and found that the Jolly stochastic method (1965) gave the best results. It is suggested that this approach be utilized since it, too, accounts for immigration and emigration. Other methods of population estimation should not be used unless the assumptions for their use can be met. For example, the method of Eberhardt (1969) would not be useful since the assumptions about recapture classes during a trapping period are not met.

Evaluation of Constants

Once the system was identified, constants were changed to evaluate their importance to the model. Extreme upper and lower values were assigned to increase the probability of including the values due to natural variation within the system.

The evaluation was done by including a looping statement (a DO-loop) that enclosed the simulation portion of the program. The statement for this process was: DO 1100 ND=NA, NB, NC.

The statement assigned the constant being incremented (ND) an initial value (NA), and the population was simulated for the year period; the constant was then incremented by NC, and the simulation was repeated. The incrementation and consequent simulation were repeated until the constant was equal to the upper value (NB). Following the last simulation for the constant, control was transferred to a DO-loop enclosing the incrementation DO-loop, the input value of the constant was reassigned, and the next constant was incremented.

The constant in the model responsible for the most change of the simulated population size was the mortality rate of the young. With a standardized mortality rate of 0.96, the population increased from 16 to 20 during the summer period; with a modified mortality rate of 0.8, the population increased from 16 to 32 during the same period. If the mortality rate had been 1, the population would have been exterminated in about five months (Bendell 1959). Bendell studied populations on control islands of Lake Opinicon, Ontario, and found that the mortality of young decreased from 0.96 to 0.6 when the populations were given additional food supplies (survival from 6/140 to 64/161).

Evaluation of the variable food/m^2 indicated that a range of 1 gram of food/m^2 (assuming a limiting range) would cause a one- to two-fold difference in the size of the population. Also, during the standardized simulation (no incrementation), the index of food availability was the only calculated variable that limited the population. These observations, and the role of food in affecting the mortality rate of the young, indicate that the study of food availability is a prime consideration for explaining the population dynamics of *P. leucopus* in the Dismal Swamp. Since there are no data available, it is particularly important to determine the amount of potential food/m² during different seasons. The food consumption has been documented by Sealander 1952), and it is probably sufficient for future studies of population dynamics. Although food availability may be of prime importance, there is also a possibility that it may not be as important as suggested by the model. Golley (1962) found that *P. leucopus* stores a large amount of seeds and nuts for winter use. Also, it was observed that mice in the Dismal Town area nested in trees, and during preliminary studies in February 1971 the white-footed mice traversed extensive areas covered with water by climbing on fallen branches. The importance of food availability may be a function of the amount of food stored and the mice's efficiency in finding the food stored.

Evaluation of the other constants of the model indicates that unless these constants are significantly different than defined by the model, their further study would not be useful for explaining the population dynamics of *P. leucopus* in the Dismal Swamp. However, significantly higher densities of mice would change the relative importance of these constants. For example, the home-range size of males had a more significant effect on the population than the home-range size of females. This difference is due to the significantly higher number of males than females in the simulation; also, if the number of adult females had been greater, the number of young/litter and the breeding season may have had more effect. If the total density had been greater, the relative size of both male and female home ranges may have had more effect.

Further simulations, evaluating more than one constant at a time, may be useful for determining experimental design. For example, the number of young/litter may have a more significant effect if the mortality rate of the young is lower. It is suggested that any future study of ecological factors affecting the populations of *P. leucopus* in the Dismal Swamp concurrently include a rigid trapping scheme for determining density and age-sex structure. If there are any significant differences between the densities in future studies and this study, the constants should be reevaluated at an early date and the experimental design modified accordingly.

CONCLUSIONS

Probably the most significant contribution of a model such as described is that of experimental design. The logical format forces the formulation of precise relationships, and, due to the operational nature of the relationships, indicates the form and amount of data required in the experiment.

The lack of experimental design is apparent in the literature of population ecology. Data used to explain population dynamics are often fragmented, incomplete, or composed of isolated values with dubious usefulness. Simulation models can decidedly assist the data-collection effort, even though such models do not represent the entire system.

The emphasis in the construction of this model has been empirical rather than analytical. By using a large number of simple equations that are solved numerically, the model is not restricted by assumptions of linearity, and it can evaluate a wide range of input data. Theory development, including model construction, is incomplete without verification, and therefore further expansion of the model will require experimentation in the laboratory and the field.

The model is not a final explanation of the population dynamics of *P. leucopus* in the study area. The constants were taken from studies done in upland forests, and data collected were those needed only to identify the selected variables of interest, i.e., the population structure. However, because the model identifies several of the most significant ecological factors affecting population dynamics of the white-footed mouse, it can be a useful guide for further studies in the Dismal Swamp.

SUMMARY

A computer simulation model was developed to explain the population dynamics of the white-footed mouse (*Peromyscus leucopus*) in an area of the Dismal Swamp. The model was designed to provide an experimental base for future studies. The model indicates relationships between food availability, home-range size, competition with the golden mouse (*Ochrotomys nuttali*), habitat selection, and reproduction.

White-footed mice were trapped in the Dismal Town site during each season from April 1972 through March 1973. The age-sex structure of the population was determined and compared with the simulated structure. Although there were significant discrepancies between the comparisons, the differences were explained and the model accepted as representing the population dynamics in the study area.

The model constants were evaluated, and it was determined that mortality rate of the young and food availability were the primary factors affecting population change. Other factors, such as home-range size and habitat selection, might be of more relative importance at higher population densities.

ACKNOWLEDGMENTS

The authors wish to express their sincerest appreciation to Mary Keith Garret and Patricia Gammon for their assistance with the field work. This study was submitted by the senior author as a thesis in partial fulfillment of requirements for the degree of Master of Science, Old Dominion University, Norfolk, Virginia, August 1973.

REFERENCES CITED

Asdell, S. A. 1964. *Patterns of mammalian reproduction,* 2d ed. Comstock Publ. Assoc. Ithaca, N.Y. 670 pp.

Bendell, J. F. 1959. Food as a control of population of the white-footed mice, *Peromyscus leucopus noveboracensis* (Fisher). *Canad. J. Zool.* 37:173–209.

Buell, M. F., A. N. Langfore, D. W. Davidson, and L. F. Ohmann. 1966. The upland forest continuum in northern New Jersey. *Ecology.* 47:416–432.

Burt, W. H. 1940. Territorial behavior and populations of some small mammals in southern Michigan. *Misc. Publ. Mus. Zool. Univ. Mich.* 45:1–58.

Clark, F. H. 1938. The age at sexual maturity of mice of the genus *Peromyscus. J. Mamm.* 19:230–234.

Eberhardt, L. L. 1969. Population estimates from recapture frequencies. *J. Wildlife Mgt.* 33:28–39.

Forrester, J. W. 1968. *Principles of systems.* Preliminary 2d ed. Wright-Allen Press, Cambridge, Mass.

French, N. R., C. O. Jorgensen, J. H. Smith, and B. G. Maza. 1971. Comparison of some IBP population estimates methods for small mammals. U.S. Natl. Comm. for Int. Biol. Prog; Office of Chairman, Spec. Rpt., July 1971.

Golley, F. B. 1962. *Mammals of Georgia: a study of their distribution and functional role in the ecosystem.* Univ. Georgia Press, Athens. 218 pp.

Jackson, W. B. 1952. Populations of the woodmouse (*Peromsycus leucopus*) subjected to applications of DDT and parathion. *Ecol. Monographs* 22:259–281.

Jolly, G. M. 1965. Explicit estimates from capture-recapture data with both death and immigration—stochastic model. *Biometrika* 52:225–247.

Kowal, N. E. 1971. A rationale for modeling dynamic ecologic systems. Pp. 123–194 *in* B. C. Patten (ed.). *Systems analysis and simulation in ecology,* v.1. Academic Press, New York.

McCarley, H. 1964. Ethological isolation in the cenospecies *Peromyscus leucopus.* *Evolution* 18:331–332.

Meanley, B. 1968. Notes on the Dismal Swamp plants. *Atlantic Nat.* 23:78–82.

Metzgar, L. H. 1971. Behavioral population regulation in the woodmouse *Peromyscus leucopus.* *Amer. Midl. Nat.* 86:434–448.

Nicholson, A. J. 1941. The homes and social habits of the woodmouse (*Peromyscus leucopus noveboracensis*) in southern Michigan. *Amer. Midl. Nat.* 25:196–223.

Platt, J. R. 1964. Strong inference. *Science* 146:347–353.

Rood, J. P. 1966. Observation of *Peromyscus* in captivity. *Amer. Midl. Nat.* 76:496–503.

Sealander, J. A., Jr. 1952. Survival of *Peromyscus* in relation to environmental temperature and acclimation at high and low temperatures. *Amer. Midl. Nat.* 46:257–311.

Sheppe, W. 1965. Characteristics and uses of *Peromyscus* tracking data. *Ecology* 46:630–634.

Snyder, D. R. 1956. Survival rates, longevity, and population fluctuations in the white-footed mouse, *Peromyscus leucopus,* in southern Michigan. *Univ. Mich. Mus. Zool., Misc. Pub.* 95. 33 pp.

Stickel, L. F., and O. Warbach. 1960. Small mammal population of a Maryland woodlot. *Ecology* 41:269–286.

Wecker, S. C. 1964. Habitat selection. *Sci. Amer.* 211(4):109–116.

MAMMALS OF THE DISMAL SWAMP: A HISTORICAL ACCOUNT

Charles O. Handley, Jr.

EXPLORATION AND SETTLEMENT OF VIRGINIA AND CAROLINA

When the English came to the coast of Virginia in the late sixteenth and early seventeenth centuries, they found mammals, both large and small, abundant throughout. Captain Arthur Barlowe discovered the Carolina Banks and Roanoke Island during his voyage of 1584. He described the islands as "beautiful to behold and rich in deer, rabbits, hares, and other animals" (Lorant 1946, p. 133). A year later Thomas Hariot, the first naturalist to visit this coast, arrived with colonists in northeastern North Carolina. In a report to Sir Walter Raleigh he observed: "the *Beares* of the countrey are commonly very fatte, and in some places there are many. . . . All along the Sea coast there are great store of *Otters.*" "*Deare,* in some places there are great store: neere unto the sea coast they are of the ordinarie bignes as ours in England, & some lesse: but further up into the countrey where there is better seed they are greater: they differ from ours onely in this, their tailes are longer and the snags of their hornes looke backward" (Hariot 1893, pp. 16 and 29).

Settlers came to the lower James River in April 1607, and George Percy wrote that they found "great store of Deere both Red and Fallow. There are Beares, Foxes, Otters, Bevers, Muskrats, and wild beasts unknowne" (Cumming et al. 1972, p. 258). Edward Williams, extolling the virtues of "Virginia in generall, but particularly Carolina" wrote in 1650: "Nor is the Land any lesse provided of native Flesh, Elkes bigger than Oxen, whose hide is admirable Buffe, flesh excellent, and may be made, if kept domesticke, as usefull for draught and carriage, as Oxen [!]. Deere in a numerous abundance, and delicate Venison, Racoones, Hares, Conyes, Bevers, Squirrell, Beares, all of a delightful nourishment for food, and their Furres rich, warme, and convenient for clothing and Merchandise" (Force, 1836–46, p. 11). John Clayton, rector of Crofton at Wakefield in Yorkshire, wrote of a visit in 1686 to

Tidewater, Virginia: "there are abundance of brave Red Deer so that
a good Woodsman, as they call them, will keep a House in Venison."
"And *Wolves* there are great store; you may hear a Company Hunting
in an Evening, and yelping like a pack of Beagles; but they are very
cowardly" (1694, pp. 122, 125).

In 1701 John Lawson made a seven weeks' trek through the Carolinas that carried him from Charleston to the sites of Salisbury, Hills-
boro, Goldsboro, and Greenville in North Carolina. His accounts of
natural history are surprisingly accurate and detailed and thus are
quite valuable. He described about 30 kinds of mammals, including
not only large and impressive species, but even rats, mice, flying squirrel, chipmunk, shrew, and bat. He found bear "very common" and
deer, a staple food, abundant, but elk and buffalo were seldom seen
near the settlements. The panther, he observed, was a great enemy
of the planters. Wolves were common. Beaver were "very numerous
in Carolina, there being abundance of their Dams in all Parts of the
Country where I traveled" (Harriss 1937, pp. 119–129). *William Byrd's
natural history of Virginia,* originally published in 1737 (Beatty and
Mulloy 1940), is largely paraphrased or copied from *Lawson's history
of North Carolina* and thus mostly does not pertain to Virginia at all.
Byrd's modifications and additions generally were not improvements
on Lawson's account.

LATE COLONIAL PERIOD

In a distressingly short time, as settlement was extended and the European population grew, the mammalian fauna began to change. The
larger species were most vulnerable. As early as 1686 John Clayton,
the rector of Crofton, wrote: "*Elke,* I have heard of them beyond the
Inhabitants . . ." but "I have never heard of any *Lions* . . . [and] *Bears*
there are, and yet but few in the inhabited part of *Virginia;* towards
Carolina there are many more" (1694, pp. 122, 124). Little more than
10 years later, Beverley (1705, v. 2, p. 37) observed that while there
were still plenty of beaver, otter, muskrat, and mink in the coastal
marshes, swamps, and savannas, and deer, rabbit, fox, raccoon, squirrel, and opossum in the uplands, it was necessary to go inland to the
"Frontier Plantations [Appomattox, etc., in the Piedmont] . . . [to]
meet with Bears, Panthers, Wild-Cats, Elks, Buffaloes" and in 1739
John Clayton, the botanist, living in Gloucester County, Virginia,
wrote that "the bears, Panthers, Buffaloes and Elks and wild cats are
only to be found among the mountains and desert parts of the countrey
where there are as yet few inhabitants and the hunting there is very
toilsome and laborious and sometimes dangerous" (1899, p. 174).

FIRST IMPRESSIONS OF DISMAL SWAMP MAMMALS

In colonial times, as now, the Dismal Swamp, bypassed by civilization, was a sanctuary for many creatures (such as bear, bobcat, and perhaps puma) already eliminated from the settled country. Our first impression of it may have come from Augustin Herrman, an early mapmaker, who may have had the Dismal Swamp in mind when he imprinted on his map of Virginia and Maryland (1673): "The Land between James River and Roanoke River is for the most parts Low Suncken Swampy Land not well passable but with great difficulty. And therein harbours Tygers Bears and other Devouringe Creatures."

It may not have seemed a sanctuary to William Byrd II, whose diary for March 1728 provided the earliest detailed information on the Swamp. There is no evidence that Byrd personally observed a single wild mammal during his brief (one-half mile) foray into the Swamp's eastern edge or on his trek around its northern borders and down to Corapeake Creek on the west. He did record that his surveyors encountered "Bever Dams & Otter holes" and that the local people reported panthers, wolves, and foxes, as well as free-ranging cattle and hogs (Boyd 1967).

Byrd's most notable contribution to mammalogy was his often quoted and often challenged negative observation on the scarcity of animal life in the Swamp. On 17 March 1728 he wrote: "Since the Surveyors had entered the Dismal they had laid Eyes on no living Creature; neither Bird nor Beast, Insect nor Reptile came in View. Doubtless, the Eternal Shade that broods over this mighty Bog, and hinders the sun-beams from blessing the Ground, makes it an uncomfortable Habitation for any thing that has life. . . . foul Damps ascend without ceasing, corrupt the Air, and render it unfit for Respiration. Not even a Turkey-Buzzard will venture to fly over it" (Boyd 1967, p. 70; see also Byrd 1789, p. 231; Ruffin 1837*b*, p. 595; Murray 1950, p. 225; and Olsen 1962, p. 70). A contrary view was expressed by George Washington, who visited the Swamp at least five times between 1763 and 1768. He found it a " 'glorious paradise' abounding in wild fowl and game" (Troubetzkoy 1961, p. 19). Bassett (1901, p. 60) observed that "Byrd's description of this swamp is too unfavorable. The place is not uninhabited at this day. Persons who live in the adjacent country go thither to hunt bears and deer as well as wild cats."

In spite of his own lack of personal observation of the Swamp, although he was on its fringes for more than two weeks, Bryd was contemptuous of the similar ignorance of the farmers living nearby. On 13 March 1728 he wrote: "Tis hardly credible how little the Bordering inhabitants were acquainted with this mighty Swamp, notwith-standing they had liv'd their whole lives within smell of it" (Boyd 1967, p. 60; also Ruffin 1837b, p. 593; and Hunter 1881, p. 3). Of Captain Wilson, in whose house he spent the night of 14 March 1728, he wrote: "This worthy Person lives within sight of the Dismal . . . and yet he knew as little of it as he did of Terra Australis Incognita. He told us a Canterbury Tale of a North Briton, whose Curiosity Spurr'd him a long way into this great Desart, as he call'd it, near 20 Years ago. . . . [He] gave such a frightful account of the Monsters he saw, and the Distresses he underwent, that no mortall Since has been hardy enough to go upon the like dangerous Discovery (Boyd 1967, p. 64; also Ruffin 1837b, p. 594; and Hunter 1881, p. 3).

PRE–CIVIL WAR PERIOD

Over a hundred years after Byrd's survey, Edmund Ruffin (1837a, p. 513), editor of the Petersburg, Virginia, *Farmers' Register,* observed the persisting lack of factual information about the Swamp:

Few strangers would ever have been induced by curiosity to attempt the great labors necessary for even a slight examination [of the Swamp]; nor would any have probably seen more than some points on the outer margin, but for the great highways now opened through the swamp—the great canal, the road on its bank, from Norfolk to North Carolina, and the railway which dips into the northern extremity of the swamp. These passages have given to thousands a rapid passing glance at certain portions of the scenery; but in every other respect, these numerous passengers have added nothing to the scant information previously possessed by the public. No visitor has made the investigation of the peculiarities of this unknown land a main object—and still less has any person paid attention to the geological and agricultural aspects in which this region well deserves consideration.

Indeed, Ruffin did concentrate his observations on geology and agriculture during his November 1836 visit, but he did mention the surprising abundance of black bear, even at that date long since exterminated in Tidewater and Piedmont Virginia, the ferocity of the bobcat and mink, the occurrence of skunks on the Swamp borders, and the singular occurrence of a lone wolf some years before (Ruffin 1837a, p. 519).

The prominent geologist Charles Lyell viewed the Swamp from the rail line between Norfolk and Suffolk on 23 December 1841. He quoted Ruffin's observations on bear, bobcat, and wolf, but contributed nothing new of his own (Lyell 1845, p. 148). "Wild cattle, noted for their ferocity, [which] roamed at large in the woods . . .," were cited by Gains (1954, p. 28) as one of the deterrents to exploration of the interior of the Swamp in prewar days.

Thus, up to the closing quarter of the nineteenth century the reported mammalian fauna of the Dismal Swamp consisted of beaver, seven species of carnivores, and domestic cattle and hogs. Most of our present knowledge of the mammals of the Swamp was accumulated in the late 1800s.

POST–CIVIL WAR PERIOD: BEGINNINGS OF SCIENTIFIC INVESTIGATION

Charles Hallock (1877, p. 167) published a sportsman's gazetteer that encouraged hunters and fishermen to visit the Swamp:

The *Dismal Swamp*, one vast morass, with little islands of solid ground scattered here and there, is the haunt of a great number of bears, panthers, deer, coons, otters, ducks, geese, swans, turkeys, partridges and other game. Cat and other varieties of fish are found in its waters. The bears and panthers are seldom shot, as they retire into the vastness of the densest and most impenetrable jungles. The swamp is but little hunted and game there is unmolested save by the lumbermen or shingle-men who depend largely upon the rifle for their subsistence. The starting point for the interior of the swamp is Norfolk, where guides, cooks, provisions, row and sail boats, or steam-tugs may be secured.

Alexander Hunter visited the Swamp in August (ca. 1880) and reported his observations in a partly historical, mostly anecdotal article marred by many factual miscues (Hunter 1881). Nevertheless, he provided the first mention of raccoon, opossum, muskrat, and white-tailed deer in the Swamp. Later he republished the same story, with a new title and with a somewhat different brand of local color, more mammal notes, and the addition of a bear hunt (Hunter 1895). Robert Arnold of Suffolk was the first local writer to mention mammals—squirrel, bear, bobcat, deer, raccoon, and skunk—in the Dismal Swamp (Arnold 1888). Unfortunately, all of his mammal notes were in the context of "tall tales."

Real scientific investigation of the Swamp was initiated by Nathaniel Shaler (1890). His description of the Swamp, in the *Annual Report of the U.S. Geological Survey*, is mostly topographical and geographical, but it does contain a few significant observations on mammals:

The mammalian life is more peculiar than that of the other groups. The rodents are conspicuous by their absence .... owing to the fact that nut-bearing trees are relatively rare, the arboreal rodents are generally absent. The inundated nature of the soil makes it unfit for occupation by the subterranean forms of that group. . . . The predaceous mammals, such as the fox and wolf, find these marshy lands unsuited to their needs . . . Bears are remarkably abundant. . . . Deer are now rare. . . . The most peculiar feature in the mammalian life is the fact that large numbers of wild horned cattle are found within the morass. . . .

The detailed description of the wild cattle, their behavior, and their conflict with bears (Shaler 1890, p. 333) have been much copied and quoted (e.g., Anonymous 1892, p. 322; Stewart 1902, p. 172; Eaton 1910, p. 27).

THE NINETIES: BIOLOGICAL SURVEYS

From 1891 through 1894 the Smithwick brothers collected small mammals near the head of Albemarle Sound in Bertie County, North Carolina, no more than 50 miles southwest of Lake Drummond (Brimley 1897, p. 237). Although not directly connected with the Dismal Swamp, their collection was important, for it was rich in bats and gives us a clue to what we should expect in the Swamp, where few bats have been collected.

Most of our knowledge of the mammals of the Dismal Swamp was gained during a surge of collecting in the years 1895–98. During this interval, collectors spent a total of about 23 weeks in and near the Swamp. Some were most interested in mammals, while others were searching primarily for birds or plants and collected mammals only incidentally. At first most activity was on the part of the U.S. Department of Agriculture's Bureau of Biological Surveys, directed by C. Hart Merriam. Merriam himself visited the Swamp briefly, in June 1895, but most of the collecting was done by A. K. Fisher and E. A. Preble, with an assist from J. H. Gaut and T. S. Palmer. Beginning in 1896, major activity shifted to William Palmer, W. J. Daniel, Jr., D. W. Prentiss, and Paul Bartsch of the U.S. National Museum; and to J. D. Figgins and Alphonso Royster, American Museum of Natural History. These persons all collected around Wallaceton, Lake Drummond, Jericho Ditch, and Suffolk. At the same time, R. T. Young, Academy of Natural Sciences of Philadelphia, trapped small mammals a short distance south and southeast of the Swamp at Chapanoke and Currituck, North Carolina.

Unfortunately, very little of this museum-based activity has found its way into the literature. Fisher (1895) published a very brief and popular report on his earliest work in the Swamp, and Rhoads and Young (1897) summarized Young's observations in northeastern North Carolina and described the meadow vole, *Microtus pennsylvanicus nigrans.* Merriam (1895*a* and *b,* 1896, and 1897) described the short-tailed shrew (*Blarina brevicauda telmalestes*), long-tailed shrew (*Sorex longirostris fisheri*), lemming vole (*Synaptomys cooperi helaletes*), and muskrat (*Ondatra zibethicus macrodon*), all based on Fisher's 1895 collections from Lake Drummond. Packard (1969) used another of Fisher's Lake Drummond specimens, this one taken in 1898, in designating a neotype for *Ochrotymys nuttalli nuttalli.* The collections of this period have been used subsequently by various authors in more than a dozen taxonomic revisions (see acounts of species). Finally, Bartsch (1901) wrote of his trip with William Palmer to the Swamp in June 1897. Most of the narrative concerned birds and plants, but Bartsch did mention half a dozen species of mammals, the most interesting of which were bats found roosting in hollow cypress snags in Lake Drummond.

Many years later A. K. Fisher told Stansbury (1925, p. 96) that he had a paper on the mammals of the Dismal Swamp underway. In searching the old Bureau of Biological Survey files, I have found some of Fisher's Dismal Swamp field notes but no manuscript. From W. J. Daniel, Jr., then residing in Lynchburg, Virginia, Stansbury (1925, p. 96) obtained a list of the mammals of the Dismal Swamp which, although lacking annotations, was by far the most comprehensive to that date. Daniel listed 29 species, but inadvertently overlooked several of the common ones, such as *Condylura* and the two species of *Peromyscus.*

EARLY TWENTIETH CENTURY

Following the great collecting effort of the 1890s, such activity declined to a very low level in the next decade, then ebbed nearly to a stop for almost 25 years. Sporadic short visits were made to the Swamp between 1902 and 1909 by Paul Bartsch, W. L. McAtee, W. J. Daniel, Jr., W. L. Ralph, and Alphonso Royster, all for the National Museum. J. B. Lewis, one of the last of the old-time naturalists, who knew birds and plants and was a keen observer of mammals as well, lived on the northern border of the Swamp from 1903 until 1911. He published some of his notes on mammals in 1928 (Lewis 1928). Fortunately, I have obtained another, unpublished, manuscript detailing additional observations of swamp mammals during those years (Lewis 1938), and I have quoted them extensively in the accounts of species.

Brimley's (1905) catalog of the meager collections of mammals of North Carolina is useful because it summarized the known mammalian fauna of the northeastern corner of the state. He had very little from this region beyond Young's Chapanoke and Currituck collections and the Smithwicks' Bertie County collection. A later summation

(Brimley 1945) added few new data for this part of North Carolina.

In his *History of Nansemond County, Virginia,* prepared for the Jamestown Exposition, Dunn (1907) devoted nine pages to the Dismal Swamp and made brief mention of some of its mammalian inhabitants (later quoted by Squires 1928, p. 154). Eaton (1910) made a boat trip into the Swamp to Lake Drummond in May 1910 and reported on a few kinds of mammals that he saw or heard about.

THE THIRTIES AND FORTIES

After a lapse of a quarter of a century, museums resumed interest in the mammals of the Dismal Swamp in the thirties, but compared to activity at the turn of the century, it was rather half-hearted and relatively few specimens were collected. G. H. H. Tate, American Museum of Natural History, visited Lake Drummond briefly in June 1930 and collected half a dozen mammals. Vernon Bailey, Biological Survey, picked up two raccoon skulls at Lake Drummond in November 1931.

In 1933 Robert Lunz, Jr., collected a few *Peromyscus leucopus* and *Ochrotomys nuttalli* for the Charleston Museum (South Carolina) in the southern reaches of the Swamp in Pasquotank County, North Carolina, and Lunz and H. S. Peters collected a *Rattus norvegicus* within the Swamp. Lee R. Dice in 1933 and Don Hayne in 1935 made collections of live *Peromyscus leucopus* and *P. gossypinus* near Cypress Chapel, Suffolk, and at Lake Drummond for genetic studies at the University of Michigan (Dice 1940, p. 14).

Watson M. Perrygo and several assistants traveled widely in eastern North Carolina in 1939 collecting birds and mammals for the U.S. National Museum. They obtained half a dozen mammals of four species in the southern portions of the Swamp, in Gates and Pasquotank counties.

Two excellent popular articles, based on personal observation in the Swamp, appeared in the thirties. John Ariza's (1932) article in the *National Geographic Magazine* was well illustrated and contained many references to mammals. Margaret Davis's (1934) charming piece in the *South Atlantic Quarterly* had only scant reference to mammals but did support Ariza's observation on the disappearance of the wild cattle. In search of birds, J. J. Murray visited the Swamp in the 1940s and wrote one of the best summaries of its history. Although he limited his mammal observations to one paragraph, notes on several species were significant (Murray 1948, p. 23).

THE FIFTIES AND SIXTIES

For the first time, individual species of mammals of the Dismal Swamp area were considered in detail when K. A. Wilson studied the role of mink, otter, and raccoon as predators of muskrats in Northwest River Marsh, Currituck County, North Carolina, from 1947 to 1951 (Wilson 1953, 1954). More studies of this sort will have to be conducted if the Swamp ecosystem is to be understood and managed.

I collected in the Swamp with snap traps on eight nights in February and June 1953 to determine whether there had been significant changes in the small mammal fauna in the fifty years since the area had last been intensively trapped. My stations were 8.2 miles W South Mills (fallow field, canal bank, canebrake), 4 miles N Wallaceton (moist fern meadow), 3 miles N Wallaceton (bayberry swamp, pine woods, honeysuckle thicket), 2 miles N Wallaceton (canebrake, cattail marsh, gum swamp, fallow field), Lake Drummond (hardwood forest), and 2 miles E Deep Creek (brackish marsh). Four other collectors (Ralph and Daniel worked together and count as one) snap-trapped the same general area half a century earlier. The results of the trapping are shown in Table 1.

Twelve species of mice and shrews were caught by the five collectors. This represents the entire known fauna of mice and shrews of the Swamp (R. T. Young caught a single specimen of *Blarina carolinensis* near Chapanoke, North Carolina, in 1897, but this species probably cannot be properly classified as an inhabitant of the Swamp).

Most of the collectors (four out of five) found *Peromyscus leucopus* the commonest small mammal. Three out of five found *Ochrotymys nuttalli* numerous, and two of five found *Blarina brevicauda* numerous. These three species can be assumed to be the most abundant and widespread mice and shrews of the Swamp. Five other species were found numerous by only one or two of the five collectors: *Peromyscus gossypinus, Synaptomys cooperi, Oryzomys palustris, Reithrodontomys humulis,* and *Sorex longirostris.* These are probably irregularly distributed and only locally common in the Swamp. Their capture depends upon fortuitous discovery of pockets of abundance. Habitat in the Swamp must be marginal and mostly unsatisfactory for the remaining four species, *Microtus pennsylvanicus, Mus musculus, Microtus pinetorum,* and *Cryptotis parva,* which were not caught in numbers by any of the collectors. They probably are uncommon in the Swamp.

The same three species most often taken at the turn of the century were captured in 1953, and no new species were taken then. The absence of the numerous but irregularly distributed species *Peromyscus gossypinus, Synaptomys cooperi,* and *Oryzomys palustris* from the 1953 collection may have been due merely to an accident of collecting. Thus, it seems likely that the passage of 50 years had little effect on the small mammal fauna of the Swamp.

During the 1950s and 1960s the Dismal Swamp became an increasingly frequent subject of newspaper, Sunday Supplement, and magazine accounts. Usually its more conspicuous mammals, or those with euphonious names, were mentioned. Troubetzkoy (1961) provided a little quotable information on mammals in an excellent and well-illustrated article in *Virginia Cavalcade*. Despite its title, "The cursed Swamp," Olsen (1962) produced a surprisingly good story, with factual history and zoology in *Sports Illustrated*. However, nothing good can be said about Sutton's (1955) "A filthy bogg" in *Saturday Review*. If only he hadn't mentioned mammals, it could have been ignored completely.

THE PRESENT

Brooke Meanley's (1973) booklet *The Great Dismal Swamp* hopefully has started a new era by setting a high standard of excellence. Meanley spent a great deal of time in the Swamp and gathered many personal observations. His two pages of mammal notes in *The Great Dismal Swamp* are tantalizingly brief.

Altogether there have been five "comprehensive" accounts of the mammals of the Dismal Swamp: the lists of Daniel (Stansbury 1925) and Meanley (1973) and the species accounts of Bailey (1946), Handley and Patton (1947), and Handley and Handley (1950). These were "comprehensive" in terms of inclusion of all of the species of mammals known to occur in the Swamp, but not in terms of information about them. Unfortunately, there were no equivalent lists for the North Carolina side of the Swamp. Brimley's (1905 and 1945) accounts of the mammals of North Carolina usually mentioned the Dismal Swamp only in the context of species peculiar to it. The same can be said of the list of Smith et al. (1960) and its revision by an anonymous author (1974).

The present historical account is a step toward a definitive work on the mammals of this unique area. More field work will have to be conducted before accounts of distribution, present abundance, and ecology of the mammals of the Swamp can be written. I have tried to review as much as possible of the literature pertaining to the mammals of Dismal Swamp and vicinity. There has proved to be much more than I anticipated at the outset. In fact, I am surprised by how much has been written about Dismal Swamp mammals. I am certain to have

missed some important titles, and was unable to locate copies of some
suspected to contain information on mammals. I have used direct quo-
tations as much as possible to bring the relevant literature together in
one place.

ACCOUNTS OF SPECIES

Order Marsupialia—Marsupials

Didelphis virginiana virginiana Kerr
Virginia opossum

The earliest settlers of Virginia marveled at the strange beast which
carried its young in a pouch on its belly, and John Smith used its
Indian name, *opassom,* when he wrote of it. However, the opossum
escaped observation by the earlier authors of works on the Dismal
Swamp and it remained for Hunter (1881, p. 9) to make the first mention of it as an inhabitant of the Swamp in an anecdotal tale: "de
swamp is full of coons and possums."

A. K. Fisher (1895) observed that opossums were "not scarce" in
the Swamp, and Young (Rhoads and Young 1897, p. 311) was told
that they were common at both Chapanoke and Currituck in North
Carolina. Eaton (1910, p. 28) saw an opossum that some sailors had
caught at the locks on the Feeder Ditch in May 1910. Lewis (1938,
p. 1) found the opossum common at the northern edge of the Swamp
in the period 1903–11, and Daniel included it in his list of Dismal
Swamp mammals (Stansbury, 1925, p. 96). One of the Swamp's mammalian noises heard occasionally by Ariza (1932, p. 130) was the opossum's "hissing snarl." Murray (1948, p. 23) regarded *Didelphis* as "very
common" in the Swamp, and I have found opossum tracks a common
sight on ditch bank roads and dead opossums frequent on highways
in and around the Swamp. Wilson (1954, p. 202) identified remains
of an opossum in the digestive track of a mink.

The National Museum has a specimen (US 75942) of opossum that
A. K. Fisher collected, 10 October 1895.

Order Insectivora—Shrews and Moles

Sorex longirostris fisheri Merriam
Southeastern long-tailed shrew

The common long-tailed shrew of the lowlands of the southeastern United States, *Sorex longirostris,* was first reported in the Dismal
Swamp by A. K. Fisher (1895, p. 220) after a trapping expedition to
the Swamp. His cryptic reference—"Among other things I got two rare

shrews"—can be interpreted only by examination of his collections in the National Museum. One "rare" shrew was *Sorex longirostris* Bachman and the other was *Blarina brevicauda* Say.

Merriam (1895*b*, p. 86) promptly named Fisher's long-tailed shrew "*Sorex fisheri,*" based on its large size and dull coloration. Rhoads almost immediately suspected that *S. fisheri* was really only a subspecies of the common southeastern long-tailed shrew, *Sorex longirostris,* for a specimen that Young caught at Chapanoke seemed to be intermediate between the two supposed species (Rhoads and Young 1897, p. 311). This relationship was eventually confirmed by Jackson (1928, p. 87), who had at his disposal, besides the Chapanoke specimen, a good series from Lake Drummond. The skull of one of the latter (US 75167) was figured in Hall and Kelson (1959, v. 1, p. 29).

Daniel included *Sorex longirostris* in his list of the mammals of the Dismal Swamp (Stansbury 1925, p. 97), and Handley and Patton (1947, p. 108) believed it to be "evidently fairly common" in the Swamp. Bailey's (1946, p. 100) detailed description of habits of *S. l. fisheri* probably was gleaned from literature and applies to long-tailed shrews in general, not specifically to *S. l. fisheri* as implied. Actually, beyond Hollister's (1911*a*, p. 380) mention of Ralph's discovery of a litter of five young in May 1905, practically nothing is known of the natural history of *S. l. fisheri.*

In addition to Young's Chapanoke specimen in the Academy of Natural Sciences of Philadelphia and one in the American Museum of Natural History that Daniel collected at Lake Drummond in 1905, the National Museum has 16 from Lake Drummond collected in 1895 and 1902 by Fisher, T. S. Palmer, Ralph, and Daniel, and one that I collected near Wallaceton in 1953.

Blarina brevicauda telmalestes Merriam
Greater short-tailed shrew

Although the black bear is the most notable mammal of the Swamp, the greater short-tailed shrew may be the most interesting mammal of the Swamp, if for no other reason than its curiously confused taxonomy and distribution. The first clue to its occurrence in the Swamp was in A. K. Fisher's (1895, p. 220) cryptic account of capturing "rare shrews" (see also account of *Sorex longirostris*).

Merriam (1895*a*, p. 15) lost no time in describing Fisher's short-tailed shrew as a new species, "*Blarina telmalestes,*" which he thought was peculiar to the Dismal Swamp. This concept has persisted to the present day. For example, see the map in Hall and Kelson (1959, v. 1, p. 53). Handley and Patton (1947, p. 112) stated: "Known only from the Dismal Swamp. . . . It is semi-aquatic and has never been found outside its swampy environment, where it is most common in dense undergrowth and cane brakes."

There are supposed to be two species of *Blarina* in the vicinity of the Dismal Swamp: the large whiter-toothed *B. telmalestes* Merriam in the Swamp and the much smaller browner-toothed *B. brevicauda carolinensis* Bachman in the surrounding uplands and throughout Tidewater Virginia and North Carolina. Further afield, brown-toothed shrews, *B. b. churchi* Bole and Moulthrop and *B. b. kirtlandi* Bole and Moulthrop, as large as *B. telmalestes,* are found in the Piedmont and in the Appalachians.

Extensive collecting in recent years in the eastern parts of Virginia and North Carolina has revealed this pattern of distribution to be a myth. Shrews which can be identified as *B. telmalestes* are found as far away from the Dismal as Southampton County, Virginia, and Dare, Hyde, and Pitt counties in North Carolina. In these places they are integrating with the large browner-toothed shrew, *Blarina brevicauda kirtlandi.* Thus, the large shrew, browner-toothed in part of its range, whiter-toothed elsewhere, has a continuous distribution. The Dismal Swamp population should be called *Blarina brevicauda telmalestes.* Unfortunately, when he described *B. telmalestes,* Merriam compared the Dismal Swamp specimens not with *Blarina brevicauda* from nearby localities in the eastern United States (which they resemble and from which they probably are sometimes indistinguishable) but with specimens from west of the Mississippi in Iowa (from which they are indeed quite different).

But what of the small *Blarina*? The recent collecting shows it to have a surprisingly discontinuous distribution in the coastal plain and lower Piedmont of Virginia and North Carolina, with numerous isolated populations. It should be called *Blarina carolinensis.* Usually the large and small *Blarina* have exclusive ranges, but I have found them together in the Northern Neck of Virginia, and Young found both kinds at Chapanoke, North Carolina (Rhoads and Young 1897, p. 310). Rhoads *almost* sorted out this puzzle correctly (Rhoads and Young 1897, p. 311), but his observations subsequently have been overlooked or ignored.

Young's specimens of *B. b. telmalestes* were taken in "moss in pine woods" at Chapanoke (two specimens) and "in a patch of *Juncus* in a wet piece of woods" at Currituck (Rhoads and Young 1897, p. 310). Daniel included *Blarina* in his list of the mammals of the Dismal Swamp (Stansbury 1925, p. 97). Wilson (1954, p. 202) found *Blarina* to be a frequent prey of mink in Currituck County.

As was the case with *Sorex longirostris fisheri,* the habits detailed by Bailey (1946, p. 104) for *B. b. telmalestes* apply to short-tailed shrews

Table 1. Mice and shrews trapped in the Dismal Swamp by five collectors and groups, 1893–1906 and 1953.

	A. K. Fisher	E. A. Preble	Wm. Palmer	W. L. Ralph J. W. Daniels, Jr.	1893–1906 Totals	C. O. Handley, Jr.
Peromyscus leucopus	26	24	7	21	78	34
Blarina brevicauda	16	17	4	—	37	2
Ochrotomys nuttalli	23	13	—	—	36	14
Peromyscus gossypinus	13	5	11	—	29	—
Synaptomys cooperi	20	—	1	—	21	—
Oryzomys palustris	13	1	2	—	16	—
Reithrodontomys humulis	—	14	—	2	16	1
Sorex longirostris	4	—	—	10	14	1
Microtus pennsylvanicus	—	7	—	—	7	1
Mus musculus	—	2	4	1	7	3
Microtus pinetorum	—	4	—	—	4	—
Cryptotis parva	1	—	—	—	1	—
Total specimens saved	116	87	29	34	266	56
Total species	8	9	6	4	—	7
Nights trapped	27	24	18	14	—	8
Months of collection	Jun Oct Nov	Apr May	May Jun	Jan May Jun	—	Feb Jun
Years of collection	1895 1898	1896 1897	1893 1896 1897 1899	1897 1902 1905 1906	—	1953

in general and not to *B. b. telmalestes* in particular. Actually, little is known of the natural history of this species in the Dismal Swamp.

The greater short-tailed shrew has been found by many collectors and is numerous in museums. There are 30 Lake Drummond specimens in the National Museum, taken by Fisher, William Palmer, and Preble, between 1895 and 1899; another, in the American Museum, was collected there by Tate in 1930. Ten USNM specimens from the vicinity of Wallaceton were taken by Preble, McIntosh, and myself, in 1896, 1946, and 1953. One in the National Museum was caught by Perrygo and Rohwer near South Mills in 1939, and the two specimens from Chapanoke and one from Currituck taken by Young in 1897 are in the Academy of Natural Sciences of Philadelphia.

Blarina carolinensis Bachman
Lesser short-tailed shrew

This species occurs near the southern and eastern margins of the Swamp, but probably not actually within it. Young caught one, together with the larger *B. b. telmalestes* Merriam, at Chapanoke, Perquimans County, North Carolina, in 1897 (Rhoads and Young 1897, p. 311). *B. carolinensis* has also been taken at Virginia Beach, Knotts Island, and Winton. It was erroneously listed by Bailey (1946, p. 107) for Lake Drummond and several other localities in Virginia where it does not occur.

Cryptotis parva parva Say
Least shrew

Frequent in fallow upland fields and in marsh edges, the least shrew is known in the Dismal Swamp only by a specimen (US 75205) that A. K. Fisher collected in short grass on the shore of Lake Drummond, 17 October 1895. There was no published mention of the specimen until Bailey (1946, p. 102) included it in his *Mammals of Virginia*.

Scalopus aquaticus aquaticus L.
Eastern mole

The eastern mole is one of the species, including cottontail, chipmunk, pine vole, house mouse, and gray fox, that benefit from swamp drainage. It invades the Swamp on road banks, waste soil dredged from canals and ditches, and in agricultural fields. In April and May 1896 E. A. Preble collected nine eastern moles around Wallaceton for the National Museum. Referring to these specimens, Jackson (1915, p. 36) stated that the "Dismal Swamp, Va., produces a mole which is as large as the typical form and has a little more tendency toward a mummy brown shade on the back." However, the differences were not great enough to justify naming.

Along the northern borders of the Swamp in Norfolk County, during the period 1903–11, J. B. Lewis (1938, p. 1) found *Scalopus aquaticus* "common in open land not subject to standing water," and Daniel included it on his list of the mammals of the Dismal Swamp (Stansbury 1925, p. 97). I found mole tunnels in a garden at the mouth of the Feeder Ditch in 1953 and on the road along Hamburg Ditch in March 1974.

Condylura cristata parava Paradiso
Star-nosed mole

This boreal mole is a characteristic inhabitant of swamps, wet meadows, and stream banks in eastern Canada and northeastern United States. Its range extends southward in the Appalachians to southwestern North Carolina and along the coast to southeastern Georgia. South of middle Virginia it seems to be absent from the intervening Piedmont. Its distribution thus is very much like that of the southern lemming vole, and it can be found in the vole's habitat. However, it is not so narrowly restricted ecologically, and its southern populations probably are not so endangered as are those of the vole.

E. A. Preble caught one star-nosed mole at Wallaceton in April 1896 (US 77813) and three at Lake Drummond in May 1896 (US 77814, 77815, and 78041). Bailey (1946, p. 94) salvaged one at the Feeder Ditch locks:

> One week end, May, 1934, while collecting in Dismal Swamp, near Lake Drummond, several of my zoölogy students and I were discussing the possibility of collecting a few star-nosed moles. Captain Cherry, the keeper of the locks at the feeder ditch said, "All sorts of moles are plentiful here—in fact my old cat almost lives on them." And, believe it or not, before he finished his story, an old mother cat came walking across the grass flat, facing the yard of the keeper's house, with a full grown female star-nosed mole. Captain Cherry took the mole from the cat—it is now preserved in alcohol in the collection at the University of Richmond.

J. B. Lewis (1938, p. 1), who lived near the northern edge of the Swamp from 1903 until 1911, found the star-nosed mole "fairly common, especially in wet soils. About as many were seen as of the common mole." Wilson (1954, p. 202) found one in the digestive tract of a mink obtained from a fur dealer at Moyock, North Carolina.

In his review of American moles, Jackson (1915, p. 91) listed the four Dismal Swamp specimens in the National Museum as *C. c. cristata* Linnaeus. Using the same Preble specimens from the Dismal Swamp, but with the advantage of more abundant material from elsewhere in the range of the star-nosed mole, Paradiso (1959) distinguished the southern specimens from *C. c. cristata* by their smaller size. He included the measurements of the Dismal Swamp specimens in his table substantiating his new subspecies, *C. c. parva*.

Order Chiroptera—Bats

Myotis keenii septentrionalis Trouessart
Eastern long-eared myotis

E. A. Preble took a specimen of *M. kennii* at Lake Drummond, 2 May 1896 (US 82176). It was listed, along with its external measurements, by Miller and Allen (1928, pp. 107 and 109) in their monograph on American *Myotis* and *Pizonyx*. Another, in the American Museum of Natural History (93177) was taken by Tate at Lake Drummond in June 1930.

Myotis lucifugus lucifugus Le Conte
Little brown myotis

Although this *Myotis* has not been found in the Dismal Swamp, Miller and Allen (1928, p. 46) reported a specimen in the Academy of Natural Sciences of Philadelphia from nearby Bertie County, North Carolina. Brimley (1897, p. 238) reported three specimens taken by the Smithwicks in Bertie County: 9 July 1891, 3 August 1892, and 17 July 1893. It probably occurs in the Swamp.

Lasionycteris noctivagans Le Conte
Silver-haired bat

A species to be sought after in hollow trees and under loose bark is the silver-haired bat. As yet it has not been found in the Dismal Swamp, but it should occur there. The Smithwicks collected half a dozen in Bertie County, North Carolina; four on 1 July 1891 and two from a hollow tree, 26 December 1892 (Brimley 1897, p. 238).

Pipistrellus subflavus subflavus F. Cuvier
Eastern pipistrelle

Daniel included the pipistrelle on his list of the mammals of the Dismal Swamp (Stansbury 1925, p. 98), but there has been no specific mention in the literature of the specimens that have been collected there. A. K. Fisher shot four in evening flight on the shore of Lake Drummond, 13 and 14 October 1895, and Ralph and Daniel collected one, also at Lake Drummond, 23 May 1905. All of these specimens are in the National Museum. One in the American Museum of Natural History was collected at Lake Drummond by G. H. Jarrell, 18 April 1964.

Eptesicus fuscus fuscus Palisot de Beauvois
Big brown bat

The big brown bat is likely to occur in the Dismal Swamp although there are no records of it there. The Smithwicks collected three specimens not far away, in Bertie County, North Carolina: 17 August 1891 and 7 March and 9 November 1893 (Brimley 1897 p. 238). One of these is in the American Museum of Natural History.

Nycticeius humeralis humeralis Rafinesque
Evening bat
  Nycticeius humeralis may be the commonest bat of the Swamp. It was found roosting in small, hollow cypress snags in the eastern edge of Lake Drummond by William Palmer, Prentiss, Daniel, and Bartsch on 19 June 1897 (Bartsch 1901, p. 67; Meanley 1973, p. 34) and one specimen was collected (US 83641). Earlier, on 8 June 1895, A. K. Fisher and C. Hart Merriam had shot three in one evening at Suffolk (US 76504, 76505, 76506), and on 13 to 15 June 1896 William Palmer collected eight in the Swamp (US 63495–63497 and 82666–82670). Another specimen from Lake Drummond, collected by Figgins, 8 June 1898, is in the American Museum of Natural History. Some of these specimens were mentioned by Miller (1897, p. 120), and their measurements were tabulated in his revision of North American Vespertilionidae.

Lasiurus borealis borealis Müller
Northern red bat
  Bartsch (1901, p. 67) described the capture of *Lasiurus borealis* Müller (as well as *Nycticeius humeralis* Rafinesque and *Plecotus rafinesquii* Lesson) from within the hollow shells of small dead cypress standing in the eastern edge of Lake Drummond. *L. borealis* usually roosts in foliage, and its discovery in hollow cypress snags seems unlikely. Perhaps Bartsch was confused on the capture site of the *L. borealis* as well as on the date, which was in June 1897, not 1899 as implied. The specimen of red bat that he, Prentiss, Daniel, and William Palmer collected has been mentioned by Miller (1897, p. 108) and by Meanley (1973, p. 34). There are three specimens in the National Museum: US 76503, shot by Fisher a Suffolk, 8 June 1895; US 83642, caught by D. W. Prentiss, Jr., at Lake Drummond, 19 June 1897; and US 144455, collected by J. H. Riley at Suffolk, 20 November 1906.

Lasiurus cinereus cinereus Palisot de Beauvois
Hoary bat
  The hoary bat has not been found in the Dismal Swamp, but it probably occurs there. The Smithwicks collected three in nearby Bertie County, North Carolina, 10 October and 1 November 1892 and 8 April 1893 (Brimley 1897, p. 237).

Lasiurus intermedius floridanus Miller
Northern yellow bat
  Most of the range of *Lasiurus intermedius* H. Allen is in tropical America, but it is common in Florida and in some other places around the

Gulf of Mexico. There are a few records for Georgia and South Carolina, and de Rageot (1955, p. 456) reported a pregnant female that was found at Willoughby Beach, Norfolk County, Virginia, 8 May 1954. It is not known whether this species occurs regularly as far north as the Norfolk area, accidentally flew there, or reached there by ship (the southern yellow bat, *Lasiurus ega* Gervais, has been recorded aboard a ship at sea). It has not been recorded in the Dismal Swamp, but it may occur there.

Plecotus rafinesquii macrotis Le Conte
Eastern big-eared bat
   Under the name *Corynorhinus macrotis,* Bartsch (1901, p. 67) reported the discovery of big-eared bats roosting in small, hollow cypress snags standing in the eastern edge of Lake Drummond. One of the bats was collected by J. W. Daniel, Jr. (US 83669). It was mentioned by Miller (1897, p. 52) in his revision of North American Vespertilionidae and by Handley (1959, p. 163) in his revision of the genus *Plecotus.* Both Daniel (Stansbury 1925, p. 98) and Meanley (1973, p. 34) also listed it as an inhabitant of the Swamp.
   Widely distributed in the southeastern United States, this big-eared bat apparently reaches its northeastern limit in the Dismal Swamp. It should be found roosting in hollow trees and abandoned houses.

Order Lagomorpha—Rabbits and Hares

Sylvilagus floridanus mallurus Thomas
Eastern cottontail
   Common in the uplands all around the Swamp, the cottontail benefits by swamp modification. Drought, drainage, road construction, clearing, and agriculture all provide the drier conditions that make it now one of the more frequently encountered mammals in the Swamp.
   Hunter (1895, p. 75) mentioned flushing rabbits on the western edge of the Swamp, and Young (Rhoads and Young 1897, p. 305) saw cottontails in northeastern North Carolina, but did not secure any specimens. Daniel included it in his list of the mammals of the Dismal Swamp (Stansbury 1925, p. 97). Lewis (1938, p. 6) found it "common, except in swamps and marshes" around the northern edge of the Dismal Swamp, 1903–11. Wilson (1954, p. 200) regarded it as "common" around Northwest River Marsh, Currituck County, and observed that it was frequently eaten by mink.
   The National Museum has five cottontails that Preble collected near Wallaceton in April 1896, one that Ralph obtained in the Swamp in May 1905, and one that Leonard Llewellyn shot near Suffolk in

March 1941. A specimen in the American Museum of Natural History was collected by Tate in June 1930 at Lake Drummond. Nelson (1909, p. 167) used the earlier of these specimens in his revision of North American rabbits. Of *S. f. mallurus* he said: "This form is larger and paler than *floridanus,* and appears to reach its extreme development about the Dismal Swamp of Virginia."

Sylvilagus palustris palustris Bachman
Marsh rabbit

An inhabitant of the marshes and swamps of the southeastern United States, the marsh rabbit reaches the northern extreme of its range in the Dismal Swamp. Young (Rhoads and Young 1897, p. 305) thought that it might occur in northeastern North Carolina but did not secure any specimens. Lewis (1938, p. 6) found it "common in the Dismal Swamp and in the freshwater tidal marshes along the headwaters of the Elizabeth River," during the years 1903–11, and in an earlier paper he (Lewis 1928, p. 95) referred to it as "blue-tail." Ariza (1932, p. 130) heard "a 'pond toes', or swamp rabbit, making his strange minklike snarl." Daniel included it in his list of the mammals of the Dismal Swamp (Stansbury 1925, p. 97).

There are several specimens of marsh rabbit in the National Museum. In 1895 and 1896, William Palmer, Preble, and Merriam collected specimens around Lake Drummond, the Feeder Ditch, and Jericho Ditch, and Preble shot one near Wallaceton. W. F. Hutchinson took one northeast of the Swamp, near Pungo, in 1912, and Perrygo got one in the southwest quarter of the Swamp near Sunbury in 1939. Specimens in the American Museum of Natural History were collected at Lake Drummond by Figgins in 1898 and by Tate in 1930. Nelson (1909, p. 268) observed that "three adults and one young from Dismal Swamp, Virginia, are true *palustris* in all external characters of size, proportions, and color, but have even heavier skulls than typical specimens from farther south."

The marsh rabbit may not be as numerous in the Dismal Swamp now as it was at the turn of the century. I have not encountered it, and Brooke Meanley (1973, p. 35) has done little better: "The Dismal Swamp is the northern limit of the marsh rabbit. I have seen only one of these mammals, and that was along the North Carolina–Virginia line in the evergreen shrub bog community on June 30, 1971. The Marsh rabbit is stockier and darker than the cottontail, which also occurs in some sections of the Swamp."

Order Rodentia—Squirrels, Beaver, Rats, and Mice

Tamias striatus fisheri A. H. Howell
Eastern chipmunk

The chipmunk is near the southern limit of its range on the Atlantic seaboard in the Dismal Swamp. Daniel included it on his list of mammals of the Dismal Swamp (Stansbury 1925, p. 96), but Ariza (1932, p. 129) thought that this species did not occur in the Swamp. Lewis (1928, p. 98) did not find chipmunks there: "Burrowing and ground dwelling mammals seem to be very scarce in the swamp, doubtless due to the fact that the soil is full of water so much of the time. I saw no ground squirrels or burrowing mice in the swamp, though they were found in the better drained country out side."

Increasing amounts of dry ground in the Swamp in later years, however, have permitted invasion by chipmunks. Meanley (1973, p. 35) found them to be "uncommon; I never see more than one a day, and these are in the best forest in the Swamp." I was told in 1974 that chipmunks are often seen on the ditch-bank roads in the Swamp. They occur also on the drier ground on the escarpment bordering the Swamp on the west. There is a specimen in the American Museum of Natural History (13841) collected by J. D. Figgins, 2 June 1898, at Suffolk (Howell 1929, p. 17).

Sciurus carolinensis carolinensis Gmelin
Gray squirrel

Judging by variation in reports of abundance, the population of gray squirrels in the Dismal Swamp must be subject to marked fluctuations. For example, Shaler (1890, p. 332) observed that "owing to the fact that nut-bearing trees are relatively rare, the arboreal rodents are generally absent." However, during a collecting trip to the Swamp in June 1895, A. K. Fisher (1895, p. 220) found squirrels "remarkably abundant. . . . [They] have discovered an easy way to get a living by going along the shores of Lake Drummond and picking up nuts and berries which have fallen into the water and drifted in windrows. They trot along the logs and fish them out with their paws."

Although he did not take any specimens, and in fact saw only one gray squirrel at Currituck, Robert Young was told that it was "fairly common in all localities" in northeastern North Carolina (Rhoads and Young 1897, p. 310). Lewis (1938, p. 4) thought that gray squirrels were "rather rare in the Dismal Swamp," 1903–11, but Eaton (1910, p. 28) saw "innumerable" squirrels that had been killed by sailors at the head of the Feeder Ditch in May 1910. Daniel included the gray squirrel in his list of Dismal Swamp mammals (Stansbury 1925, p. 96). Murray (1948, p. 23) echoed Shaler's observation that "there are not many squirrels, as nut trees do not grow well in the water." On the other hand, Wilson (1954, p. 200) found gray squirrels "common" around Northwest River Marsh in Currituck County and occasionally eaten by mink.

There are numerous specimens of gray squirrel from the Dismal Swamp in the National Museum. Nine were collected by Figgins, Fisher, William Palmer, Preble, Ralph, and Daniel on the shores of Lake Drummond and along the Feeder Ditch in 1895, 1896, and 1905. Royster took one at Suffolk in 1905, and Perrygo obtained one near South Mills in 1939.

Sciurus niger niger L.
Fox squirrel

In colonial times the fox squirrel may have been common in southeastern Virginia, and it probably varied periodically in abundance as it now seems to do in western Virginia. When first mentioned by Captain John Smith in 1612, it apparently was uncommon in the Jamestown area: "Their Squirrels—some as neare as greate as our smallest sort of wilde rabbits [= fox squirrel]; some blackish or blacke and white [= fox squirrel], but the most are gray [= gray squirrel and fox squirrel (?)]" (Arber 1910, pp. 59 and 355).

On the other hand, it seems to have been common when John Clayton (1694, p. 123) visited Virginia in 1686: "The first [of three species of squirrels] is the great Fox Squirrel, much larger than the *English*, and gray, almost as a common Rabbet. These are very common." John Lawson, writing in 1701, listed four species of squirrels in eastern North Carolina but did not comment on abundance: "The first is the Fox-Squirrel, so called because of his large Size, which is the Bigness of a Rabbet of two or three Months old. His Colour is commonly gray; yet I have seen several pied ones, and some reddish and black; his chiefest Haunts are in the Piny Land" (Harriss 1937, p. 128).

Although declining in numbers, the fox squirrel persisted in southeastern Virginia at least until the end of the nineteenth Century. A. K. Fisher recorded in his field notes in October 1895: "Rather rare on high ground—said not to occur in the swamp." Daniel included it in his list of Dismal Swamp mammals (Stansbury 1925, p. 96). Possibly it no longer occurs at all in southeastern Virginia, although I was told in 1953 that "black squirrels" were sometimes found in the Swamp. Meanley (1973, p. 35) observed: "The fox squirrel is either rare or extirpated; I have not seen one in 15 years of work in the Swamp." It should be sought in stands of mature pines.

Glaucomys volans volans L.
Southern flying squirrel

The flying squirrel had been "reported at Chapanoke [North Carolina]" according to Young (Rhoads and Young 1897, p. 311), and Daniel included it in his list of the mammals of the Dismal Swamp (Stansbury 1925, p. 97). During the years 1903–11, near the northern edge of the Swamp, in Norfolk County, Lewis (1938, p. 5) found flying squirrels "abundant, especially about farm buildings that were near woods. Sometimes they are destructive to stored corn and other grain." A specimen in the National Museum (US 142113) was collected by Royster in December 1905 at Suffolk (A. H. Howell 1918, p. 24).

Castor canadensis carolinensis Rhoads
Beaver

Beavers probably once abounded in and around the Dismal Swamp. There is even speculation that beavers may have been responsible for the formation of the Swamp. For example, Hill (1973, p. 24) quoted Gary Soucie as dismissing a geological explanation:

> "There just isn't much geological or paleobotanic evidence to support it," he wrote recently. Soucie favors another wilder theory which he says is finding growing acceptance. That is that the Dismal Swamp was created by beavers.
>
> The Northwest and Nansemond Rivers drain the Dismal Swamp and, according to the beaver theory, these were dammed by a prehistoric beaver community. The beavers created the conditions for swamp development. The forest trapped in the resultant marsh laid down peat over a subsurface which was already impermeable hard clay, the peat acted to conserve water and slow drainage, and the "beaver bog" became a self-sustaining swamp. [See Oaks and Whitehead, this volume, pp. 20–21.]

Early visitors to the coasts of Virginia and North Carolina often remarked about the presence and sometimes about the abundance of beavers. Among these were Percy, 1607 (Cumming et al. 1972, p. 258), Williams, 1650 (Force 1836–46, p. 11), Clayton the rector, 1686 (1694, p. 124), Lawson, 1701 (Harriss 1937, p. 123), Beverley (1705, v. 2, p. 37), and Clayton the botanist, 1739 (1899, p. 174). On the eastern approaches to the Dismal, in the swamp between the North and Northwest rivers, William Byrd's boundary surveyors on 9 March 1728, "met with Beaver Dams & Otter holes, which it was not practicable to pass in a direct line" (Boyd 1967, p. 53). No further mention of beavers has been found in the chronicles of the Dismal Swamp, and this animal probably has been long extinct in the Swamp. Brimley (1945, pt. 9, p. 1) had a report from T. A. Smithwick of beavers in nearby Bertie County, North Carolina, as late as 1903. However, Brimley was somewhat dubious and thought that they might have been exterminated earlier. Apparently there are no beavers from the Dismal Swamp region in museums.

In recent years the beaver, by way of introductions, has reoccupied much of its former range in Tidewater Virginia. Perhaps eventually it will make its way back into the Dismal Swamp, or maybe it can be restocked there to help maintain the water level in the Swamp. If it is restocked, southern animals should be used, so as to match the original indigenous population as nearly as possible. [See p. 24.]

Oryzomys palustris palustris Harlan
Marsh rice rat

Most of the rodents that inhabit the Dismal Swamp do not have a particular affinity for water. In fact, the majority of them probably do not like to get their feet wet. Exceptions are the muskrat, rice rat, and a newcomer, the nutria (formerly also the beaver). Among these the rice rat is peculiar in requiring fairly extensive marsh vegetation along with the water. Thus, in the Dismal Swamp it is local in its distribution and not often encountered.

Specimens of this species were reported as "rice mice" by A. K. Fisher (1895, p. 220) among rodents and shrews that he trapped in the Swamp, and Daniel included it as "rice field mouse" in his list of Dismal Swamp mammals (Stansbury 1925, p. 97). Wilson (1954, p. 202) found rice rats to be relatively plentiful and a popular autumn food of mink in Northwest River Marsh, Currituck County. He (1953, p. 118) also discovered that unused muskrat houses were frequently used as nest sites by rice rats. According to his unpublished field notes, a specimen that Fisher caught at Lake Drummond on 7 June 1895 contained nine embryos.

There are 19 specimens of *O. palustris* from Lake Drummond in the National Museum (Goldman 1918, p. 24), collected between 1895 and 1905 by Fisher, William Palmer, Prentiss, and Royster; seven from the same area are in the American Museum of Natural History, collected in 1893, 1898, 1902, and 1930, by Figgins, Daniel, and Tate. In addition, the National Museum has a single specimen from Wallaceton, collected by Preble in 1896, and two from Suffolk, trapped by Royster in December 1905 and January 1906.

Reithrodontomys humulis humulis Audubon and Bachman
Eastern harvest mouse

A substantial number of harvest mice were trapped, presumably in grassy habitats, by Preble, Ralph, and Daniel in the vicinity of Wallaceton and Lake Drummond. However, there has been no published mention of them, except in Daniel's list of the mammals of the Swamp (Stansbury 1925, p. 97) and in the works of Howell and Hooper mentioned below.

Young found the harvest mouse to be numerous in northeastern North Carolina, where he caught 2 at Chapanoke and 14 at Currituck. "At the latter place the conditions were more favorable. . . . Here they were trapped in marshy meadows grown up with *Juncus* and grass. Such places are scarce at Chapanoke, and there they were . . . obtained in cultivated fields and in patches of *Hypnum* in the pine woods" (Rhoads and Young 1897, p. 310).

Hooper (1943, p. 14) observed that specimens from northeastern North Carolina and the Dismal Swamp area of Virginia exhibit the rufescent upper parts characteristic of typical *R. h. humulis* Audubon and Bachman from farther south. Cranially, however, the same specimens resemble *R. h. virginianus* A. H. Howell of the Virginia Piedmont in large size, broad, deep braincase, and widely spreading zygomata. Thus, the Dismal Swamp populations can be regarded as intergrades between the two subspecies.

From Wallaceton there are 14 specimens of harvest mice in the National Museum, collected by Preble in 1896; also 2 obtained by Ralph and Daniel at Lake Drummond in 1905, and 1 that I caught near Deep Creek in 1953. One in the American Museum of Natural History was collected at Lake Drummond by Tate in 1930. Currituck is represented by 14 in the Academy of Natural Sciences of Philadelphia, 7 in the Cleveland Museum, and 4 in the National Museum. There is 1 specimen each in the Academy of Natural Sciences of Philadelphia and the National Museum from Chapanoke. Some of these specimens were mentioned by Howell (1914, p. 20) and Hooper (1943, p. 16) in their papers on the taxonomy of *Reithrodontomys.*

Peromyscus gossypinus gossypinus Le Conte
Cotton mouse

The mice *P. gossypinus* and *P. leucopus* are very similar both morphologically and genetically. It is probable that they evolved from a common ancestor whose range was fragmented into southeastern and southwestern segments by the last glaciation (Handley 1972, p. 294). The southwestern segment, which continued to occupy the majority of the ancestral home in Mexico and adjacent parts of the United States evolved into *P. leucopus.* The other segment, evolving into *P. gossypinus,* survived in a smaller pocket in Florida and vicinity. With the retreat of the glaciers and removal of ecological barriers, these sibling species began to disperse from their refugia. Where they first met, in the lower Mississippi Valley, they eventually accommodated to each other, and their ranges there now overlap extensively. In contrast, along the Atlantic seaboard, where the encounter has been more recent, there is very little overlap of distribution—*P. gossypinus* is generally confined to the coastal lowlands and *P. leucopus* is in the uplands of the interior. The northeastern limit of *P. gossypinus,* the Dismal Swamp and south bank of the James River, is a critical area for understanding the relationships of these species.

The history of collection of the cotton mouse in the Dismal Swamp reveals curious variations. Most of the persons who trapped in the Swamp between 1895 and 1898 found it to be a more or less common species, whereas those who collected there in the next decade did not find it at all. Dice and Hayne (see below) encountered it in numbers again in the early 1930s, but it seemed to be absent when I trapped in the Swamp twenty years later. During the same interval, populations of *P. leucopus* have been consistently high.

Lee R. Dice and Don Hayne made collections of live *Peromyscus* in the Dismal Swamp in 1933 and 1935 for genetic studies at the University of Michigan (Dice 1940, p. 14). They took *Peromyscus gossypinus* only in swampy habitats near Cypress Chapel (30 specimens) and at Lake Drummond (3 specimens), whereas they found *P. leucopus* in both swamp and upland habitats. Neither species seemed to be really numerous anywhere in the region. The two species readily hybridized in the laboratory and produced fertile offspring, but there was no evidence that they interbred in the Swamp, despite the fact that they occurred in the same habitat and could even be caught in the same trap lines. Dice was unable to determine what the isolating mechanism in nature might be and assumed that it must be some psychological factor. Much remains to be learned about the social and ecological relationships of these two species.

Aside from Dice's comments, very little has been written about the cotton mouse in the Swamp. Young caught two at Currituck, North Carolina, "in a patch of *Juncus* in a wet piece of woods" (Rhoads and Young 1897, p. 309). Osgood (1909, p. 137) gave measurements of specimens from the Dismal Swamp and listed 44 specimens that had been captured there.

There are 29 specimens of *P. gossypinus* in the National Museum from Lake Drummond, collected in June, October, and November 1895–98, by Fisher, William Palmer, and Prentiss; 13 in the American Museum of Natural History from the same place were collected in June and July 1898 by Figgins and Royster. Five from Wallaceton in the National Museum were collected in April 1896 by Preble. Young's 2 specimens from Currituck are in the Academy of Natural Sciences of Philadelphia.

Peromyscus leucopus leucopus Rafinesque
White-footed mouse

Unquestionably the white-footed mouse is the commonest and most widespread mammalian inhabitant of the Dismal Swamp. It seems to be equally at home in dry and wet situations, in forest and in brush, within the Swamp as well as in the surrounding uplands. It is the small mammal most likely to be caught when mouse traps are set in the Swamp (see Paschal et al., this volume).

In northeastern North Carolina, Young (Rhoads and Young 1897, p. 309) found the white-footed mouse to be the commonest mammal in his trap lines and caught it in "all kinds of situations." Altogether, Young saved 12 specimens from Chapanoke and 10 from Currituck. Wilson's (1954, p. 202) study of the food habits of mink in Currituck County revealed *Peromyscus* of undetermined species to be a popular fall and winter food of mink. Bartsch (1901, p. 56) described trapping *P. leucopus* on the shore of Lake Drummond.

Dice and Hayne found the white-footed mouse widespread, but uncommon in the Dismal Swamp region in 1933 and 1935. They took two in upland brush near Suffolk, five in a cypress swamp near Cypress Chapel, and four at Lake Drummond. Although *Peromyscus gossypinus* was taken in the same swampy habitats, they found no evidence of hybridization in the wild (Dice 1940, p. 14).

White-footed mice from the Dismal Swamp are abundant in museums. I know of nearly 200 specimens and undoubtedly there are more. From Lake Drummond there are 65 in the National Museum and 22 in the American Museum of Natural History, collected by Daniel, Figgins, Fisher, William Palmer, Preble, Ralph, Royster, Tate, and me. The National Museum contains 19 specimens from Wallaceton, collected by Preble and me, 3 that I caught near Deep Creek, and 18 obtained by Fisher, Gaut, and Royster near Suffolk. The American Museum also has one that Figgins trapped near Suffolk. Young's specimens from northeastern North Carolina are distributed between the Academy of Natural Sciences of Philadelphia and the National Museum: Chapanoke, 10 (ANSP) and 2 (USNM); Currituck, 6 (ANSP) and 4 (USNM). Perrygo, Rohwer, and I collected 16 (USNM) near South Mills, North Carolina. The Charleston (South Carolina) Museum contains 6 *P. leucopus* that Lunz caught in the Swamp. From amongst all of these Osgood (1909, p. 116) listed in a series of 79 specimens of *P. leucopus* from the Dismal Swamp which he had examined. He placed the series "with *leucopus*, although it shows decided tendencies towards *noveboracensis.*"

Ochrotomys nuttalli nuttalli Harlan
Golden mouse

Very likely there is no other place in Virginia and few in North Carolina where the golden mouse is so abundant as it is in the Dismal Swamp. Cane brakes, wet and dry; bay thickets; cypress, cedar, and pine forests; bracken lights; and deciduous forests and thickets—all provide suitable habitat for it. The original description of the species was based on a specimen from Norfolk (Harlan 1832, p. 446), perhaps taken near the Dismal Swamp. Subsequently, A. K. Fisher (1895, p. 220) mentioned trapping golden mice in the Swamp, and Robert Young caught 4 at Chapanoke, North Carolina (Rhoads and Young 1897, p. 309). Bartsch (1901, p. 56) took *O. nuttalli* on the shore of Lake Drummond near the mouth of Jericho Ditch. By the time Osgood (1909, p. 225) prepared his monograph on *Peromyscus,* there were 40 specimens of golden mice from the Dismal Swamp in museums. He listed measurements of Dismal Swamp specimens as representative of typical *O. nuttalli.* Daniel included the golden mouse in his list of Dismal Swamp mammals (Stansbury 1925, p. 97) (see also Paschal et al, this volume).

On 6 June 1895, near the mouth of Jericho Ditch, A. K. Fisher (unpublished field notes in Bureau of Biological Survey files) found a nest something like that of a marsh wren about two feet above the ground in fallen brush. When the nest was disturbed, a golden mouse with three or four young attached to her nipples ran out.

Because the original type had been lost and no other specimens of golden mice were known to have been taken at Norfolk, Packard (1969, p. 401) designated one of Fisher's Lake Drummond specimens (US 95889) as neotype of *Ochrotomys nuttalli nuttalli* Harlan. He examined 34 Dismal Swamp specimens in the National Museum and 4 in the American Museum of Natural History and found them to represent the large extreme of the species.

Altogether, I know of 67 specimens of golden mice from the Dismal Swamp in museums: 4 in the American Museum of Natural History, collected at Lake Drummond by Figgins; 1 in the Charleston Museum, caught by Lunz near Elizabeth City and another caught in the southern part of the Swamp; and 61 in the National Museum, taken near Wallaceton, Lake Drummond, and 8.2 mi W. South Mills, by Daniel, Fisher, William Palmer, Preble, Ralph, and myself.

Sigmodon hispidus virginianus Gardner
Cotton rat

The cotton rat is listed in *A checklist of North Carolina mammalian species* (Anonymous 1974, p. 4) as occurring in the "northern Coastal Plain, Dismal Swamp area"—probably based on the erroneous distribution map in Hall and Kelson (1959, v. 2, p. 673). Actually, this mammal is only known to occur well inland in the Piedmont and is unknown in the Dismal Swamp area.

Synaptomys cooperi helaletes Merriam
Southern lemming vole

Among the rodents that A. K. Fisher (1895, p. 220) trapped in the

Swamp were "lemming mice." He observed that this species "is hard to catch, because it will not take any sort of bait; the only way to capture it is to set a trap in its runway. I set my traps in dry places out of water." Fisher's field notes for October 1895 recorded it as "common in all the cane patches bordering the lake, but difficult to trap." He caught one lemming vole by hand in a nest in a dry clump of grass. The nest was made of coarse fibers and was lined with finer material. Because of their more massive rostrum, Merriam (1896, p. 59) thought that Fisher's specimens represented a distinct species, which he named *Synaptomys helaletes.*

Young (Rhoads and Young 1897, p. 305) captured "two specimens, male and female, the latter containing four well advanced embryos . . . in a patch of *Juncus setaceus* in a damp piece of open ground bordering pine woods at Chapanoke, March 11, 1897. The runways were filled with cut stems of *Juncus,* on which they had evidently been feeding." These specimens were mentioned by Brimley (1905, p. 11, and 1945, pt. 13, p. 1). The lemming vole was included on Daniel's list of the mammals of the Dismal Swamp (Stansbury 1925, p. 97), and Handley and Patton (1947, p. 169) reported its habitat there to be "cane brakes, sphagnum bogs, and occasionally dry grassland."

The southern lemming vole probably has a shrinking distribution. Its present range is northeastern and north central United States, adjacent Canada, and the Appalachian highlands. Relict populations have been isolated in Nebraska, Kansas, and in the Dismal Swamp, and fossils of Pleistocene age have been collected in Florida. Within the past 100 years it has been found on the Eastern Shore of Maryland, around Washington, D.C., and near Lynchburg, Virginia. Now it may occur no nearer to the Dismal Swamp than the Appalachians.

In his revision of the genus *Synaptomys,* Howell (1927, p. 17) found that southern Maryland lemming voles verged morphologically toward *S. helaletes.* He observed that although bogs in the Middle Atlantic states were shrinking and that "there may now be a definite hiatus between the ranges [of *helaletes* and its upland neighbors] . . . there are not sufficient grounds for considering the Dismal Swamp animals as being more than subspecifically distinct [from *S. cooperi*]." In a more recent revision, Wetzel (1955, p. 16) was even more emphatic about the taxonomic relationships of *S. helaletes.* He regarded it as only slightly differentiated from the upland *S. c. stonei* Rhoads. "This close relationship with *stonei* is indicative of its origin from the latter form after the loss of interconnecting range. This isolation may well have been accomplished by marine encroachment upon the intervening range as well as habitat destruction by white man."

There are 24 specimens of Dismal Swamp lemming voles in museums. All were collected in the four-year interval 1895–98. There is

1 each in the Academy of Natural Sciences of Philadelphia and USNM, collected by Young at Chapanoke; 1 from Wallaceton (USNM), collected by Fisher; and 21 from Lake Drummond, collected by Fisher and William Palmer, all in the USNM. The last of these specimens was trapped in November 1898. Has the lemming vole disappeared from the Dismal Swamp? Or have recent collectors sampled its habitat inadequately? It is included on Virginia's list of endangered species, and Taylor (1974, p. 27) suggested that "draining and habitat modification may have already exterminated this isolated, relic population."

Ondatra zibethicus macrodon Merriam
Muskrat

The muskrat was first mentioned as an inhabitant of the Dismal Swamp in an anecdotal tale by Hunter (1881, p. 13). Young found it to be "fairly common at Chapanoke . . . [and] at Currituck they were numerous in the marshes, where two specimens were secured" (Rhoads and Young 1897, p. 309.)

Fisher collected specimens at Lake Drummond which Merriam (1897, p. 143) thought represented a new species and which he named *Ondatra macrodon* on the basis of its large teeth and coloration. In his taxonomic revision of the muskrats a few years later, Hollister (1911*b*, p. 19) reduced *O. macrodon* to be a subspecies of the widespread *Ondatra zibethicus.* Hollister listed specimens from Lake Drummond (5), Suffolk (6), Wallaceton (2), and Currituck (2).

The muskrat was included on Daniel's list of the mammals of the Dismal Swamp (Stansbury 1925, p. 97), and Lewis (1938, p. 5) found it to be "common along the freshwater marshes of the Elizabeth River," 1903–11. Ariza (1932, p. 129) thought that there were few muskrats in the peaty section of the Swamp, but as Edwin Way Teale (1951, p. 256) boated up the Feeder Ditch a dripping muskrat scrambled up the bank, fleeing from us paradoxically by land instead of by water."

Wilson (1953) found circumstantial evidence that raccoons were significant predators of muskrats in forest-bordered marshes in northeastern North Carolina. In such marshes most muskrat houses (83 to 100 percent) were dug into by raccoons in May, June, and July, when parturition among muskrats was believed to be highest. Raccoon depredations on muskrat houses at other seasons were negligible. Wilson judged predation on muskrat litters by unusually high raccoon populations to be responsible for the drastic declines (up to 90 percent) in muskrat production in northeastern North Carolina in the late 1940s.

On the other hand, Wilson (1954, p. 202) found muskrats, usually young, to be of minor importance in the fall and winter diet of mink in Currituck County. He reported that 30 to 40 thousand muskrats were usually harvested by trappers each winter in Currituck County. About 75 percent of them came from marsh habitats. Evidence accumulated during Wilson's (1953, p. 113) study showed that muskrats preferred diked marshes to undiked ones: "seasonal insufficiency of water . . . is an important factor limiting muskrat production, both directly and also by lowering the quality of marsh flora." Higher stabilized water levels and the use of herbicides and controlled burning substantially increased the proportion of the muskrat's favorite food plants, Olney three-square (*Scirpus olneyi*) and cattails (*Typha*, four species) in the diked marshes. Wilson (1953, p. 118) also observed that "muskrat houses in the Northwest River area, and especially unoccupied ones, frequently housed rice rats (*Oryzomys palustris palustris*), meadow mice (*Microtus* sp.) and very likely other small mammals."

The National Museum contains two muskrats collected by Young at Currituck, North Carolina; seven from Lake Drummond caught by Daniel, Fisher, and Ralph; two that Preble obtained at Wallaceton; and eight that Ralph and Royster got at Suffolk. There are five Suffolk specimens in the American Museum of Natural History, collected by Royster.

Microtus pennsylvanicus nigrans Rhoads and Young
Meadow vole

The marsh-inhabiting meadow vole has not been found very often in the Dismal Swamp. A. K. Fisher (1895, p. 220) reported it (as "field mice") among the rodents and shrews that he trapped in the Swamp. Young trapped 13 at Currituck, North Carolina "in *Juncus* and grass of marshy fields as well as in marshy patches of ground where mint and other weeds, on which they fed, were abundant" (Rhoads and Young 1897, p. 308). Rhoads and Young distinguished the Currituck vole (as *M. p. nigrans*) from the inland *M. p. pennsylvanicus* Ord on the basis of its larger size and darker coloration. Daniel included it in his list of the mammals of the Dismal Swamp (Stansbury 1925, p. 97). Wilson (1953, p. 118) found meadow voles nesting in abandoned muskrat houses in Northwest River marsh, and observed (1954, p. 202) that meadow voles were frequent fall and winter prey of mink in that area.

The National Museum contains seven *M. pennsylvanicus* that Preble collected at Wallaceton in April 1896, and six of Young's Currituck specimens (Bailey 1900, p. 19). There is a specimen in the American Museum of Natural History, collected by Royster at Lake Drummond, in July 1898, and another from Suffolk, collected by Figgins in February 1899.

Microtus pinetorum pinetorum Le Conte
Pine vole

Very little is known about the pine vole in the Dismal Swamp. Young found it "common at Currituck [North Carolina], where they obtained in runways in the escarpment along shore and in the *Juncus* in wet woods along the shore." Altogether he saved 17 specimens (Rhoads and Young 1897, p. 309) which are in the Academy of Natural Sciences of Philadelphia and in the National Museum. Four pine voles that Preble collected at Wallaceton in April 1896 are in the National Museum (Bailey 1900, p. 64), and its occurrence at Suffolk was listed by Bailey (1946, p. 243).

Rattus norvegicus Berkenhout
Norway rat, brown rat

Probably common in urban areas around the Dismal, the brown rat is infrequent within the Swamp. However, H. S. Peters and G. R. Lunz, Jr., collected one there, 3 April 1933, and Bailey (1946, p. 255) reported it at Lake Drummond. Wilson (1954, p. 202) found remains of *Rattus norvegicus* in three out of 568 digestive tracts of mink that he examined in Currituck County.

Rattus rattus L.
Roof rat, black rat

The animal variously known as black rat, roof rat, Alexandrine rat, and fruit rat is found at least in coastal areas in most of the warmer parts of the world. It may have originated in southern Asia, but it has been dispersed to its present almost cosmopolitan range by ships and other commercial conveyances.

In some places two or three color morphs of this rat occur together; other places seem to be exclusively inhabited by a single form. This has caused great confusion and controversy. The three forms have been thought to represent distinct species, *Rattus rattus* Linnaeus, *R. alexandrinus* E. Geoffroy, and *R. frugivorus* Rafinesque, and different behavior and ecological preferences were ascribed to each. Alternatively, the three have been regarded as subspecies of a single species, *Rattus rattus*. Still another opinion makes them color phases of a single taxon, *Rattus rattus rattus*, without individual nomenclatural recognition.

Whatever the true biological relationship may be, these exotic rats arrived in this area at least as early as 1609, with Capt. John Smith at Jamestown: "In searching our casked corne, wee found it half rotten and the rest so consumed with the many thousand rats, increased first from the ships, that we knewe not how to keepe that little wee had" (Arber 1910, p. 154). Subsequently, *Rattus rattus* probably spread throughout colonial Virginia and North Carolina.

Two of the forms have been found in the Dismal Swamp. Black-backed, gray-bellied individuals ("*Rattus rattus*") were captured by A. K. Fisher at Lake Drummond, 9 October 1895 (US 75225), and by F. N. Blanchard, somewhere in the Swamp, 16 July 1918 (Univ. Mich. Mus. Zool. 53150—in alcohol). These have been reported by Bailey (1946, p. 251), Handley and Patton (1947, p. 178), and Handley and Handley (1950, p. 267) as "*Rattus rattus.*"

Brown-backed, white bellied individuals ("*Rattus frugivorus*") were trapped at Lake Drummond, 17 May 1905 (US 140774) and 23 May 1905 (US 140775) by W. L. Ralph and J. W. Daniel, Jr. These specimens have been erroneously reported by all authors as "*Rattus alexandrinus,*" which is brown-backed, gray bellied (Lantz 1909, p. 12; Daniel, *in* Stansbury 1925, p. 97; Bailey 1946, p. 253; Handley and Patton 1947, p. 179; and Handley and Handley 1950, p. 167). Brimley (1945, pt. 144, p. 2) listed a specimen of this form from Bertie County, North Carolina.

As late as the turn of the century Brimley (1905, p. 9) regarded "*Rattus alexandrinus*" as the common house rat throughout North Carolina. At that date there was only one record of *Rattus norvegicus* for the state. The roof rat does not compete well with *Rattus norvegicus*, and Bailey (1946) and Handley and Patton (1947) have ventured the opinion that it may no longer occur in the Dismal Swamp. However, in recent years populations of *Rattus rattus* have been discovered in a number of rural and wild areas in Virginia not inhabited by *Rattus norvegicus*. It is possible that it still occurs in the Dismal Swamp.

Mus musculus L.
House mouse

This Old World pest most likely arrived in North Carolina and Virginia with the first waves of settlers. It invaded the Dismal Swamp on the heels of clearing, draining, agriculture, and house construction. Habitat is apparently marginal for it in the Swamp, and it is still uncommon there.

Young collected two house mice in northeastern North Carolina, probably at Chapanoke (Rhoads and Young 1897, p. 310), and Wilson (1954, p. 202) found one in the digestive tract of a mink in Currituck County. Daniel included it in his list of Dismal Swamp mammals (Stansbury 1925, p. 97).

There are 11 specimens of house mice from the Dismal Swamp in the National Museum: 3 from Lake Drummond were collected by Daniel, William Palmer, and Ralph (2 of these were taken beneath the old hotel at the mouth of Jericho Ditch), 3 were caught by Preble and me at Wallaceton (mine in a fallow field), 1 from Suffolk was trapped by Gaut, and 2 others collected by William Palmer are not labeled with a more precise locality than "Dismal Swamp." In addition, I caught 1 in a marsh edge near Deep Creek and another in a fallow field west of South Mills. One in the American Museum of Natural History was collected by Figgins at Lake Drummond.

Myocastor coypus bonariensis E. Geoffroy
Nutria

A marsh-inhabiting native of southern South America, the nutria has been widely introduced in the United States (probably first in Louisiana in the 1930s) as a furbearer. Evans (1970, p. 57) mapped it as widely established around Chesapeake Bay and in northeastern North Carolina.

According to *A checklist of North Carolina mammalian species* (Anonymous 1974, p. 5), it has been introduced in Northampton, Currituck, and Dare counties, North Carolina. There is a specimen in the National Museum from Duck, Dare County, collected by Goldsborough in August 1971. Meanley (1973, p. 35) has recorded it in the Dismal Swamp: "In June 1970, I saw a nutria, an exotic mammal that has been introduced into nearby North Carolina marshes. It seemed out of place deep in the swamp forest."

Order Carnivora—Wolves, Foxes, Bears, Weasels, Cats, etc.

Canis lupus lycaon Schreber
Gray Wolf

Wolves were a part of the Swamp fauna in colonial times, according to Wertenbaker (1962, p. 29). They were "protected from the huntsman by the marshy nature of the ground and the impenetrable undergrowth."

Evidently wolves were still numerous around the Swamp at the time of the boundary survey. While waiting on the west edge of the Swamp for the surveyors to complete their transect, William Byrd wrote on 27 March 1728: "Betwixt this [Corapeake] and Edenton there are many thuckleberry Slashes, which afford a convenient Harbour for Wolves and Foxes. The first of these wild Beasts is not so large and fierce as they are in other countries more Northerly. He will not attack a Man in the Keenest of his Hunger, but run away from him, as from an Animal more mischievous than himself. . . . The Inhabitants hereabouts take the trouble to dig abundance of Wolf-Pits, so deep and perpendicular, that when a Wolf is once tempted into them, he can no more Scramble out again" (Boyd 1967, p. 94; Stansbury 1925, p. 99).

A century later the wolf had been long gone from the Dismal Swamp, and Edmund Ruffin (1837*a*, p. 519) found the local populus buzzing over the reappearance of a lone individual, the last to be recorded in this area:

The most singular recent fact with respect to beasts of prey, is the appearance here of a solitary wolf a few years ago. As no wolf has been heard of east of the mountains for many years, the kind of this destructive animal was not suspected until long after he had been committing his ravages on the sheep about Suffolk—and more than a year passed before he was at last killed. His howling had often been heard by the inhabitants of that town, so near did he forage—but as his shelter in the swamp was perfectly secure from intrusion, and he moved out only by night, and as no dog would pursue him, it seemed long impossible to destroy him. He at last, like many warlike or predatory heroes, from Sampson down to Macbeath, fell a prey to female attractions. Tired of celibacy, he was seeking a mate though of a different race—a bitch at a farm house: and her other suitors made so great an outcry over the foreign intruder, that his presence was discovered, and he was shot.

Urocyon cinereoargenteus cinereoargenteus Schreber
Gray fox

On 27 March 1728 William Byrd also observed that "the Foxes are much bolder [than the wolves], and will sometimes not only make a Stand, but will likewise assault any one that would balk them of their Prey" (Boyd 1967, p. 94; Stansbury 1925, p. 99). Such an aggressive attitude sounds like the behavior of rabid animals. Could it be that the Dismal Swamp foxes of the early eighteenth century were afflicted with rabies? In recent times rabies has sometimes been prevalent in wild foxes in Virginia.

Shaler (1890, p. 332) observed that "the predaceous mammals, such as the fox and wolf, find these marshy lands unsuited to their needs." However, Bartsch (1901, p. 68) saw one in the edge of the Swamp on the trail between the head of Washington Ditch and Sanders, Virginia, in June 1899, and Daniel included the gray fox on his list of the mammals of the Dismal Swamp (Stansbury 1925, p. 97). Ariza (1932, p. 129) thought that there were no foxes in the Swamp, and Murray (1948, p. 23) believed, like Shaler, that "the territory is rather wet for foxes." A more detailed assessment was provided by Meanley (1973, p. 35): "The gray fox is common around the upland edge of the Swamp and may hunt in the Swamp at night." It is very likely that foxes use ditchbank roads for access to the Swamp.

Ursus americanus americanus Pallas
Black bear

Unquestionably the most notable mammal of the Dismal Swamp is the black bear. Herrman's 1673 map of Virginia and Maryland indicated presence of bears in the "low, suncken, Swampy Land" between the James and Roanoke rivers—referring possibly to the then unnamed Dismal Swamp. Somehow bears escaped the notice of William Byrd when his men surveyed the boundary line through the Swamp in 1728, and it remained for Edmund Ruffin (1837a, p. 520), quoting Toby Fisher, a shingle-getter and eyewitness of the great fire of 1806, to provide the first definite information about bears in the Dismal: "At last, the fire approached so near that the falling of great trees was heard in rapid and continued succession, like the reports of guns heard at a distance—and when still nearer, bears and other 'varmunts' were seen fleeing from destruction, and some times singed and lamed from having been forced through the fire." When he visited the Swamp in November 1836, Ruffin (1837a, p. 519) was astonished by the abundance of bears:

It is known to most persons that bears still inhabit the Dismal Swamp, though long ago driven from every other part of lower and middle Virginia. But probably most have thought, as I did before this visit, that they were so rarely met with, that the killing of a single one would be a matter for great exultation, and cause of some notoriety to the huntsman who was so lucky. But I now learned that they were so numerous, that there were but few men who resided near the margin of the swamp who had not killed one or more. A young gentleman of our party had shot several dozens of these beasts. He told me that the largest weighed, after being skinned and gutted, more than 500 pounds. They do not usually weigh half as much. It is difficult to raise many cattle or hogs on the adjacent farms, though the swamp furnishes such abundant food for both, owing to the slaughter committed on them by the bears. A bear will with ease kill a full grown cow, and has strength to drag away the carcass to a suitable hiding place. No dogs will hunt these animals to much purpose, and therefore it is not often attempted. The most numerous pack will seldom even bring them to bay, and will never attempt to seize on them. The bears are traced and found by the hunters, by listening for the noise of their nightly depredations in corn fields, or among live stock, or when breaking the limbs of the trees they climb in search of acorns or gum berries: or they are baited and killed by traps, or heavily loaded set muskets, the latter being a common and successful mode of destroying them. I heard related by the gentlemen of our party, and by the boatmen, sundry accounts of such adventures—and enough could easily be had to fill a second volume of Davy Crockett. Indeed, the story of one remarkable adventure which has been bestowed in print on Crockett, I believe, or if not, on some other western bear hunter, I found had been pilfered from the honors of an old borderer of the Dismal Swamp: for whether the story be true or false, (and it is fully believed here,) it had been told by the hero of it for forty years before his death.

Some more formal testimony of the great number of bears in the swamp was presented at the recent meeting of the Land Company, in a written proposal submitted to them by an individual for getting up their oak timber.

This paper stated as a reason for their taking such measures, that the oaks were suffering, and many dying, under the effects of the depredations of the bears. This statement which would otherwise have been to me impossible to conceive a meaning for, was explained by the account received of the habits of these animals. Heavy and apparently clumsy as they are, they are expert climbers, and in that manner seek the gum berries and acorns, which, in their season, form a favorite part of their food. To reach the acorns on the extremities, they draw to them and break off the limbs, even when a large size—and into these broken places worms of a particular kind enter, or eggs are laid, as in the case of the pine bug, and in time the trees are killed by their borings.

Evidently bears were holding their own very well within the Swamp throughout the nineteenth century. Strother (1856, p. 455) heard a story in Suffolk of a bear eating a pig in the Swamp, and Hunter (1881, p. 9) said the bears were fond of green corn and watermelons. Bishop (whose authorship of an 1882 article is indicated only by the initials "W. H. B.") during a boat trip into the Swamp in November 1882 was told that bears in great numbers were driven into the open by fires in the Swamp. Fifty years after Ruffin was astonished by the abundance of bears, Shaler (1890, p. 333) observed that "bears are remarkably abundant. About two hundred are killed each year within the limits of this field of morasses." Shaler further commented on conflict between bears and wild cattle (see account of *Bos taurus*).

Hunter (1895, p. 74) told of hunting bears in the Swamp with dogs, and credited one hunter with killing 21 bears in a single year. Fisher (1895, p. 220) in the same year observed that "bears are numerous. In autumn they feed greedily on the fruit of the sour gum." In his unpublished field notes Fisher wrote: "Very common—in the fall of 1893 George Nichols shot 13. He usually paddled along the lake shore and shot them from sweet [sic] gum trees, the berries of which they are very fond" (Handley and Patton 1947, p. 15). Young (Rhoads and Young 1897, p. 311) found bears to be "not rare in the wilder sections of country near Chapanoke." Dunn (1907, p. 63) observed that bears "abound" in the Swamp and repeated Shaler's estimate of a yearly kill of at least 200. Eaton (1910, p. 29) said that bears "still abound" in the Swamp and paraphrased some of Shaler's (1890) data on wild cattle–bear conflict.

Lewis (1928, pp. 95 ff.) lived near the Swamp in Norfolk County and often saw bears:

One of my special delights was to watch the bears, that were still numerous, in spite of the fact that they were within fifteen miles of the big city of Norfolk, one of the oldest towns in the United States.

When a logging gang goes into a section of the swamp the bears move out and are seen no more until the cutting is finished and the roar of the "skidders," the crash of falling trees and the whistle of the "dinkey" locomotives has died away; and then, almost as soon as the tracks are pulled up, they are back again.

I will never forget my first sight of a bear in its wild state. It was in mid September. A gang of dusky laborers were "bushing down" ditch banks half a mile from the nearest gum slough. Late in the afternoon, seeing that the line of ditch on which the men were working would keep them busy until sunset, I answered the call of the wild and walked across the level stretch of potato field toward the slough. The hazy sun was at my back. A flock of migrating tree swallows circled and twittered overhead, and the ringing cuck-cuck-cuck-cuck of a pileated woodpecker sounded from among the ranks of tupelo trunks that were almost silver-gray in the light of the lowering sun. Between the edge of the potato field and the gum slough was a "reed meadow" one hundred and fifty yards wide, the reeds being about four feet high. I stepped upon the earth bank from the ditch that separated the potato field from the reeds and stood admiring the wall of gum trunks in the soft, hazy light. Suddenly my eyes caught the shaking of the reed tops about fifty yards from me. These reeds were not "shaken of the wind," as there was only the slightest breath of air stiring, and, luckily for me, it came toward me. The shaking of the reeds came quartering in my direction. Now and then it stopped for an instant, only to begin again. Suddenly a big bear mounted a huge fallen tree trunk that brought his hulking body above the reeds. He deliberately walked the length of it, paused for an instant to sniff the air and then jumped down. The reed shaking continued through another thirty yards, quartering to me, but drawing nearer, and then Bruin arose on his hind feet, bent down a prickly ash with a big paw and began leisurely to eat the berries. He was only thirty-five yards from me, I afterwards stepped the distance. On a sudden impulse I drew the .38 revolver from my belt, and almost as quickly put it back. Why disturb his meal? Better to enjoy watching him while I had the chance. I could hardly hope to kill him with that revolver anyway. The berries finished, he came down on all four again, came a few steps nearer, scratched in the ground a little, and then turned and went back toward the gum slough, without having suspected my presence.

In October the berries of the gums ripen and then it is that one has the best opportunity to see the bears, as they climb the trees and pull in the branches with outstretched paws to eat the blue-black berries. I once saw four bears in the trees at once, all busily eating berries, and none of them more than a quarter of a mile from me.

It is wonderful to see how easily the big, lumbering fellows "shin up" the trees, and still more wonderful to witness the celerity with which they can get down again when they scent the approach of their arch enemy—man.

Twice have I seen badly frightened individuals turn loose and drop twenty-five or thirty feet, hitting the ground with a resounding whack; but in each instance they "lit a-running."

Bears have a high appreciation of roasting ears and are often very destructive to corn planted near their haunts. The second year of my stay in the swamp we had corn planted on the extreme outer edge of our cleared land and only a quarter of a mile from a gum slough. When this corn reached the roasting ear stage the bears made nightly raids on it, carrying the juicy ears to the reeds where they could be eaten in seclusion. There was a full moon during the time of their feast, and I spent several nights watching for them with my rifle; but luck was against me, as not a bear came to the field during my vigils. After the loss of sleep began to weary me, I loaned my rifle to a colored field hand who was anxious to try his skill as a hunter. He posted himself on the same ditch bank on which I had been keeping watch, and waited the appearance of "Brr Bar."

About nine o'clock, as I lay near an open window at the headquarters, a mile or more from the corn field, I heard the report of the rifle, faintly in the still night air, and said to myself, thank goodness Ed has frightened a bear, at least.

The next morning at sunrise, as I was assigning the men their work for the day, I saw Ed, rifle in hand, walking rapidly from the direction of the swamp. I called to him, "Ed, did you get him last night?" The reply came in tones of great excitement—"naw sah, Cap'in, I didn't gitem, but he mighty nigh got me." "I was stan'in on de ditch bank whar you done to' me to stan', and fust I know dar was a bar in de aidge o' de co'n right 'cross de cart paff fwom me. I gets mighty shakey, but I done shot at em, an den I run for John Jones's house wif de bar right arfter me, and de farster I run de farster de bar done run too, twill I git to de house an' bus' in at de doo'." John Jones was another farm hand who lived in a little house a third of a mile from where Ed shot at the bear, and in the direction of the headquarters. As there had been rain the day before, I knew that the whole story would be written out in the soft, peaty soil, much more plainly than the excited negro could tell it, so I instructed him not to go to work with the others, but to go with me to look for the bear tracks.

Arrived on the scene we found Ed's tracks where he had stood on the ditch bank, and a very obvious record of his tremendous strides in the direction of John Jones's house, but no sign of the bear's tracks following him. Ed scratched his head and continued to look for the missing signs of his pursuer of the night before. "Dat ar bar sure done chase me plum to John Jones's house," he kept repeating.

Walking back to Ed's stand on the ditch bank, I crossed the cart road to the edge of the corn, and there found the tracks of a bear, just where he had indicated it to have been when he shot. It had walked up a corn row to the edge of the field, where it had evidently paused to reconnoiter, giving Ed a chance to shoot. The tracks indicated a slight scuffle following the shot, and then led off at right angle to the corn rows in the direction of the gum slough. I called to Ed to come with me, and we followed the trail about sixty yards, where we came upon the bear, stone dead. Ed had shot him through the chest, and the bear, mortally wounded, had run in one direction and the "nigger" in the other.

Old bear hunters who saw Ed's prize pronounced it a two-year-old, moderate fat, and we found it weighed one hundred and ninety pounds. Those same old hunters told of big bears that weighed three hundred and fifty, and I have no reason to doubt them, but this was the only one I actually weighed. I was told that only under two circumstances are the black bears of the Dismal Swamp dangerous. That is, when wounded and brought to bay, and when a mother bear sees her young in danger. Personally I have had no experience with either case, but was near where the following incident occurred. A colored man went into the swamp with his "houn dawg" and shot gun to hunt rabbits. About a mile back in the swamp his dog "bayed treed" and on going to him the hunter found him barking into the hollow stump of an immense old cypress. The negro investigated and had just pulled two tiny bear cubs out of the leaves and pine tags in the stump, when his dog whirled about and began barking in the direction of the thick reeds. The hunter dropped the cubs and turned just in time to fire his gun at close range into the breast of the mother bear, as she ran at him, rising on her hind feet as she neared him. At a range of only a few feet the shot had the effect of a bullet and killed the bear almost instantly. The hunter tried to raise the clubs [sic], but they were too young at least for his crude methods, and soon died.

Additional observations on bears are to be found in Lewis's (1938, p. 2) later unpublished manuscript on mammals:

Bears have a habit of "sharpening" their claws by standing erect facing a big tree and raking them diagonally downward through the bark, one downward and to the left, the other downward and to the right, making rough, diamond figures.

I have now in my collection the skull of an old bear that was shot and mortally wounded by my brother-in-law, Dr. George C. Faville, then of Norfolk, on the property of my employers, September 9, 1904. This bear was not found until a week later, after its bones had been picked by other bears and buzzard. . . . The statement that other bears had been eating the carcass is based on the fact that there were 14 deposits of bear excrement lying around it, and all contained black hair.

Col. William H. Stewart of Portsmouth, who lived part of his life in the Dismal, gave a picturesque discription of a bear enjoying gum berries on Smith's Ridge in the eastern portion of the Swamp:

When the leaves are falling from the frosting nights, go down in the swamp as the twilight shadows are growing; you may chance to see a black bear mount from the thick reeds and rush up a great gum tree to sup on gumberries; watch him as he reaches the top, straddles a strong limb, listens with sharp ears, turns his head to scent the air for a moment for enemies, and then satisfied to safety, reaches out with both fore-paws and draws in the switches laden with fruit. Now see how he shakes his head in gathering the berries from the sprigs, and how he chews them with supreme enjoyment. His antics are musing, for his awkward nimbleness brings a smile to one fortunate enough to witness a bear feasting on gumberries or acorns after the frosts have ripened them under the withered leaves of the great swamp trees. [Stansbury 1925, p. 197]

Next to wild cattle, bears are the largest mammals in the Swamp. Probably not as large, however, as Stansbury (1925, p. 95) believed. He credited Captain Wallace with killing an 859-pound bear, along with 29 smaller bears, by means of "spring guns" set around his cornfields in the Swamp in the winter of 1888. Better documented was one that W. N. Haldeman of Hampton, Virginia, killed in the Swamp in November 1944 (Handley and Patton 1947, pp. 15 and 127; Richards 1953, p. 16; Carpenter 1973, p. 2). Haldeman reported that its skull measured 12.5 inches in length and 31 inches in circumference (measured at the hinge of the jaw), and before skinning the distance between the ears was 8.5 inches and from ears to tip of snout 15.5 inches. The Jonas Brothers, who mounted the head, estimated that the bear may have weighed 700 pounds. The weight could only be guessed, since Haldeman and his hunting companion could scarcely roll the bear over, much less carry it out of the Swamp.

An even larger bear was killed in the Swamp by W. H. Harrison in December 1924. Its skull was 12 ⅞ inches long and 8 inches wide. It ranked second in the Boone and Crockett Club's *Records of North American big game* (Waters 1964, p. 333) among black bear from the eastern United States. The only larger bear was found in Centre County, Pennsylvania.

Stansbury (1925, pp. 33 and 96) seems to have been the first writer to mention the local belief in several kinds of bears in the Dismal Swamp. Besides the large black bear (described to me in 1953 by swamp people as the "cattle beast bear" because of its large size and fondness of preying on cattle), Stansbury listed "grizzly bear," "gray bear," "hog bear" (so called because of its small size), and "Seneca bear," a white breasted variety. Local beliefs notwithstanding, these all seem to be variants of a single species.

The black bear was included on Daniel's list of the mammals of the Dismal Swamp (Stansbury 1925, p. 97), and bears were mentioned in Nelson's (1930, p. 18) travelogue of the Swamp. Murray (1950, p. 226) stated that as many as 55 bears have been killed in the Swamp in one season, and a "swamper" told Stansbury (1925, p. 96) that "he had counted twenty-seven bears crossing a 'gum' road one morning on their way to a field on the Suffolk side of the swamps." Wilson (1954, p. 200) found bear in the larger swamps in Currituck County. In fact, the bear is fairly widespread in the swamps of eastern North Carolina (Brimley 1945, pt. 6, p. 1). In Virginia, on the other hand, it is isolated in the Dismal Swamp and in the Appalachians.

Bear sign is more often seen in the Swamp than the bears themselves. There are footprints in damp ground. In season the berry-laden droppings of bears are commonly found along woods roads and trails.

"At the height of the hunting season, in November and December" Ariza (1932, p. 129) found that bears came nightly to his camp in the Waste Weir clearing—"luscious pokeberries and trees laden with sweet-gum berries are the lures. A pail of wild honey left on a table in front of the camp was devoured by a bear one night. . . . [There are] bear trails, where old Bruin swims the canal in passing from open space to open space" (Ariza 1932, p. 121), and "wherever bears walk—and they walk nearly everywhere in Dismal—ticks are left on the grass and lie in wait for victims. Bears and deer are infested with them" (Ariza 1932, p. 129). Bear wells are another evidence of unseen bears: "Instead of walking miles to lake or stream when he is thirsty, the swamp's black bear digs a 'well' down to the water level—in dry seasons several feet" (Ariza 1932, p. 120).

Although Murray (1948, p. 23) believed that "there is no place in the State and few anywhere in the country where black bears are so common," he had to admit, "I have never been able to see one there, but I have heard the sounds of bears crashing through the brush in the distance, and along the secluded Jericho Ditch every log shows signs of their scratching." Olsen (1962, p. 82) quoted Shelton Rountree as telling him: "Every once in a while [at night] you'll hear a bear rippin' away at some decayed old tree on the lakeshore, tryin' to get at the bugs. And he'll rip and rip at that tree until it comes down with a crash that just about takes your ears off."

The diet of bears in the Swamp varies with the season. On a logging road in the clear-cut area below Corapeake Ditch I found bear droppings in March loaded with what appeared to be inkberries (*Ilex glabra*). Meanley (1973, p. 34) further elaborated a seasonal cycle:

Bears occur in all plant communities in the Swamp. In the spring and early summer of 1971, I saw bears on a number of occasions along the north end of Jericho Ditch. I found the honey tree of a yearling bear with numerous claw marks along the trunk. The bee gum was in the end of a hollow limb of a huge tulip poplar about 50 feet from the ground, and the shrubs beneath the bee hollow were often dripping with honey. I saw the yearling on at least a half-dozen occasions near the honey tree. About a half-mile up the Jericho Ditch from the honey tree was an active den of a female with small cub. The den was in a large swamp black gum, only about one mile from the city of Suffolk. Large tracks, apparently those of a male bear, were also observed in this area.

During the summer I saw fresh bear signs along Corapeake Ditch, just south of the North Carolina–Virginia border in the recent cutover sections of the Atlantic white cedar forest, where the animals had been feeding on blueberries and blackberries. In late summer and early fall, bears occasionally pilfer cornfields that border the Swamp; some caught in the act are shot by farmers.

Troubetzkoy (1961, p. 22) believed that populations of the black bear were on the decline. "The swamp is the only remaining haunt in eastern Virginia of the diminishing black bear. However, even allowing for considerable exaggeration, the turn-of-the-century estimates of 200 bears killed a year is very far from the 12 taken last year on one 40,000 acre tract belonging to the Union Bag–Camp Paper Corporation." In a similar vein Hill (1973, p. 24) wrote: "I've heard that wildlife has been diminishing in recent years, especially bear. But I've seen in years past three or four bear on a single outing." Meanley (1973, p. 34) also observed a decline: "the bear population [of the Swamp] is diminishing, and probably fewer than 100 are left."

The accompanying graph (Fig. 1) of the reported bear kill in Nansemond and Norfolk counties for the past 28 years seems to show a stable or slightly declining population, with an average kill of 13 bears per winter. There were peaks of 25 bears killed in 1953, 47 in 1955, 31 in 1958, 21 in 1960, 18 in 1964, and 25 in 1971, and depressions to as few as 2 to 5 bears killed in seven years. Variables such as weather and hunting effort have not been accounted for and might be responsible for some of the observed variation in kill. The occasional peaks of 18 to 47 bears killed in a winter in the Virginia portion of the Swamp make Meanley's guess of a population of "fewer than 100" bears in the whole Swamp look a bit low if the equation "kill $\times$ 5 = population" (Carpenter 1973, p. 7) is used for an estimate. Unfortunately, detailed records of bear kill have not been kept for the North Carolina portion of the Swamp.

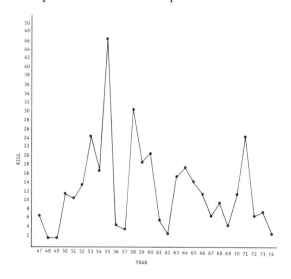

Fig. 1. Bear kill reported at check stations in Nansemond and Norfolk counties, 1947–74 (data from Carpenter 1973, p. 12).

Despite its abundance, few specimens of the Dismal Swamp black bear have found their way into museums. The National Museum has six, most of them received from hunters. The most notable is the record skull collected by W. H. Harrison (US 240613). The others are US 75046, 75256, 120713, 222782, and 282852.

Procyon lotor lotor L.

Raccoon

Hallock's (1877, p. 167) observation in his "Sportsman's Directory" that "coons" were plentiful in the Dismal Swamp still holds true today. Authors who have mentioned Dismal Swamp mammals have been unanimous in the same opinion. An anecdotal story by Hunter (1881, p. 9) commented that "de swamp is full of coons." Another article by the same author (Hunter, 1895, p. 71) gave more detail: The shingle-getters

have fat coons for meals seven days of the week. . . .

Around and on the hogbacks, the coons swarmed, if we could judge from the signs; we smelled coons, we saw coon-skin coats, coon-skin hats, coon-skin waist coats, while on the trees around the shingle camp were nailed scores of coon skins. The darkeys catch them in a peculiar trap; a great log, some eight feet long, is laid on the ground, and fenced in by shingles or palings being driven down on either side, thus when one of the logs is raised there is apparently a hollow running beneath it. A trigger is set and baited, and the coon has his life crushed out if he meddles with the dead chicken or fish on the end of the blade.

After a collecting trip to the Swamp, Fisher (1895, p. 220) observed that raccoons are "not scarce." His unpublished field notes for that trip were more explicit about raccoons: "Abundant—as many as a dozen must have come every night to feed on the fish imprisoned [in puddles of water]—nowhere in the Swamp were signs of raccoons absent." Young found them to be "fairly common" and saw skins taken near Chapanoke, Northeastern North Carolina (Rhoads and Young 1897, p. 310). Dunn (1907, p. 63) reported raccoons to be "very numerous" in the Swamp, and Eaton (1910, p. 28) observed raccoons that some sailors had caught at the locks on the Feeder Ditch in May 1910. Daniel included raccoon in his list of Dismal Swamp mammals (Stansbury 1925, p. 97), and Lewis (1938, p. 2) observed that during the interval 1903-11 raccoons were common in the Dismal Swamp, but elsewhere in the vicinity were found only occasionally, where large tracts of woods remained. Ariza (1932, p. 128) noted that raccoons preyed heavily on fish when the water was low in Lake Drummond. When he visited the Swamp in the 1940s Murray (1948, p. 23) found the raccoon to be "very common," and Wilson (1954, p. 200) called it "abundant" in all swamp-marsh cover types around Northeast River Marsh, Currituck County. He thought that destruction of muskrat litters by raccoons must have been responsible for the catastrophic drop (up to 90 percent) in muskrat populations in Currituck County between 1948 and 1952. He regarded the marshes as "infested" with raccoons (Wilson, 1953).

There are several specimens of raccoon in the National Museum from the Dismal Swamp: three collected by Fisher at Lake Drummond in 1895 and two at the same place by Bailey in 1931, one on the Washington Ditch by Bartsch and Barber in 1906, one at Wallaceton by Preble in 1896, and from near Coinjock, Currituck County, one by McAtee in 1909 and two by Dozier in 1942. One in the American Museum of Natural History was collected by Jarrell at Lake Drummond in 1964. Some of these specimens were used by Goldman (1950, p. 36) in his revision of the raccoons of North and Middle America.

Mustela frenata noveboracensis Emmons
Long-tailed weasel

According to Young (Rhoads and Young 1897, p. 312), the long-tailed weasel was "reported at Currituck. Probably occurs sparingly throughout the Albemarle region [of North Carolina]." Brimley (1945, pt. 7, p. 1) reported it from Pasquotank County, North Carolina, and Daniel included it in his list of the mammals of the Dismal Swamp (Stansbury 1925, p. 97), but Lewis (1938, p. 3) did not observe or hear of weasels during his residence near the northern edge of the Swamp in Norfolk County from 1903 to 1911. There is a specimen in the National Museum (US 77801) that Preble collected at Wallaceton in April 1896, and another (US 83670) taken in the Swamp in June 1897 by William Palmer.

Mustela vison mink Peale and Palisot de Beauvois
Mink

Although his description was somewhat ambiguous, Edmund Ruffin (1837a, p. 519) probably had in mind a mink as the smaller of "two species of what are called [in the Dismal Swamp region] *wild cats*. . . . The smaller kind [mink] is mole-colored, and has a long tail."

Entirely unequivocal were Young's observations of mink in northeastern North Carolina: "Several skins seen, which had been taken at Chapanoke, but no specimens obtained (by me) either there or at Currituck. They were reported as common in suitable localities at each place. They are considered very destructive to poultry." (Rhoads and Young 1897, p. 310).

Dunn (1907, p. 63) found the mink to be "very numerous" in the Swamp, Daniel included it in his list of Dismal Swamp mammals (Stansbury 1925, p. 97), and Lewis (1938, p. 3) observed that it was "present in the Dismal Swamp," 1903–11. Ariza (1932, p. 128) found that mink, along with otters and raccoons, took a heavy toll of fish when the water was low in Lake Drummond. Murray (1948, p. 23) thought that mink were "very common" when he visited the Swamp in the 1940s.

In the course of a four-year study 1947–51 of ecology and management of the muskrat in Currituck County, North Carolina, Wilson (1954) collected much data on food habits of mink. He believed that because of an abundance of food, mink populations were large and that those in swamps did not travel as far to find food as those in the uplands. He quoted the fur dealer J. J. Flora, in Moyock, as saying that Currituck County trappers harvested about 200 mink annually, mostly from swamps. Wilson's analysis of digestive tracts of swamp mink showed that in fall and winter about two-thirds ate quantities of minnow-sized fish and crayfish that inhabit shallow water; one-third contained remains of mammals, mostly *Peromyscus* and *Microtus;* and a few had eaten birds, frogs, and snakes. Mink scats found in Northwest River Marsh in autumn contained mostly *Oryzomys* and *Peromyscus* remains and smaller amounts of birds, crayfish, fish, and frogs. Wilson found that, contrary to popular belief, mink seldom preyed on muskrats, although these were abundant in mink habitat. Wilson supposed that when food was abundant mink took easy-to-get small prey in preference to strenuous conflict with large muskrats. After all, the local mink averaged 1 lb. 8 oz. (33 adult males) and 1 lb. 1 oz. (13 adult females) while 488 adult muskrats averaged almost 3 lb. in weight.

A specimen in the National Museum (US 75941) was taken by Fisher at Lake Drummond in October 1895.

Mephitis mephitis nigra Peale and Palisot de Beauvois
Striped skunk

Apparently the striped skunk has always been uncommon in the vicinity of the Swamp. It was first noted there by Edmund Ruffin (1837a, p. 519): "Pole cats are . . . sometimes found in the borders of the swamp." Ariza (1932, p. 129) attested to the rarity of skunks in the peaty part of the Swamp: "only one skunk has been captured there in 30 years." Daniel included it in his list of Dismal Swamp mammals (Stansbury 1925, p. 97), but Lewis (1938, p. 3) had no records or reports of skunks during his residence near the northern edge of the Swamp in Norfolk County, and Brimley (1945, pt. 7, p. 2) believed it to be "absent or scarce . . . in the northeastern portion of [North Carolina]."

Lutra canadensis lataxina F. Cuvier
River otter

The otter was one of the first mammals recorded in the Dismal

Swamp and it is still frequently seen there. William Byrd's boundary surveyors saw it first, on 9 March 1728, in the Swamp between the North and Northwest rivers: "met with Bever Dams & Otter holes, which it was not practicable to pass in a direct line" (Boyd, 1967, p. 53).

Traveling by barge down Jericho Ditch toward Lake Drummond, David Strother (writing as "Porte Crayon"), on 19 March 1856 observed sign of otter: "There, upon a decayed log, lay coiled a dead snake, dragged untimely from his winter retreat by a hungry otter" (Strother 1856, p. 444). The noise of an otter rippling the water as it swam was mentioned in an anecdotal tale by Hunter (1881, p. 13) as one of the summer night sounds of Lake Drummond.

According to Young (Rhoads and Young 1897, p. 312), "A few [otters have been] reported from the swamps around Chapanoke [North Carolina]," and Lewis (1928, p. 95) found it infrequent in the northern part of the Swamp during the period 1903–11. Daniel included it in his list of the mammals of the Dismal Swamp (Stansbury 1925, p. 97).

Much maligned by fishermen and trappers as a predator of sport fish and muskrats, the otter survived in some numbers in the Dismal Swamp while it became rare near the turn of the century in most other parts of Virginia and North Carolina. Dunn (1907, p. 63) observed that otters are "very numerous" in the Swamp. Ariza (1932, p. 121) found otter slides on the ditch banks and observed that otters take a heavy toll of fish when the water is low in Lake Drummond. He pictured an otter taken by a fur trapper (p. 125). Following trips to the Swamp in the 1940s, Murray (1948, p. 23) wrote: "Otter slides are frequently seen along the Feeder Ditch. They are probably more common here than anywhere in Virginia. . . . Except for the otter and muskrat, there are few mammals [in the Swamp] that live underground." Similarly, Meanley (1973, p. 34) observed: "The river otter is still a common mammal [in the Swamp] and is mainly associated with the ditches or canals. In April 1968, I observed a pair with two pups about two-thirds grown at their den in a bank of the Jericho Ditch. I could sit across the ditch, ten feet from the den, and watch the otter family as long as I wished, as they seemed not to be concerned with me. I could hear the pups occasionally crying and watched them swim two or three feet into the canal as one of the parents returned after a quarter-mile trip up Jericho."

When Wilson (1954, p. 205) went to Currituck County, North Carolina, in 1947 he found that

trappers complained of destruction of muskrat populations and other deeds committed by otter. The principal complaints were that otters tear open houses and devour muskrats in their beds, consume muskrats in traps and create panic among muskrats, causing them to leave their homes. Scats at two large otter toilets on the outer banks were shown to me by a bitter trapper in 1949, but examination revealed that what looked like muskrat hair was actually shredded feather remains of waterfowl. At the time [January], the waterfowl season had just closed and marshes contained the remains of dead coots, . . . other dead waterfowl, and some crippled ducks unable to fly. Of many hundred droppings the author has observed at toilets or pulverized for quick examination in the hand, almost everything, excepting occasional feathers, has appeared to be either fish or crustaceans.

Examination of 54 digestive tracts of otters showed that by volume 80 percent of all food consumed was fish and 15 percent was crustaceans (crayfish, crab, decapod, and shrimp). The remaining fraction contained water beetles, birds, frogs, clam, and hair of one muskrat.

Until the refuge was established in the northwestern quarter of the Swamp, otters were systematically trapped there as vermin because they were supposed to eat sport fish. However, otter scats that Pat Gammon and Mary Keith Garrett examined in that area were loaded with crushed crayfish carapaces. To determine the frequency of game fish in the otter diet in Currituck County, Wilson (1954, p. 206) analyzed ten stomachs and twenty droppings of otters. He found the frequency of forage fish such as carp, suckers, and killifish to be 57 percent, while that of sport fish, mostly sunfish, catfish, perch, and pickerel, was 43 percent.

Felis concolor couguar Kerr
Puma, mountain lion

Most sixteenth- and seventeenth-century writers who had anything at all to say about the natural history of coastal Virginia and North Carolina spoke of panthers, lions, and tigers (all = *Felis concolor?*), often in terms of considerable abundance. Possibly referring to the Dismal Swamp, Augustin Herrman (1673) said that the swampy land between the James and Roanoke rivers was inhabited by "Tygers."

William Byrd encountered the puma far to the west of the Swamp during the 1728 boundary survey but knew of its presence in the Swamp only secondhand. On 13 March 1728 his surveyors were camped near the eastern edge of the Swamp, about to begin their transect of it. The local people were: "simple enough to amuse our men with Idle Stories of the Lyons, Panthers and Alligators, they were like to encounter in that dreadful Place" (Boyd 1967, p. 60; Ruffin 1837*b* p. 593; Stansbury 1925, p. 139).

Subsequently, there was little further reference to the puma by most of the numerous authors who mentioned Dismal Swamp mammals. An exception was Hallock (1877, p. 167) who listed it in his "Sportsman's Directory" as plentiful in the Swamp: "The *Dismal* . . .

is the haunt of great numbers of bears, panthers . . . and other game. . . .
The bears and panthers are seldom shot, as they retire into the vastness
of the densest and most impenetrable jungles."

True (1891, p. 599) thought Hallock's reference was surprising, since
he (True) knew of no other contemporary record of occurrence of the
puma in the coastal lowlands of the South Atlantic States, except in
Florida. However, in Young and Goldman's monograph on the puma,
Young (1946, p. 37) did not question the validity of Hallock's statements. He observed: "the Dismal Swamp area appears to have been
the section where the animal held out longest." Apparently none of
the many museum collectors who worked in the Swamp in the 1890s
and 1900s found evidence of puma, but, possibly influenced by Hallock
or other rumor, Stansbury (1925, p. 96) included "panther" among
contemporary mammals of the Swamp. Apparently Ariza (1932, pp.
124 and 130) also was misled by rumor to believe that there were
panthers in the Swamp, for he "listened in vain for panthers."

Actually, it seems probable that there have been no pumas in the
Dismal Swamp since Byrd's time. Apparently they disappeared very
early from the low country at this latitude, although they did survive
for another 150 to 200 years in the nearby Appalachians. Their early
disappearance is somewhat puzzling in view of the persistence of an
adequate food supply—deer and wild cattle—and a sufficiently large
area of wild habitat to make them relatively inaccessible to hunters
and trappers. Perhaps the pumas of these latitudes were somehow not
adapted to swamp life as are their surviving relatives in Florida and
the Gulf Coast.

Felis rufus floridanus Rafinesque
Bobcat, wildcat

Prominent among the mammals of the Dismal Swamp recorded by
most authors, the bobcat was first mentioned by Edmund Ruffin
(1837a, p. 519). "A still more ferocious animal [in comparison to the
black bear] found here is the larger of two species of what are called
wild cats. This name is certainly misapplied—but my acquaintance
with this branch of natural history is not sufficient to enable me to
fix the kind of either animal, from the descriptions given. The larger
is brown, with a short tail, and is about as large as a middle sized or
rather stout dog." (Cf. Mink, p. 341—ed.)

After a trip to the Virginia portion of the Swamp to collect birds
and small mammals, Fisher (1895, p. 220) observed that "wildcats . . .
are not scarce." At about the same time, Young (Rhoads and Young
1897, p. 312) found it to be "rare, but of general distribution" in northeastern North Carolina. Lewis (1928, p. 98) wrote of experiences with
bobcats in the Dismal during the years 1903–11:

Wild cats were not uncommon in the swamp and were an interesting lot, and sometimes became quite bold. A negro who lived a short distance from the headquarters had two hound puppies that were the apple of his eye. In late winter they were about two-thirds grown and at an age when they had more nerve then discretion. One night when a light snow was on the ground both puppies were killed at the edge of the reeds sixty yards from the house, and the tracks of a big wild cat told the tale.

A few nights later, just before dawn, I was awakened by a terrific cater-wauling almost under my window. Grabbing a gun, I ran downstairs, but by the time I got the back door open all was quiet. After daylight we found a very large, old domestic tom cat that had taken up his abode at our place, still alive, but so terribly mangled that I put an end to his suffering with a revolver bullet. Again the tracks of a big wild cat led from the scene of the murder toward the swamp. Judging from the few specimens that came under my observation a full grown wild cat is about twice the weight of a large domestic cat, with feet and legs larger in proportion, and with a short tail, which gives rise to one of the common names, "Bob Cat."

The crys of a wild cat heard at night are almost as terrifying to the uninitiated as those of the coyote. One gave us several demonstrations of his skill as a vocalist during our two years' stay in the edge of the swamp, and in spite of our assurances that he was only singing to them always frightened the children.

The *Washington-Herald* for 5 November 1920 reported that a large bobcat killed in the Dismal Swamp measured 4 feet long from nose to tips of hind feet (Handley and Patton 1947, p. 143). This species was included in Daniel's list of the mammals of the Dismal Swamp (Stansbury 1925, p. 97), and it was mentioned at several other places in Stansbury's book (pp. 33, 84, 96, and 148). Nelson (1930, p. 18) observed that bobcats still roamed the Swamp as they did three centuries earlier when the first English settlers arrived in the vicinity. Ariza (1932, p. 130) believed that he observed that bobcats are troubled by ticks but manage to rid themselves of them. Murray (1948, p. 23) regarded the bobcat as "very common" in the Swamp in the 1940s, and Meanley (1973, p. 34) thought it was "still common" in the early 1970s. Pat Gammon and Mary Keith Garrett of the refuge staff told me in 1974 that they had seen two bobcats, both on ditch-bank roads, in the two years that they have been traveling about the refuge. In contrast, I have seen three bobcats in 40 years in the Appalachins where they are common. Although the bobcat probably is found nowhere in eastern Virginia outside of the Dismal Swamp, it is fairly widespread in the swamps of eastern North Carolina (Brimley 1945, pt. 8, p. 2).

There are in the American Museum of Natural History three specimens of *Felis rufus* from the Swamp (AMNH 14367, 15691, 15692) and one from Suffolk (AMNH 15676), colleted by Figgins and Royster. The National Museum has one (US 75254) that A. K. Fisher obtained on the shore of Lake Drummond, 11 October 1895. Its stomach contained two lemming voles (*Synaptomys*) and a song sparrow. Another bobcat (US 73685) was obtained by William Palmer for the National Museum in the winter of 1896. Many years later Peterson and Downing (1952, p. 14) examined the three Dismal Swamp bobcats in the American Museum of Natural History. Because of the narrowness of the skulls, they concluded that these specimens represented the southeastern subspecies, *F. r. floridanus.*

Order Artiodactyla—Hogs, deer, goats, etc.

Sus scrofa L.
Domestic hog

Wertenbaker (1962, p. 29) found that branding hogs and cattle and running them into the Swamp where they could find free feeding grounds was already a common practice in the early eighteenth century. William Bryd observed free-ranging hogs in March 1728 on the boundary survey: "Both Cattle and Hoggs ramble in the Neighbouring Marshes and Swamps, where they maintain themselves the whole Winter long, and are not fetch'd home till the Spring" (Boyd 1967, p. 54). However, he noted: "At this time of the Year [March] both the Cattle and Hoggs had forsaken the Skirts of the Dismal, invited by the Springing Grass on the firm Land" (Boyd 1967, p. 78).

When he visited the Swamp almost 200 years later, Stansbury (1925, pp. 33 and 94) found that the wild hog was considered to be a game mammal. The fate of this animal in the Swamp, however, is uncertain. There seems to be no recent mention of it in the literature.

Odocoileus virginianus virginianus Zimmermann
White-tailed deer

Why this conspicuous animal was not mentioned by early visitors to the Swamp is a mystery. Hunter (1881, p. 11) related that Lake Drummond was discovered in Revolutionary War days by a huntsman in pursuit of a wounded deer, but since the discovery of the lake was misdated by about a hundred years, the part of the deer in the legend may be no more accurate.

Nevertheless, the white-tailed deer was a part of the Swamp fauna. It was sometimes abundant and sometimes rare. Hallock (1877, pt. 2, p. 167), in his "Sportsman's Directory" advised that it was plentiful in the Swamp at that date. By the late nineteenth century Shaler (1890, p. 333) observed that "deer are now rare, but they have been somewhat plenty." Hunter (1895, p. 75) described finding a doe in a

canebrake and a buck in a field beside the Swamp in the course of a
bear hunt. In the same year Fisher (1895, p. 220) observed that "deer
are common but hard to get. In the fall hunters run them into the lake
and catch them with dogs." Young (Rhoads and Young 1897, p. 311)
was told that deer were "not uncommon in the wild regions about
Chapanoke [northeastern North Carolina]." Dunn (1907, p. 63) observed that deer were "plentiful" in the Swamp, and Eaton (1910,
p. 29) said they abounded there. However, Lewis (1938, p. 6) who
resided near the Swamp remarked of the white-tailed deer: "Confined to the Dismal Swamp, where it was not common." Daniel included it in his list of the mammals of the Dismal Swamp (Stansbury
1925, p. 96) and Nelson (1930, p. 18) mentioned its occurrence in the
Swamp. Ariza (1932, p. 126) observed that particularly in the Swamp
quadrant east of Jericho Ditch "deer abound." He (p. 129) also noted
that Swamp deer commonly are infested with ticks. When he visited
the Swamp in the 1940s Murray (1948, p. 23) found deer "very common." Wilson (1954, p. 200) reported deer in the larger swamps in
Currituck County, North Carolina.

Sometimes the population of deer in the Swamp grows very large. I
found such a "high" in February 1953. When I made my way through
some of the drier places back into the woods, I found signs of deer
everywhere. In the nearly impenetrable thickets of bay, and in the
bracken "lights," well-worn deer trails crisscrossed in unbelievable
abundance. The sharp hooves of the deer had worn the pathways deep
into the soft swamp soil. Hardly a clump of maple or willow sprouts
or patch of blackberry failed to show evidence of deer browsing. In
the course of my short walk I jumped two deer that had been bedded
down for the day in the security of thickets. As time passed, I came to
realize that deer were among the most abundant, and by far the most
evident, of the larger animals in the Swamp.

A few years later Troubetzkoy (1961, p. 22), visiting the Swamp in
May, saw "several white-tailed deer—one doe bounding off with
honeysuckle in her mouth." He also observed that "the high browse
lines of deer this May indicate that their food level is getting low and
where the canopy of trees is closing over, undergrowth disappears and
this is not conducive to an increase."

Probably there is considerable natural fluctuation of the deer
population in the Swamp, unrelated to hunting pressure. This is
illustrated in Figure 2, which includes the deer killed in the Virginia
portion of the Dismal Swamp, as well as in other parts of Nansemond
and Norfolk counties, from 1947 through 1974. A rapidly growing
population outstripped the ability of the habitat to support it, peaked
in 1958, and began to decline. Doe seasons beginning in 1962 reduced
the population, but a new upward trend became evident in 1971.

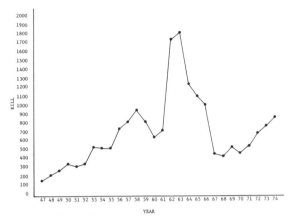

YEAR

Fig. 2. White-tailed deer kill reported at check stations in Nansemond and Norfolk counties, 1947–74 (data from Virginia Commission of Game and Inland Fisheries).

The practice of hunting deer from stands, long the custom in the Dismal, was described by Olsen. He also described the deer:

The bucks come big and fat, but their horns are short and oddly formed and sometimes [superficially] resemble the horns of cattle. Many of the bucks have a single horn, or tiny horns that would look more natural on a chamois. The hunters of the Dismal Swamp say that these deer have been produced by natural selection, that deer with huge spreading racks could not survive the thickness of the swamp and were quickly culled out by predators. Scientists say that the deer have deformed horns simply because the soil is thin in the mineral content that produces big racks. [Olsen 1962, p. 75]

Another idiosyncrasy of these deer, according to Olsen (1962, p. 79) is their reaction to hounds: "they must have jumped a buck and a doe that were lying together. One went one way and one went another. Most deer won't do that; they'll run right together. But in Dismal Swamp they'll always split up." Olsen (1962, p. 80) also believed that some Swamp deer are transients: "The bane of the huntmaster's existence is the migrating deer, who is merely passing through the Dismal Swamp. If a dog picks up the scent of a migrating deer, he will stay on the trail for miles, and the huntmaster has to scratch one hound from his list." One of the silent evidences of deer in the Swamp, observed Olsen (1962, p. 82), is the stump of a tree where "a deer has polished his horns."

Bos taurus L.
Domestic cattle

Evidently feral cattle were commonplace in early colonial times in Virginia. John Clayton (1694, p. 121) observed that "*Wild Bulls* and *Cows* there are now in the uninhabited Parts, but such only as have been bred from some that have strayed, and become Wild, and have propagated their kind, and are difficult to be shot, having a great Acuteness of Smelling."

Wertenbaker (1962, p. 29) found records of cattle in the Dismal at a very early date. "The great swamp was used also as a free feeding ground for cattle and hogs. One would secure from the county court an official mark or brand, place it upon the stock, and turn them loose to feed. At the proper seasons one would slaughter his cows and hogs, provided they could be found in the wilderness of trees and bushes."

Later the custom of running branded cattle into the Swamp to forage for themselves proved to be a curse to the farmers. Once the cattle were established as feral animals in the Swamp, it became necessary to fence the Swamp side of farmlands to keep the cattle out of the planted fields.

The best account of the wild cattle has been provided by Shaler (1890, p. 333):

The most peculiar feature in the mammalian life is the fact that large numbers of wild horned cattle are found within the morass. These have feralized from domestic herds about the swamps. Estimates as to the number of these creatures vary considerably. I am inclined to think that there are probably about five hundred now living within this area. They are extremely wild, and when hunted are often dangerous to the sportsman. Several observant persons have reported to me that fierce combats frequently take place between the bulls and the bears. Mr. Wallace, of Wallaceton, states that he has several times heard the bellowing of the horned cattle when they were engaged in such combats. Another observer stated to me that some years ago he found a bull and a bear lying dead beside each other, both having been killed in the combat.

It is said that the bears have a peculiar habit in their assault upon the horned cattle; they spring upon their backs and rend the muscles which support the head of their prey, and thus escape the danger from its horns. The evidence as to this peculiar habit rests upon the fact that where the horned cattle have been killed in their contests with the bears the neck muscles are found divided.

I have not myself had an opportunity of seeing any of these cattle, but it is stated that they are generally of a black color and of small size. They appear to range through all portions of the swamp, but during the breeding season to prefer the slightly elevated portions where the canes abound. . . . They feed mainly on the tenderer shoots of the cane, and are said to dwell generally in herds of from twenty to fifty individuals. Occasionally members of the wild herds are tolled out into the cultivated fields by offerings of salt, and are led to join the domestic cattle. The greater part of the wild cattle, however, evidently live for generations without obtaining access to saline materials, a fact which shows that salt is not really necessary to them, for within the morass they can have no opportunity whatever of obtaining it. There are no salt springs, the tidal rivers which penetrate to the swamp are all fresh, and there are no licks, such as were afforded by the slightly saline clays of the Mississippi Valley, to which the buffalo abundantly resorted.

After a collecting trip for small mammals, Fisher (1895, p. 220) observed: "There are plenty of cattle in the swamp—small, dark and very wild. They are the progeny of animals that have strayed from domesticated herds. Hunters stalk and shoot them like deer." Dunn (1907, p. 63) observed: "Wild cattle, as fleet and as wary as the deer, make their home on the ridges that run through the swamp." Eaton (1910, p. 27) did not personally see any cattle when he visited the Swamp in May 1910 and had to be content to paraphrase Shaler (1890) in his account.

Stansbury (1925, p. 98) apparently believed that the "so-called" wild cattle found in the Swamp were not feral: "They are in origin merely wanderers from herds of domestic cattle." Nevertheless, he listed them among the game mammals of the Swamp (pp. 33 and 84). Nelson (1930, p. 19) quoted Anne Ellis of the Tidewater Automobile Association: "In open spaces here and there [along the Feeder Ditch] herds of semi-wild and totally wild cattle that live in the swamp may be seen grazing."

However, according to Ariza (1932, p. 129), "it was thought several years ago that by exterminating Dismal Swamp's wild cattle, ticks would be eradicated. The cattle have disappeared, but there are as many ticks as ever." Margaret Davis (1934, p. 177) also got the impression from the Swamp people that the wild cattle were gone: "the wild cattle of an earlier day that you used to hear so much about but [you] don't hear of any more." However, Murray (1948, p. 23) observed, following visits in the 1940s: "Years ago the cattle that escaped into the Swamp bred a fierce strain that made them the most dangerous of all the swamp creatures. Possibly a few of them still exist, although marines were sent into the Swamp some years ago on a campaign of extermination."

The present status of wild cattle in the Swamp is uncertain. I was assured by local residents in 1953 that the organized attempts to eradicate the cattle had been unsuccessful. I was told tales of bear and "cattlebeast" encounters resembling some of those that Shaler heard. One is worth repetition:

In the early days of this century a particularly big and strong "cattlebeast" bull frequented the "Desert" northwest of Elizabeth City. Scars on his hide showed that this particular bull had had several encounters with bears, and he was widely known for his strength and endurance. One day, great bellows of terror and rage issued from the swamp, and eventually the bull came out into the farmland, so decimated by a bear that he could not raise his head. However, inspection of the scene of the struggle revealed a large area of flattened and trampled swamp vegetation and a gored, dead bear.

Capra hircus L.

Domestic goat

Another domestic mammal possibly feral in the Dismal is the goat, as Hill (1973, p. 24) has reported the Swamp to be inhabited by "some domesticated goats gone wild." Its status is uncertain, however, for it has not been mentioned by other authors.

ACKNOWLEDGMENTS

I was aided greatly in my search for pertinent references by Jane E. Ailes. She and my wife, Darelyn Handley, did most of the reading to locate passages relating to mammals. Helen Hutchinson typed the manuscript. I am indebted to each of these persons for their part in producing this paper. Stuart Critcher, North Carolina Wildlife Resources Commission, and Dick Cross, Virginia Commission of Game and Inland Fisheries, kindly provided information. My thanks go also to Paul Kirk for inviting me for participate in the Dismal Swamp Symposium.

The material from J. B. Lewis's 1938 manuscript is quoted with the kind permission of Florence Lewis Batson. The material from Meanley (1973) is reprinted by permission of the Audubon Naturalist Society of the Central Atlantic States, Inc. The paragraph from Olsen (1962) is reprinted by permission of *Sports Illustrated*.

REFERENCES CITED

Anon. 1892. The Virginia Dismal Swamp. *Sci. Amer.* 66(21 May):322. [by J. Ralph?]

Anon. 1974. *A checklist of North Carolina mammalian species.* N.C. Wildlife Resources Comm. 21 pp.

Arber, E. 1910. *Travels and works of Captain John Smith,* pt. 1. Edinburgh. 382 pp.

Ariza, J. F. 1932. Dismal Swamp in legend and history. *Natl. Geog. Mag.* 62(July):120–130.

Arnold, R. 1888. *The Dismal Swamp and Lake Drummond: early recollections, vivid portrayal of amusing scenes.* Green, Burke & Gregory, Norfolk. 78 pp.

Bailey, J. W. 1946. *The mammals of Virginia.* Publ. by the author. Williams Printing Co., Richmond. 416 pp.

Bailey, V. 1900. Revision of American voles of the genus *Microtus. N. Amer. Fauna* 17:1–88.

Bartsch, P. 1901. A trip to the Dismal Swamp. *Osprey* 5:35–37, 55–56, 67–69.

Bassett, J. S. (ed). 1901. *The writings of "Colonel William Byrd of Westover in Virginia Esqr."* Doubleday, Page & Co. New York. 461 pp.

Beatty, R. C., and W. J. Mulloy. 1940. *William Byrd's natural history of Virginia.* Dietz Press, Richmond. 95 pp. + appendix (109 pp., orig. German text).

Beverley, R. 1705. *The history and present state of Virginia.* v. 1, pp. 1–104; v. 2, pp. 1–40; v. 3, pp. 1–64; v. 4, pp. 1–83.

B[ishop], W. H. 1882. To the Great Dismal Swamp. *Nation* (New York) 35(14 Dec.):502–504.

Boyd, W. K. 1967. *William Byrd's histories of the dividing line betwixt Virginia and North Carolina.* Dover Publ., N.Y. 341 pp. (Reprint of work first published in 1929 by the N.C. Historical Comm., Raleigh.)

Brimley, C. S. 1897. An incomplete list of the mammals of Bertie Co., N.C. *Amer. Nat.* 31:237–238.

————. 1905. A descriptive catalogue of the mammals of North Carolina, exclusive of the Cetacea. *J. Elisha Mitchell Sci. Soc.* 21:1–32.

————. 1945. The mammals of North Carolina. *Bull. Dept. Agric.* 18 pts., 36 pp. (also published in 18 parts in *Carolina Tips,* 1944–46, 39 pp.).

Byrd, W., II. 1789. A description of the Dismal Swamp, in Virginia; with proposals for and observations on the advantages of draining it. *Columbian Mag.* (Philadelphia) 3(Apr.):230–234.

Carpenter, M. 1973. *The black bear in Virginia.* Va. Comm. Game and Inland Fisheries, Richmond. 22 pp.

Clayton, J. 1694. Account of Virginia; giving a short description of the beasts and serpents thereof. *Philos. Trans.* 18:121–135.

Clayton, J. 1899. Virginia game, and field sports (description of them by the botanist Clayton in 1739). *Va. Mag. Hist. Biog.* 7:172–174.

Cumming, W. P., R. A. Skelton, and D. B. Quinn. 1972. *The discovery of North America.* Amer. Heritage Press, New York 304 pp.

Davis, Margaret. 1934. "Great Dismal" pictures. *S. Atlantic Quart.* 33(Apr.): 171–184.

de Rageot, R. H. 1955. A new northernmost record of the yellow bat, *Dasypterus floridanus. J. Mamm.* 36:456.

Dice, L. R. 1940. Relationships between the wood-mouse and the cotton-mouse in eastern Virginia. *J. Mamm.* 21:14–23.

Dunn, J. B. 1907. *The history of Nansemond County, Virginia.* Publ. by Nansemond Co., Suffolk, Va. 71 pp.

Eaton, W. P. 1910. The real Dismal Swamp. *Harper's Monthly Mag.* 122(Dec.): 18–30.

Evans, J. 1970. About nutria and their control. *U.S. Dept. Int., Bur. Sports Fish. and Wildlife, Resource Publ.* 86:1–65.

Fisher, A. K. 1895. The Dismal Swamp and its occupants. *Sci. Amer.* 73(5 Oct.):220.

Force, P. 1836–46. Virginia, by E. Williams. 2d ed, 1650. *Collection of Historical Tracts* 3:9–19.

Gains, W. H. 1954. Men against the Swamp. *Va. Cavalcade.* 4(winter):23–29.

Goldman, E. A. 1918. The rice rats of North America (genus *Oryzomys*). *N. Amer. Fauna* 43:1–100.

————. 1950. Raccoons of north and middle America. *N. Amer. Fauna* 60:1–153.

Hall, E. R., and K. R. Kelson. 1959. *The mammals of North America.* Ronald Press Co., New York. v. 1, pp. 1–546 + *1–79* (index); v. 2, pp. 547–1083 *1–79* (index); 553 figs., 500 maps.

Hallock, C. 1877. A sportsman's directory to the principal resorts for game and fish in North America, pt. 2. Pp. 1–208 in *The sportsman's gazeteer and general guide,* etc. Forest & Stream Publ. Co., New York.

Handley, C. O., Jr. 1959. A revision of American bats of the genera *Euderma* and *Plecotus. Proc. U.S. Natl. Mus.* 110:95–246.

———. 1972. Appalachian mammalian geography—Recent Epoch. Pp. 263–303 *in* P. C. Holt (ed). The distributional history of the biota of the Southern Appalachians. Pt. 3: Vertebrates. *Va. Polytech. Inst. and State Univ. Res. Div. Monographs* 4.

Handley, C. O., Jr. and C. O. Handley, Sr. 1950. Mammals. Pp. 235–276 in *The James River Basin: past, present and future.* Va. Acad. Sci., Richmond.

Handley, C. O., Jr., and C. P. Patton. 1947. *Wild Mammals of Virginia.* Va. Comm. Game and Inland Fisheries, Richmond. 220 pp.

Hariot, T. 1893. *Hariot's narrative of the first plantation of Virginia in 1585.* Bernard Quaritch, London. 111 pp.

Harlan, R. 1832. *Arvicola nuttali:* description of a new species of quadruped of the genus *Arvicola,* of Lacepede, or *Hypudaeus,* of Illiger. *Monthly Amer. J. Geol. & Nat. Sci.* (Philadelphia) 1:446–447.

Harriss, F. L. (ed). 1937. *Lawson's history of North Carolina.* Garrett & Massie, Richmond. 259 pp.

Herrman, A. 1673. Map of Virginia and Maryland. London.

Hill, D. 1973. The great Swamp's brightened future: anything but dismal. *Commonwealth* 40(Apr.):19–24, 48–52.

Hollister, N. 1911a. Remarks on the long-tailed shrews of the eastern United States, with description of a new species. *Proc. U.S. Natl. Mus.* 40:377–381.

———. 1911b. A systematic synopsis of the muskrats. *N. Amer. Fauna* 32:1–47.

Hooper, E. T. 1943. Geographic variation in harvest mice of the species *Reithrodontomys humulis. Univ. Mich. Mus. Zool., Occas. Pap.* 477:1–19.

Howell, A. B. 1927. Revision of the American lemming mice (genus *Synaptomys). N. Amer. Fauna* 50:1–38.

Howell, A. H. 1914. Revision of the American harvest mice (genus *Reithrodontomys). N. Amer. Fauna* 36:1–97.

———. 1918. A revision of the American flying squirrels. *N. Amer. Fauna* 44:1–64.

———. 1929. Revision of the American chipmunks (genera *Tamias* and *Eutamias). N. Amer. Fauna* 52:1–157.

Hunter, A. 1881. Through the Dismal Swamp. *Potter's Amer. Monthly* 17(July):1–15.

———. 1895. The Great Dismal Swamp. *Outing* 27:70–76.

Jackson, H. H. T. 1915. A review of the American moles. *N. Amer. Fauna* 38:1–100.

———. 1928. A taxonomic review of the American long-tailed shrews (genera *Sorex* and *Microsorex). N. Amer. Fauna* 51:1–238.

Lantz, D. E. 1909. The brown rat in the United States. *U.S. Dept. Agric., Biol. Surv. Bull.* 33:1–54.

Lewis, J. B. 1928. Wild life of the Dismal Swamp. *Game & Fish Conservationist* (Va.) 8(Nov.-Dec.):95–98.

_____. 1938. List of mammals observed in Amelia, Brunswick and Norfolk counties. MS. 6 pp.

Lorant, S. 1946. *The New World: the first pictures of America.* Duell, Sloan & Pearce, New York. 292 pp.

Lyell, C. 1845. *Travels in North America in the years 1841–1842: with geological observations on the United States, Canada and Nova Scotia.* v. 1, 316 pp. v. 2, 271 pp. London.

Meanley, B. 1973. *The Great Dismal Swamp.* Audubon Nat. Soc. Cent. Atlantic States, Washington, D.C. 48 pp.

Merriam, C. H. 1895*a*. Revision of the shrews of the American genera *Blarina* and *Notiosorex. N. Amer. Fauna* 10:5–34.

_____. 1895*b*. Synopsis of the American shrews of the genus *Sorex. N. Amer. Fauna* 10:57–100.

_____. 1896. Revision of the lemmings of the genus *Synaptomys,* with descriptions of new species. *Proc. Biol. Soc. Washington* 10:55–64.

_____. 1897. Description of a new muskrat from the Great Dismal Swamp, Virginia. *Proc. Biol. Soc., Washington* 11:143.

Miller, G. S., Jr. 1897. Revision of the North American bats of the family Vespertilionidae. *N. Amer. Fauna* 13:1–141.

Miller, G. S., Jr., and G. M. Allen. 1928. The American bats of the genera *Myotis* and *Pizonyx. U.S. Natl. Mus. Bull.* 144:1–218.

Murray, J. J. 1948. The Great Dismal Swamp. *Raven* 19(3–4):14–26.

_____. 1950. Birds. Pp. 213–233 in *The James River Basin: past, present and future.* Va. Acad. Sci., Richmond.

Nelson, E. W. 1909. The rabbits of North America. *N. Amer. Fauna* 29:1–314.

Nelson, R. F. 1930. Visiting Great Dismal Swamp. *Natl. Repub.* 18(May): 18–20.

Olsen, J. 1962. The cursed Swamp. *Sports Illus.* 17(22):68–82.

Osgood, W. H. 1909. Revision of the mice of the American genus *Peromyscus. N. Amer. Fauna* 28:1–285.

Packard, R. L. 1969. Taxonomic review of the golden mouse, *Ochrotomys nuttalli. Univ. Kansas Mus. Nat. Hist., Misc. Pub.* 51:373–406.

Paradiso, J. L. 1959. A new star-nosed mole (*Condylura*) from the southeastern United States. *Proc. Biol. Soc., Washington* 72:103–107.

Peterson, R. L., and S. C. Downing. 1952. Notes on the bobcats (*Lynx rufus*) of eastern North America with the description of a new race. *Roy. Ontario Mus. Zool. Paleo Contrib.* 33:1–23.

Rhoads, S. N., and R. T. Young. 1897. Notes on a collection of small mammals from northeastern North Carolina. *Proc. Acad. Nat. Sci.* Philadelphia (1897):303–312.

Richards, E. V. 1953. Virginia's black bear—good or bad? *Va. Wildlife* 14(2): 16–17, 21, 23.

Ruffin, E. 1837*a*. Observations made during an excursion to the Dismal Swamp. *Petersburg* (Va.) *Farmers' Register* 4(1 Jan.):513–521.

_____. 1837*b*. The earliest passage through the Dismal Swamp. Extract from the Journal of Col. William Byrd, of Westover. *Petersburg* (Va.) *Farmers' Register* 4:593–599.

Shaler, N. S. 1890. General account of the fresh-water morasses of the United

States, with a description of the Dismal Swamp district of Virginia and
North Carolina. *U.S. Geol. Surv., Ann. Rpt.* 10:255–339.

Smith, E. R., J. B. Funderberg, Jr., and T. L. Quay. 1960. *A distributional list
of the Recent mammals of North Carolina.* N.C. Wildlife Resources Comm.
19 pp.

Squires, W. H. T. 1928. *The days of yester-year in colony and commonwealth.* Print-
craft Press, Portsmouth, Va. 301 pp.

Stansbury, C. F. 1925. *The lake of the Great Dismal.* Albert and Charles Boni
Publ. Co., New York. 238 pp.

Stewart, W. H. 1902. *History of Norfolk County, Virginia, and representative citizens.*
Biographical Publ. Co., Chicago. 1042 pp.

Strother, D. H. [Porte Crayon]. 1856. The Dismal Swamp. *Harper's New
Monthly Mag.* 13(Sept.):441–455.

Sutton, H. 1955. A filthy bogg. *Sat. Rev. Lit.* 38(6 Aug.):38–39.

Taylor, J. W. 1974. The Dismal Swamp lemming mouse. *Va. Wildlife* 35(5):27.

Teale, E. W. 1951. *North with the spring.* Dodd, Mead & Co., New York. 361 pp.

Troubetzkoy, U. 1961. The Great Dismal Swamp. *Va. Cavalcade* 10:19–27.

True, F. W. 1891. The puma, or American lion: *Felis concolor* of Linnaeus. *Ann.
Rpt. Nat. Mus.* (1888–89):591–608.

Waters, R. S. 1964. *Records of North American big game.* Holt, Rinehart, and
Winston, New York. 398 pp.

Wertenbaker. T. J. 1962. *Norfolk: historic southern port.* Duke Univ. Press, Durham, N.C. 417 pp.

Wetzel, R. M. 1955. Speciation and dispersal of the southern bog lemming,
Synaptomys cooperi (Baird). *J. Mamm.* 36:1–20.

Wilson, K. A. 1953. Raccoon predation on muskrats near Currituck, North
Carolina. *J. Wildlife Mgt.* 17:113–119.

———. 1954. The role of mink and otter as muskrat predators in northeastern
North Carolina. *J. Wildlife Mgt.* 18:199–207.

Young, S. P. 1946. History, life habits, economic status, and control (of the
puma), pt. 1. Pp. 1–174 *in* S. P. Young and E. A. Goldman. *The puma,
mysterious American cat.* Amer. Wildlife Inst., Washington.

The following works were either overlooked or were not available when this
manuscript was written. Thus, they are not cited in the text.

Anon. 1900. The Dismal Swamp of Virginia. *Sci. Amer.* 82:249–250. (P. 250
paraphrases Shaler, 1890, re. bear, deer, and cattle in the Swamp.)

Anon. 1901. Some Swamp experiences. *Forest and Stream* 57:286. (Adventure
with wounded black bear in the Dismal Swamp).

Anon. 1920. Not so dismal after all. *Literary Dig.* 64(6):88–90. (P. 90: "Bears
frequently stir the brake, rabbits scamper about, muskrats and fish swim
in the placid amber waters.")

de Rageot, R. H. 1957. Predation on small mammals in the Dismal Swamp,
Virginia. *J. Mamm.* 38:281. (*Blarina brevicauda telmalestes,* food of copperhead snake; *Mus musculus* preyed upon by saw-whet owl; *Blarina brevicauda
telmalestes, Microtus pennsylvanicus, Microtus pinetorum,* and *Mus musculus* in
barn owl pellets).

Stansbury, C. F. 1907. In the Great Dismal Swamp. *Eclectic Mag.* 148(1):3–17.
    (Pp. 8–9 paraphrase all of Shaler's [1890] remarks on mammals. Also,
    pp. 13–14 say that "there were grizzly, gray and black bears, wild cattle,
    wild hogs, wild cats, coons, 'possums, rabbits and squirrels galore" at the
    time of Stansbury's visit.)
(See also the papers in this volume by Garrett and Sonenshine, and Paschal,
Sonenshine and Richardson, each based on a recent Master's thesis at Old
Dominion University.)

ESSAY ON THE LITERATURE OF THE DISMAL SWAMP

Peter C. Stewart, Paul W. Kirk, Jr., and
Harold G. Marshall

One proof of the sustained interest in the Dismal Swamp is its voluminous and varied literature. Naturalists have long been interested in the Swamp's unique physical and biological characteristics, and although the area is virtually uninhabited, the Dismal has been the subject of a surprising amount of nonscientific literature, as well. This essay describes and comments upon some of the primary source materials and other literature on this enduring topic. It is hoped that both the general reader and the more serious scholar will be served by this paper and will want to pursue the subject further. The essay selections have an economic and cultural bias, and those relating to the natural sciences either have special relevance to the history of science or are generally regarded as popular rather than strictly scientific accounts of the Swamp. Nevertheless, the latter observations can have scientific value, as Handley has shown in this volume. Moreover, in the older literature especially the distinction between "popular" and "scientific" becomes rather arbitrary. In no way should this commentary be considered a complete bibliography of the entire subject. Many additional items not cited in the essay have been listed at the end in a Supplemental Bibliography, and attention is also called to the many references given in the preceding papers and elsewhere in this volume. The references presumed to be of greatest interest to naturalists and environmentalists are designated in the lists with an asterisk*, and a separate article emphasizing the more technical scientific literature follows this one. Serious investigators who take a holistic view of natural and human history should find pertinent references in both bibliographies.

Government records—British, federal, state, and local—all contain information. British Custom's Records (Great Britain Naval Office Returns, 1730–72), for example, reveal the volume and value of the colonial lumber trade, much of which originated in the Swamp. Federal documents, other than those that deal with the sciences, mostly pertain to the United States interest in the Dismal Swamp Canal. These documents include survey maps and proposals submitted to and by various branches of the federal government, and are now in the Library of Congress and the National Archives. The Virginia State Library in Richmond holds published annual reports of the Canal and its branches telling of the work done, tolls collected, and the volume and nature of commerce. Since part of the Canal and the Swamp through which it runs are located in North Carolina, that state's archives also contain documents. Various local jurisdictions in both Virginia and North Carolina offer probate and land transfer information about those who claimed title to the Swamp.

Manuscript collections contain the largest untapped supply of materials. The Virginia State Archives, in addition to published records, houses the unpublished manuscripts of the state's Board of Public Works, including information on the Canal Company as well as the two antebellum railroads that crossed portions of the Swamp. Duke University, Durham, N.C., has the most valuable of all primary collections in the papers of the Dismal Swamp Land Company. This collection contains several thousand pieces and includes quarterly production and sales reports, plus letters detailing management and ownership problems. The College of William and Mary holds an important adjunct collection of Land Company materials classified as the [E. G.] Swem Dismal Swamp Papers. The collection contains the original list of the 154 petitioners who received the land grant as well as the results of some surveying done by Gershom Nimmo. Berkeley and Berkeley (1976) make extensive use of these early papers and cite numerous other sources in their detailed historical account "Man and the Great Dismal." Duke University also holds the John Kilby Papers, which should have additional information, as the Kilby family controlled portions of the swampland in the nineteenth century.

The senior author's interest in this topic was rekindled by inadvertently coming upon some letters that covered incidents in the history of the Swamp. The *Loyalists Claims* of the Birtish Public Record Office, available in this country on microfilm, have several items of special interest, including the petition of Isaac Hildreth, a house carpenter who surveyed for a canal before the Revolution when he joined Lord Dunmore in the capacity of an engineer. Also included is the petition of Captain Joliffe, a Portsmouth loyalist who hid in the Dismal Swamp while spying for Benedict Arnold and then helped in guerilla operations. Joliffe takes credit for the ambush of a notorious rebel leader, Captain Nott (Survey Report no. 2395). Another letter discusses the affairs of the Dismal Swamp Land Company after the Revolution (Anon. 1783). The papers of Charles Stewart at the National Library of Scotland, also available on microfilm, contain a letter from James Parker (15 November 1769) which deals with this later loyalist's efforts to cut paths into the Swamp in pursuit of lumber. It also refers to the work of others at the same time. Unfortunately, such peripheral letters are not indexed in a way that would allow scholars of the Dismal Swamp to learn of their existence except by happenstance. There is simply no way of knowing how much additional fugitive material may exist.

With the major exception of the writings of William Byrd II, only a limited amount of primary manuscript material on the Dismal Swamp has ever been published. In 1925 John C. Fitzpatrick edited *The diaries of George Washington, 1748–1770* and between 1931–44 *The writings of George Washington, 1745–1799.* The latest edition of *The diaries of George Washington* is by Jackson (1976). The diary contains an account of one of Washington's forages around the Dismal Swamp and the other source has numerous letters pertaining to Swamp affairs scattered through its many volumes. Another relatively recent publication of a primary source, edited by Eleanor P. and Charles B. Cross, Jr. (1968), is *Glencoe diary: the war-time journal of Elizabeth Curtis Wallace.* This account vividly describes the troubles endured by a family who ran a plantation on the east side of the Swamp during the tumultous Civil War years.

A more comprehensive study of newspapers would also aid a great deal to our knowledge of the Swamp and Swamp life. A considerable amount of material on routine Swamp affairs appears in nineteenth- and twentieth-century local newspapers. In the late 1930s C. L. Morton wrote feature articles for the *Norfolk Virginian-Pilot* and the *Richmond Times-Dispatch.* A local historian, John C. Emmerson, Jr., of Portsmouth (1950), made a compilation of newspaper clippings entitled *Dismal Swamp Canal,* which may be found in the Mariner's Museum Library in Newport News, Virginia. A similar collection for the history of the entire Swamp should be of great value. Despite its unpretentious title, *The hotel of the Great Dismal Swamp and contemporary events thereabouts,* by Jesse Forbes Pugh and Frank T. Williams (1964), starts in the right direction. The book notes newspaper accounts of events in upper North Carolina and employs local archives for marriage records to validate matrimonial matters at the Half Way House.

The work of the archaeologist is, of course, vital to obtain an understanding of the Dismal Swamp. For articles representative of the type of work being done see Ben McCary (1963, 1968) and Edward Bottoms and Floyd Painter (1972 and in this volume). These articles and several others scattered through the *Quart. Bull. Archeol. Soc. Va.* and the *Chesopiean* offer some fascinating, if inconclusive, evidence of early man's encounter with the Swamp.

The literature by and about William Byrd staggers the scholar. The "conqueror" of the Dismal Swamp not only wrote at least two accounts of the episodes related to surveying the boundary line between Virginia and North Carolina, but about nearly everything else he did as well. His "Secret Diaries," which disappeared and were rediscovered piecemeal, were written in shorthand and had to be deciphered. A product of Virginia planter society, Byrd's diaries reveal much about life in eighteenth-century Virginia. Though less crude and with many more intellectual pursuits, Byrd at times seems to be an American version of Squire Western, a character in Fielding's *Tom Jones,* who thoroughly enjoyed physical activity. A good recent biography of Byrd is Pierre Marambaud's (1971) *William Byrd of Westover, 1674–1744.* There are many places to find Byrd's ideas. John Spencer Bassett (1901) *The writings of "Colonel William Byrd of Westover in Virginia Esqr.,"* Earl Gregg Swem (1922) *Descriptions of the Dismal and a proposal to drain the Swamp,* William K. Boyd (1929) *William Byrd's histories of the dividing line betwixt Virginia and North Carolina,* and Louis B. Wright (1966) *The prose works of William Byrd of Westover Virginia* are all helpful. One of Byrd's papers, April 1789, "A description of the Dismal Swamp in Virginia . . ." contains his usual proposal to drain the Swamp and build a canal, but it also includes the comments of a writer in 1789 who thought that such a canal would freshen the water in Norfolk's harbor, thus reducing the destruction by shipworms. Produced at the time the Canal Company received its charter and needed financial assistance, the idea illustrates that the promotional side of man's mind knows no bounds.

Nearly all the source material cited thus far has focused on the economic exploitation of the Dismal Swamp, but there also exists a considerable body of cultural artifacts. The Mariner's Museum in Newport News, holds one copy of the famous Williamson drawing that Mr. Hall of Norfolk turned into a lithograph. The work shows the Canal and Half Way House. An engraving entitled *The lake of the Dismal Swamp,* done on steel under the name of J. G. Chapman (1839) appears in *Knickerbocker Magazine.* Another early engraving with George Washington and his horse in the foreground and Lake Drummond in the background can be found in a private archive in New York, but it also appeared on the cover of the Dismal Swamp issue of *Contact* magazine (Freston 1973).

Other sketches of life in the Swamp can be found in several nineteenth-century periodicals. The most extensive work of this type goes under the pseudonym Porte Crayon (David Hunter Strother), a reporter born in Winchester, Virginia. Strother, who entered the Swamp from the Suffolk side, wrote an 1856 article, "The Dismal Swamp," which includes much philosophy, some history, a few legends, personal experiences while touring the Swamp, and a couple of fabrications. Since the magazine had a wide circulation, many people knew about the Swamp only vicariously through his account.

The primary literature and poetry are generally available in anthologies and articles dealing with the Dismal Swamp or Lake Drummond. Thomas Moore's famous ballad "The lake of the Dismal Swamp" has been reproduced several times since the 1846 edition. The same applies to Henry Wadsworth Longfellow's "The slave in the Dismal Swamp." Harriet Beecher Stowe's *Dred; a tale of the Great Dismal Swamp* is the best-known novel to use the Swamp as background. First published in Boston in 1856, this was reprinted in 1972. An anonymous short story in 1886, "An adventure in the Dismal Swamp: a story of the rebellion," purports to describe guerilla activities during the Civil War, but though some skirmishing undoubtedly took place in the Swamp during war, this short story could have taken place nearly anywhere, for the Swamp is not a factor in the story. John Hamilton Howard's book (1906) *In the shadow of the pines* was sufficiently popular that many public libraries possess a copy.

The legends about the Swamp are distributed through many travel and descriptive accounts. Two available secondary sources are Margaret Davis's (1934) " 'Great Dismal' pictures" and Hubert J. Davis's (1971) *The Great Dismal Swamp, its history, folklore and science.* Despite the title, Margaret Davis's article has no photographs, but does deal with some curious tales about the area. One deals with "Old Johnny Culpepper," who carried on a conversation with a bear. A bear sentence followed this pattern: "Gumpty sifty, Gumpty sifty, Google claw." Other than suggesting that the bear repeated itself, the words obviously tell us very little. Johnny also told of the time he found a deer with a poem hanging from its neck, which offered this plea: "When Julius Caesar here did reign/ About my neck he hung this chain/ and whosoever me shall take/ Save me for Julius Caesar's sake." A reader who believes any of the foregoing should also accept the notion that the deer was actually William Byrd reincarnate, for that worthy liked to make classical reference. Possibly the bear resembles the Virginia cavalier more closely, for Byrd also coded his remarks to make them difficult to understand.

Hubert J. Davis does an even more elaborate job, particularly on Indian legends. The book also has some historical coverage, but it is very difficult to know where legends end and history begins. Written for the edification of children, the book includes a story about George Washington climbing a tree to escape a bear. There is a sketch of a very youthful-looking George in said tree with an accompanying comment that the future president probably had never before faced a more difficult situation. Since George had already led Virginia's troops against the French and had his hands full as part of Brad-dock's disastrous experience, the whole idea is a little preposterous. That yarn, along with another crediting Washington with giving Deep Creek, a village on the eastern edge of the Swamp, its name for remarking on the depth of the water into which he accidentally fell, makes one wonder if Parson Weems has met his match. On the whole, however, *The Great Dismal Swamp* has value, for readers of all ages.

Nineteenth- and twentieth-century travel accounts and memoirs sometimes give historical information, but their greatest value lies in their descriptions of what was taking place at the time. As might be expected, such sources are prone to exaggerate and mislead. The nineteenth-century materials include Strother's previously cited article written in 1856, an anonymously written article entitled "The Dismal Swamp" (1850), which appeared in *Chambers's Edin-burgh Journal,* and Frederick Law Olmstead's (1904) *A journey in the sea-board slave states in the years 1853–54 with reports on their economy,* in 2 volumes. The anonymous traveler (probably a Scot) who toured the lowlands of North Carolina and Virginia commented on the shingle business. He observed that cypress shingles served as American sub-stitutes for roofing slate. Slaves and escaped bondsmen (as many as a thousand, he heard) produced shingles deep in the Swamp. This particular traveler was thoroughly unimpressed with the Swamp, Swamp life, the Half Way House (especially its food), Elizabeth City, and practically everything else he saw. Olmstead, later the founder of Central Park in New York City, journeyed into the Swamp to find out more about slavery and its impact on the southern economy. He offers a detailed analysis of the employment of blacks in the lumber business.

Other nineteenth-century accounts include the memoirs of Robert Arnold (1888), *The Dismal Swamp and Lake Drummond: early recollections, vivid portrayal of amusing scenes.* Arnold, a resident of Suffolk, mentions talking with an old Negro guide who claimed to have escorted Thomas Moore from Suffolk into Lake Drummond in the early part of the century. Other sources claim Moore went to the Half Way House along the Canal. He may have gone to neither place. The subtitle of Arnold's book, *Uncle Alick and the mule,* gives some indication of the credibility of this work. One of the better accounts is that of W. H. B[ishop], "To the Great Dismal Swamp" (1882). The author took the steamer *Thomas Newton* down the Canal, stayed at the Wallace plantation for a time, and entered Lake Drummond from the Feeder Ditch. He described the Swamp, the plantation, and the people who lived in the area.

The turn of the century brought even more interest in seeing and reporting about the Swamp, including contributions by women. Harriet E. Freeman and Emma G. Cummings (1901), in "Dismal Swamp and how to go there," offer a charming account of how "two enterprising New England women" barely made it from Hampton to Norfolk, took the railroad to Elizabeth City, then against the advice of well-meaning males boarded a canal boat going to Norfolk, sat and watched the scenery, and then had the audacity to advise people on how to find the Dismal Swamp. Another article, "A day in the Great Dismal Swamp" (Catlin 1905), concerns the experiences of two ladies who stayed overnight in Suffolk. There they found a black guide who fascinated them far more than the Swamp through which he conducted them.

Other early twentieth-century articles are Walter Prichard Eaton (1910), who reported on "The real Dismal Swamp" and mentioned Nathaniel Shaler's suggestion for draining; and Frederick Street (1903), "In the Dismal Swamp," which gives the views of still another reporter who toured the Swamp. Street termed "delicious" the meat of wild cattle encountered in the Swamp. He also noted a rumor that a western syndicate planned to redeem a major tract of the Dismal Swamp for traditional agriculture. Like many folk in the early twentieth century, Street seemed unaware of the vast amount of peat that made farming difficult, if not impossible. The reporter predicted a relatively early demise for the entire Swamp. Along the same line of thought, but from the perspective of the U.S. Geological Survey at the time Theodore Roosevelt's conservation program was well underway (1907), is Herbert Wilson's "Reclaiming the swamp lands of the United States." Wilson called for draining vast portions of America's wetlands, including the Dismal Swamp.

By far the best twentieth-century account is Charles F. Stansbury's (1925) *The lake of the Great Dismal*, which deals extensively with the literature and history of Lake Drummond. Stansbury, a newsman, was the first person to fly over the Dismal Swamp and to land on Lake Drummond in a seaplane. Two other fairly good travel and descriptive accounts are John Francis Ariza (1932), "Dismal Swamp in legend and history," and R. F. Nelson (1930), "Visiting Great Dismal Swamp." The first also delves into historical matters.

Sportsmen have long had a deep interest in matters relating to the Dismal Swamp. Alexander Hunter wrote two articles and a book on hunting expeditions into the Lake Drummond area. These are "The Great Dismal Swamp" (1895), "Through the Dismal Swamp" (1881) and *The huntsman in the South* (1908). They all contain anecdotes and descriptions with some historical references. The author manages to misplace the discovery of Lake Drummond by a little over a hundred years, but his descriptions of some of the human residents are invaluable. The chapter on the Dismal Swamp in the book is very similar to the article written by him over a quarter of a century earlier. Today's sports-minded people are still interested in the Swamp; note the continued historical orientation in Ellington White's (1973) "George Washington dug here."

The historical scholarship in the Dismal Swamp remains somewhat limited, but there are several items that deserve comment. Two of these are especially useful. "History of the Dismal Swamp Land Company of Virginia," by Robert H. Reid (1948) makes good use of the land company records housed at Duke. Much more can be done, however, not only with the Land Company's development, but also with the activities of other individuals and corporations that have exploited the Swamp. "The literature and legends of the Great Dismal Swamp," by Robert H. Morrison (1947), is a first-rate thesis about the poets, novelists, and others who have used the theme of the Swamp in their cultural works. Morrison's bibliography has 134 entries.

Published materials include the efforts of Alexander Crosby Brown (1947), who authored a brief article, "The lady of the lake in the Dismal Swamp," and two book-length studies, both entitled *The Dismal Swamp Canal.* The second (1970) is simply an enlargement of the first (1967), some of which appeared as installments in *Amer. Neptune* in July 1945 (5:203–222), October 1945 (5:297–310) and January 1946 (6:51–70). The books are thorough studies using government documents, a variety of primary journals, and Norfolk newspaper notations collected by John C. Emmerson, Jr. (1950). The bibliography in the 1970 edition is extensive and includes many federal documents, pp. 218–220. In the post–World War II era a rash of works on canal building in America appeared. Brown's books filled a major void by examining the history of one of the major links in the Atlantic coast's network of nineteenth-century canals. Through Brown's work we now know a great deal about the story of construction and maintenance, but economic historians will want to know more of the kind and volume of commerce which flowed over the Canal in order to evaluate the importance of the project in the local and national economies.

A particularly facinating, though very tiny, pamphlet is Dr. John A. Muscalus's (1965) *The Dismal Canal and Lake Drummond Hotel on paper money, 1838–1865.* Produced for the Historical Paper Money Research Institute (historical inquiries often make strange bedfellows), this study explores the use of Thomas Williamson's drawing of the Canal and Lake Drummond Hotel (Half Way House) on various currencies. The pamphlet includes pictures of the money.

Several short articles have appeared in *Virginia Cavalcade,* the popular state-sponsored historical journal. William Harris Gains wrote two (1954*a* and *b*), "Men against the Swamp" and "The minstrel sang of a dusky lake." The first includes the Williamson sketch and a good, though brief, discussion of the history of man's involvement with the Dismal Swamp. The second article examines Thomas Moore's visit to Norfolk and the background of the famous poem. Another short but accurate historical account in the same journal was written by Ulrich Troubetzkoy in 1961, "The Great Dismal Swamp." This author also wrote four historically oriented articles for *Virginia Wildlife* (1967*a–c*, 1968). Not nearly of the same quality is Horace Sutton's (1955) "A filthy bogg," and still lower in any reasonable assessment of recent articles on the Swamp falls Carrol Hughes's (1945) "The Great Dismal Swamp."

Local history books can often be helpful on the Swamp's history. The Norfolk County Historical Society of Chesapeake produced a short book written by Betty Hathaway Yarborough and researched by Jayne Cosby Wilkinson (1965), *The Great Dismal,* which could have been expanded. William H. Stewart (1902), *History of Norfolk County, Virginia, and representative citizens,* contains a fairly large segment on the Dismal which appears to have been based on Shaler's earlier comments about reclamation. Also, Rogers Dey Whichard's three-volume *The history of lower Tidewater* has one chapter on the Swamp written by Floyd McKnight (1959). Alvah Duke (1973), a local resident who has worked diligently on the preservation of the Dismal Swamp, privately produced a pamphlet titled *Dismal Swamp wildlife.* The work contains some errors on man's early encounters with the Swamp, but includes useful documentation of the current conservation movement.

Scientific journals and books, both popular and scholarly, supply a considerable body of material not only on matters with which naturalists are normally concerned, but with cultural and economic interests as well. One of the best-known naturalists to examine the Swamp was Sir Charles Lyell, who in 1845 published *Travels in North America in the years 1841–1842: with geological observations on the United States, Canada and Nova Scotia.* In volume 1, chapter 7, he describes a railroad trip across the "pine barrens" of southeastern Virginia. Although only viewing that portion of the Swamp through which the train passed, Lyell explained the geological development of the Swamp and used its presence to theorize about coal formation. Lyell, despite his short tenure in the Swamp, was quite descriptive, even describing his train. J. W. Chickering (1873), in "The flora of the Dismal Swamp," avoids cultural commentary, but A. B. Webster's (1875) "On the physical and geological characteristics of the Great Dismal and the eastern counties of Virginia" succumbed to temptation and claimed George Washington was twenty-one years of age in 1763. The article also briefly refers to Lyell's theory of coal formation. Charles Louis Pollard (1896) reports on a scientific expedition along the Jericho canal route, whereas Arthur Hollick (1912) briefly analyzes tree growth and includes two pages of illustrations.

Several articles appeared in *Scientific American* in the 1890s. A. K. Fisher (1845) described cattle, other Swamp animals, and fish. He also discussed the lack of malaria, the condition of timber, the process of shingle making, and a number of other matters in a surprisingly short article. An anonymous writer (1898) offered diagrams and related information on the rebuilding of the Dismal Swamp Canal under the title "Reconstruction of the Dismal Swamp Canal." Another worthwhile article, presumably written by J. Ralph (Anon. 1892), "The Virginia Dismal Swamp," describing animals, including the bears and cattle, which often fought. The description of the bears defeating the wild horned bulls by climbing on their necks is undoubtedly taken from Shaler's 1890 paper, which he cites (see excerpt p. 350). The anonymous writer also discussed prospects for claiming the Swamp for agricultural purposes.

Nathaniel S. Shaler's (1890) "General account of the fresh-water morasses of the United States" was a landmark study of the swamplands that stressed the Dismal Swamp's medicinal value and determined the cost and value of reclaiming the wetlands. Even Thomas H. Kearney's (1901) botanical study of lower Virginia suggested reclamation by noting that the type of groundcover often gave indications of the possible use of the soil.

As the twentieth century has progressed, scientists have become less interested in reclamation, perhaps because most of the potential farmland has been brought under cultivation, or because of a greater concern for preservation of natural forest lands. Whatever the explanation, the core or center of the Swamp is no longer threatened by farming or timber interests. The recent gifts to The Nature Conservancy from the Union Camp Corporation of the old Land Company acreage, and from the Georgia Pacific Company of some of the New Lebanon holdings, have protected the central area of the Dismal Swamp. Scientists in their various specialties may now explore the intriguing natural aspects of the Swamp with a comparative peace of mind.

What, then, is the task of the historian? The preceding bibliographical essay offers many possible avenues of investigation, depending on one's definition of the Dismal Swamp. If a broad approach is taken and the studies include more than the peatlands and unreclaimable soil, the historian, in effect, is studying the history of much of lower Tidewater Virginia and a great deal of the northeastern corner of North Carolina. If one takes the narrowest definition, then the primary focus would be on land roughly three times the amount recently turned over to the federal government.

No matter which definition is used, there are several topics intimately connected to the Swamp's history which need inquiry. The only related topic having received rather complete coverage is the history of the Dismal Swamp Canal. A thorough historical study of lumber operations compared to similar work elsewhere should be interesting. An examination of farm practices in the general area of the Swamp would enhance our knowledge about former agricultural habits and techniques. Historians would certainly be interested in the use of slaves, free blacks, and other laborers who worked in the forests or on the farms. Intensive combing of Virginia and North Carolina archives for the papers of people who lived near the Swamp or held interests there should be fruitful for all of these topics.

These few suggestions by no means exhaust the list of possibilities. The guerilla activities of loyalists like Josiah Phillips during the Revolution or of rabid secessionists during the Civil War may interest the military historian. It should be apparent from this essay that the Dismal Swamp affected the thinking of many people who were never within a hundred miles of the place. Our comments have barely scratched the surface of this particular role of the Swamp.

REFERENCES CITED

Anon. 1783. Letter to Samuel Gist, 7 Nov. 1783, in Robert Gilmour Petition. *Loyalist Claims*. Great Britain. Public Record Office. Survey Report 2394.

Anon. 1850. The Dismal Swamp. *Chambers's Edinburgh J.* 23(14 Dec.):373–375.

Anon. 1886. An adventure in the Dismal Swamp: a story of the rebellion. *Cosmopolitan* 1:99–101.

*Anon. 1892. The Virginia Dismal Swamp. *Sci. Amer.* 66(21 May):322. [by J. Ralph?]

*Anon. 1898. Reconstruction of the Dismal Swamp Canal. *Sci. Amer.* 78(5 Mar.):145, 153–154.

*Ariza, J. F. 1932. Dismal Swamp in legend and history. *Natl. Geog. Mag.* 62(July):120–130.

*Arnold, R. 1888. *The Dismal Swamp and Lake Drummond: early recollections, vivid portrayal of amusing scenes*. Green, Burke & Gregory, Norfolk. 78 pp.

*Bassett, J. S. (ed). 1901. *The writings of "Colonel William Byrd of Westover in*

Virginia Esqr." Doubleday, Page & Co., New York. 461 pp. (Reprinted in 1971 by Burt Franklin of New York.)

*Berkeley, E., and Dorothy Berkeley. 1976. Man and the Great Dismal. *Va. J. Sci.* 27:141–171.

*B[ishop], W. H. 1882. To the Great Dismal Swamp. *Nation* (New York) 35(14 Dec.):502–504.

*Bottoms, E., and F. Painter. 1972. Bola weights from the Dismal Swamp region of Virginia and North Carolina. *Chesopiean* 10:19–30.

*Boyd, W. K. (ed). 1929. *William Byrd's histories of the dividing line betwixt Virginia and North Carolina.* N.C. Hist. Comm., Raleigh. 341 pp. (Reprinted in 1967 by Dover Publ. Co., New York.)

Brown, A. C. 1947. The lady of the lake in the Dismal Swamp. *Amer. Neptune* 7(Jan.):66.

———. 1967. *The Dismal Swamp Canal.* Norfolk Co. Hist. Soc. Chesapeake, Va. 144 pp.

*———. 1970. *The Dismal Swamp Canal,* rev. and enlarged ed. Norfolk Co. Hist. Soc. Chesapeake, Va. 234 pp.

*Byrd, W. 1789. A description of the Dismal Swamp, in Virginia; with proposals for and observations on the advantages of draining it. *Columbian Mag.* (Philadelphia) 3(April):230–234.

Catlin, Louise E. 1905. A day in the Great Dismal Swamp. *Mag. Amer. Hist.* 2:339–345.

Chapman, J. G. 1839. The lake of the Dismal Swamp. *Knickerbocker* 13 (May):367 (an engraving).

*Chickering, J. W. 1873. The flora of the Dismal Swamp. *Amer. Nat.* 7(Sept.): 521–524.

Cross, Eleanor P., and C. B. Cross, Jr. 1968. *Glencoe diary: the war-time journal of Elizabeth Curtis Wallace.* Norfolk Co. Hist. Soc. Chesapeake, Va. 156 pp.

Davis, H. J. 1971. *The Great Dismal Swamp, its history, folklore and science,* rev. ed. Johnson Publ. Co., Murfreesboro, N.C. 182 pp.

*Davis, Margaret. 1934. "Great Dismal" pictures. *S. Atlantic Quart.* 33(Apr.): 171–184.

*Duke, A. 1973. *Dismal Swamp wildlife.* Adams Press, Chicago. 97 pp.

*Eaton, W. P. 1910. The real Dismal Swamp. *Harper's Monthly Mag.* 122 (Dec.):18–30.

*Emmerson, J. C., Jr. (comp). 1950. *Dismal Swamp Canal.* Mariner's Museum, Newport News, Va.

*Fisher, A. K. 1845. The Dismal Swamp and its occupants. *Sci Amer.* 73(5 Oct.):220.

Fitzpatrick, J. C. (ed). 1925. *The diaries of George Washington, 1745–1799,* v. 1–4. Houghton Mifflin Co., Boston.

———. (ed). 1931–44. *The writings of George Washington 1745–1799,* v. 1–39. U.S. Govt. Print. Off., Washington. (Index to Dismal Swamp entries v. 38, p. 179)

Freeman, Harriet E., and Emma G. Cummings. 1901. Dismal Swamp and how to go there. *Chatauquan* 33(Aug.):515–518.

*Freston, T. E. (ed). 1973. *Contact* 8(1). Dismal Swamp issue. Union Camp Corp., Wayne, N.J. 24 pp. (Portions reprinted in *Va. Wildlife*, 1974, Apr., pp. 19–20, 24; also *Va. Wildlife Federation Record*, 1973.)

*Gains, W. H. 1954a. Men against the Swamp. *Va. Cavalcade* 4(Winter):23–29.

———. 1954b. The minstrel sang of a dusky lake. *Va. Cavalcade* 4(Winter): 30–31.

Great Britain Naval Office Returns, 1730–72. Lower James River District. (Univ. Virginia microfilm.)

*Hollick, A. 1912. The Dismal Swamp of Virginia. *Amer. Forests* 18(July): 431–434.

Howard, J. H. 1906. *In the shadow of the pines.* Eaton and Mains, New York. 249 pp.

Hughes, Carrol. 1945. The Great Dismal Swamp. *Coronet* 17(Jan.):31–33.

*Hunter, A. 1881. Through the Dismal Swamp. *Potter's Amer. Monthly* 17 (July):1–15.

*———. 1895. The Great Dismal Swamp. *Outing* 27:70–76.

*———. 1908. *The huntsman in the South.* Neale Publ. Co., New York, 318 pp. Includes a chapter on the Swamp.

Jackson, D. (ed). 1976 to date. *The diaries of George Washington*, v. 1–4. Univ. Press of Va., Charlottesville.

*Kearney, T. H. 1901. Report on a botanical survey of the Dismal Swamp region. *Contrib. U.S. Natl. Herbarium* 5:321–585.

Longfellow, H. W. 1908. *The complete poetical works of Henry Wadsworth Longfellow.* Houghton Mifflin Co., Boston. 689 pp.

*Lyell, C. 1845. *Travels in North America in the years 1841–1842: with geological observations on the United States, Canada and Nova Scotia,* v. 1 and 2. Wiley & Putnam, New York.

*McCary, B. 1963. The archaeology of the western area of the Dismal Swamp in Virginia. *Quart. Bull. Archeol. Soc. Va.* 17:40–48.

*———. 1968. Bannerstones of the Dismal Swamp area in Virginia and North Carolina. *Quart. Bull. Archeol. Soc. Va.* 22:118–155.

McKnight, F. 1959. The Great Dismal Swamp. Pp. 181–190 *in* R. Whichard (ed). *The history of Tidewater Virginia,* v. 2. Lewis Hist. Publ. Co., New York.

Marambaud, P. 1971. *William Byrd of Westover, 1674–1744.* Univ. Press of Virginia, Charlottesville. 297 pp.

Moore, T. 1846. *Poetical works of Thomas Moore.* D. Appleton and Co., New York. 747 pp.

Morrison, R. H. 1947. The literature and legends of the Great Dismal Swamp. Master's Thesis Univ. North Carolina (Chapel Hill). 107 pp.

Muscalus, J. A. 1965. *The Dismal Canal and Lake Drummond Hotel on paper money, 1838–1865.* Historical Paper Money Res. Inst., Bridgeport, Pa. 8 pp.

*Nelson, R. F. 1930. Visiting Great Dismal Swamp. *Natl. Repub.* 18(May): 18–20.

Olmstead, F. L. 1904. *A journey in the seaboard slave states in the years 1853–54 with reports on their economy,* v. 1 and 2. G. P. Putnam's Sons, New York.

*Pollard, C. L. 1896. Notes on a trip to the Dismal Swamp. *Garden and Forest* 9(18 Nov.):462–463.

Pugh, J. F., and F. T. Williams. 1964. *The hotel of the Great Dismal Swamp and contempory events thereabouts.* Old Trap, N.C. 174 pp.

*Reid, R. H. 1948. History of the Dismal Swamp Land Company of Virginia. Master's Thesis Duke Univ. 167 pp.

*Shaler, N. S. 1890. General account of the fresh-water morasses of the United States with a description of the Dismal Swamp district of Virginia and North Carolina. *U.S. Geol. Survey, Ann. Rpt.* 10(pt. 1):261–339.

*Stansbury, C. F. 1925. *The lake of the Great Dismal.* Albert and Charles Boni Publ. Co., New York. 238 pp.

*Stewart, W. H. 1902. *History of Norfolk County, Virginia, and representative citizens.* Biographical Publ. Co., Chicago. 1042 pp.

Stowe, Harriet B. 1856. *Dred; a tale of the Great Dismal Swamp.* v. 1, 242 pp. v. 2, 391 pp. Sampson Low, Son and Co., London. (A 1972 reprint is available from AMS, New York.)

Street, F. 1903. In the Dismal Swamp. *Frank Leslie's Popular Monthly Mag.* 55(Mar.):527–531.

*Strother, D. H. [Porte Crayon]. 1856. The Dismal Swamp. *Harper's New Monthly Mag.* 13(Sept.):441–455.

*Sutton, H. 1955. A filthy bogg. *Sat. Rev. Lit.* 38(6 Aug.):38–39.

*Swem, E. G. (ed). 1922. *Descriptions of the Dismal Swamp and a proposal to drain the Swamp.* Charles F. Heatman, Metuchen, N.J. 32 pp.

*Troubetzkoy, U. 1961. The Great Dismal Swamp. *Va. Cavalcade* 10(Spring): 19–27.

*_____. 1967a. Seasons in the Dismal Swamp—spring. *Va. Wildlife* 28(6): 17–20.

*_____. 1967b. Seasons in the Dismal Swamp—summer. *Va. Wildlife* 28(8): 4–5, 22–23.

_____. 1967c. Seasons in the Dismal Swamp—autumn. *Va. Wildlife* 28(10): 6–8, 17.

*_____. 1968. Seasons in the Dismal Swamp—winter. *Va. Wildlife* 29(3):6–7, 19–22.

*Webster, A. B. 1875. On the physical and geological characteristics of the Great Dismal and the eastern counties of Virginia. *Amer. Nat.* 9(May): 260–277.

*White, E. 1973. George Washington dug here. *Sports Illus.* 38(16 Apr.):87.

*Wilson, H. 1907. Reclaiming the swamp lands of the United States. *Natl. Geog. Mag.* 18(May):292–301.

Wright, L. B. (ed). 1966. *The prose works of William Byrd of Westover, narratives of a colonial Virginian.* Harvard Univ. Press, Belknap Press, Cambridge, Mass. 438 pp.

*Yarborough, Betty Hathaway, and Jayne C. Wilkerson. 1965. *The Great Dismal.* Norfolk Co. Hist. Soc. Chesapeake, Va. 18 pp. (unnumbered). Includes wildlife photos.

SUPPLEMENTAL BIBLIOGRAPHY

This supplemental list includes only work not mentioned in the text of the preceeding essay. It consists of three parts: (1) older items, including two federal documents not cited by Brown (1970); (2) comparatively recent newspaper, periodical, and miscellaneous material; and (3) the nonscientific reports and summaries of the comprehensive Dismal Swamp Study (P.L. 92–478). Most of the periodial citations (part 2) are intended primarily for the general reader as they stress popular views on the topic, but some are of a scientific nature while having literary value or containing historical observations. For a more detailed analysis of scientific literature, including the remainder of the Dismal Swamp Study reports, see the following bibliographical essay in this volume.

1. Older Sources and Federal Documents

Anon. 1858. The Dismal Swamp Canal. *DeBow's Review* 25(Sept.):365–366.

Anon. 1867/1869. Annual report of the president and directors to the stockholders of the Dismal Swamp Canal Company, for fiscal year ending Sept. 30, 1868. Kirn Memorial Library, Norfolk, Va.

*Anon. 1900. The Dismal Swamp of Virginia. *Sci. Amer.* 82:249–250.

*Anon. 1901. Some Swamp experiences. *Forest and Stream* 57:286.

*Anon. 1920. Not so dismal after all. *Literary Dig.* 64(6):88–90.

*Brickell, J. 1737, *The natural history of North-Carolina.* James Carson, Dublin. 417 pp. (1969 reprint by Johnnson Reprint Corp., New York.)

Brougham, J. 1856. Dred: of the Dismal Swamp: a play in five acts. Dramatized from Harriet Beecher Stowe's novel. No. 145 in *French's American drama.* S. French, New York. 43 pp. (Univ. Michigan microfilm.)

Caldwell, H. 1866. *Oliatta and other poems.* J. S. Redfield, New York. 200 pp.

Dunn, J. B. [1907?] *The history of Nansemond County, Virginia.* Map and 71 pp. n.p., Kirn Memorial Library, Norfolk.

*Farley, J. 1826. Plan of the Dismal Swamp Canal. U.S. Army, MS map, July. National Archives. Senate Collection No. 25222.

King, J. T. 1878. The great North American natural curiosity—the Dismal Swamp of North Carolina. *University Mag.* (Univ. North Carolina [Chapel Hill]) 1(Apr.):55–61. Mentions health aspects.

Luetscher, G. D. 1908. Atlantic coastwise canals: their history and present status. *Ann. Amer. Acad. Pol. Soc. Sci.* 31(Jan.):92–101.

Lyell, C. L. 1842. Great Dismal Swamp. *Petersburg* (Va.) *Farmer's Register* 10:353. An extract from Lyell's lectures.

*Ralph, J. 1892. Virginia Dismal Swamp. *Sci. Amer.* 66(21 May):322.

*Ruffin, E. 1837. Observations made during an excursion to the Dismal Swamp. *Petersburg* (Va.) *Farmers' Register* 4(1 Jan.):513–521.

*Stansbury, C. F. 1907. In the Great Dismal Swamp. *Eclectic Mag.* 148(1): 3–17.

*Swem, E. G. 1919. An analysis of Ruffin's Farmers' Register, with a bibliography of Edmund Ruffin. *Va. State Lib. Bull.* 11(3 and 4). 144 pp.

*U.S. Congress. House of Representatives. 1906. Drainage of Dismal Swamp of North Carolina and Virginia. 22 June. Washington, 59th Cong., 1st. sess., Rpt. on 4994. (See Brown, 1970, for congressional sources.)

2. Recent Articles in Newspapers, Periodicals and Miscellany

*Anon. 1943. Survey of Dismal Swamp area to be made by forest service. *Norfolk Virginian-Pilot* (13 Feb.).

*Anon. 1952. The Great Dismal Swamp. *Norfolk and Western Mag.* (July):414–418, 432.

*Anon. 1970–71. The fabled Swamp. *Living Wilderness* 34(Winter):28. By the editor, accompanying articles by Delzell, de Rageot, and Meanley.

*Anon. 1972. Industry steps in to save the land. *U.S. News and World Rpt.* 74(19 Mar.):63–64.

*Anon. 1972. Union Camp donates a swamp. *Business Week* (20 Jan.):23.

*Anon. 1973. Preserving ye Great Dismal for posterity. *Scientific News* 103 (3 Mar.):132–133.

Anon. 1974. Twenty-two research projects at refuge. *Suffolk News-Herald* (29 Dec.): Sunday supplement.

*Anon. 1974. A swamp reprieved. Pp. 140–147 *in* Jane D. Alexander (ed). *1974 nature/science annual.* Time-Life Books, New York.

*Anon. 1975. Dismal Swamp explorations planned. *UNews,* Old Dominion Univ. 4(30 May):8.

Anon. 1976 to date. *Dismal Swamp Explorations.* Newsletter of Office of Dismal Swamp Programs, Old Dominion Univ. Published irregularly. Largely the work of G. F. Levy, Program Director.

Anon. 1978. Swamp's past hotels shady. *UNews,* Old Dominion Univ. 7(10 Mar.):2.

Brady, P. M., and K. B. Cumming. 1971. Black crappie fishing in black water. *Va. Wildlife* 32(6):4–5.

Brown, J. 1978. The Great Dismal Swamp. *Norfolk Virginian-Pilot* (26 March): C1, 3.

*Brown, W. R. 1976. Environment education activity packets. No. 3, Dismal Swamp (ages 12–14); No. 9, The Great Dismal Swamp Canal (ages 12–14); No. 18, A trip to the Swamp (ages 12 up); No. 20, The Great Dismal Swamp—Future? (ages 10 up); No. 21, Dismal Swamp Challenges: I (age 5 up); No. 22, Dismal Swamp Challenges: II (age 5 up); No. 23, Fire Bird—The Slave (age 10 up). Science Education Center, School of Education, Old Dominion Univ.

*Bushnell, D. 1975. The Great Dismal Swamp. *Pace: the inflight mag. of Piedmont Airlines.* 2(May–June):5–7, 22, 29.

*Byrd, B. 1974. Past, present, and future of Swamp. *Mace and Crown,* Old Dominion Univ. (25 Mar.):1.

*City of Chesapeake. Dept. Parks and Recreation. 1975. Chesapeake scenic waterways. Dept. Parks, P.O. Box 15225, Chesapeake, Va. 23320. Information booklet with maps.

*Cobb, R. 1976. A Dismal Swamp island of history: prime hunting land goes on market. *Norfolk Virginian-Pilot* (13 June):D1.

*Conservation Council of Virginia. Dismal Swamp Preservation Comm. 197[?]. *The Great Dismal Swamp of Virginia and North Carolina.* 12 pp. illus.

Courage, E. 1961. I hiked across Dismal Swamp. *Va. Wildlife* 22(7):18–19, 21–22.

*Craig, J. B. 1973. Dismal's bright future. *Amer. Forum* 79(May):10–11.

Cross, C. B., Jr. 1975. True Dismal Swamp legend one of the mysterious hermit. *Norfolk Ledger-Star* (15 Dec.):A12.

Cross, Eleanor P., and C. B. Cross. 1966. From the archives. Norfolk Co. Hist. Soc. Chesapeake, Va. 53 pp. (esp. pp. 27–32).

*Davis, B. 1972. The Great Dismal Swamp. *Ford Times* (Aug.):8–14.

*Dean, G. W. 1969. Forests and forestry in the Dismal Swamp. *Va. J. Sci.* 20:166–173.

*Delzell, D. E. 1970–71. Dismal Swamp: its natural history. *Living Wilderness* 34(Winter):29–33.

*de Rageot, R. H. 1965. An introduction to the Great Dismal Swamp. *Wildlife in N.C.* 29(May):7–9, 23.

*_____. 1973. Dismal Swamp to be preserved. *Parks and Recreation* 8(Mar.):4.

*Duke, A. 1969*a.* Dismal Swamp—land of drainage ditches. (*Newport News–Hampton Daily Press*) *New Dominion Mag.* (29 June): 1, 4–9.

*_____. 1969*b.* This too was Eden. *Natl. Humane Rev.* (May–June):10–13.

*Ennis, J. 1973. Documentary videotape on the Dismal Swamp (approx. 30 min., color). WTAR-TV, Norfolk. (Script filed at Dismal Swamp Refuge headquarters.)

Freeman, D. S. 1951–56. *George Washington, a biography* v. 3–7. Charles Scribner's Sons, N.Y.

*Friddell, G. 1974. Now, at last, the truth about "Old Dismal." *Norfolk Virginian-Pilot* (21 Apr.):C3.

*Gooch, B. 1976. Wildlife refuge crisis. *Va. Wildlife* 37(5):8–9.

*Harris, J. 1976. A giant in failing health. *New Norfolk* 14((Aug.):10–13.

*Harrison, G. H. 1960. The Great Dismal Swamp. *Va. Wildlife* 21(7): 14–15.

*_____. 1974. Painting a bright future for the Great Dismal Swamp. *Natl. Wildlife* 12(6):50–55.

*Hass, Patricia C. 1974. The Great Dismal Swamp. *Richmond Times-Dispatch* (21 July):F1.

*Hill, D. 1961. Whittling down the Great Dismal Swamp. *Commonwealth* (Apr.):17, 18, 31, and (May):19–21, 24.

*_____. 1973*a.* The great Swamp's brightened future: anything but dismal. *Commonwealth* 40(Apr.):19–24, 48–52.

*_____. 1973*b.* The Great Dismal models for our leading artists.. *Norfolk Virginian-Pilot* (3 June):C2 and C3.

*_____. 1973c. Dismal Swamp size defined by U.S. study. *Norfolk Virginian-Pilot* (29 July).

*_____. 1975. Some folks might call it a dismal performance. *Norfolk Virginian-Pilot* (2 Mar.):C3.

*Jones, T. D. 1969. A visit to the Dismal Swamp. *Va. Wildlife* 30(7):8–9.

*Juren, E. 1973. The Great Dismal Swamp. *ODU Mag.* 1(Fall–Winter):13–18.

*Keller, Eugenia. 1973. The great Dismal Swamp. *Chemistry* 46(10):17–21.

*Lasley, J. 1976. The Dismal Swamp. *Durham* (N.C.) *Morning Herald* (18 Apr.):E1.

*_____. 1976. Dismal Swamp object of preservation effort. *Durham* (N.C.) *Morning Herald* (18 Apr.):E20.

*Marshall, H. G. 1972. Lake Drummond: the heart of the Great Dismal Swamp. *Atlantic Nat.* 27(2):60–64.

*Mason, C. R. 1952. Mapping in Dismal Swamp. *Military Engineer* 44(Mar.–Apr.):120–125.

*Meanley, B. 1970–71. The Dismal Swamp: its flora and fauna. *Living Wilderness* 34(Winter):34–37.

*_____. 1972. A bear's honey tree in the Dismal Swamp. *Atlantic Nat.* 27(2):87.

Moeller, J., and B. Moeller. 1974. Intracoastal: who's afraid of the Dismal Swamp? *Motor Boating and Sailing* 134(Sept.):52–53.

Morton, C. B. 1937. Now you may see Swamp's wild beauty. *Richmond Times-Dispatch Mag.* (19 Sept.).

_____. 1940. Hunters paradise: the Dismal. *Norfolk Virginian-Pilot* (15 Dec.).

Olsen, J. 1962. The cursed Swamp. *Sports Illus.* 17(22):68–82.

Owens, G. 1976. Mother nature pollutes where the buffalo used to roam. *Norfolk Ledger-Star,* (8 June). Viewpoints page.

*Parker, J. 1961. The Dismal Swamp: memoranda concerning its history and ownership from 1763 to 1962. Union Bag–Camp Paper Corp., Franklin, Va. 27 pp. Kirn Memorial Library, Norfolk.

*Payne, M. 1971. Great Dismal Swamp. *Natl. Parks and Conservation Mag.* 45(Feb.):9–31.

Price, S. 1977. Canoe camping in the Dismal Swamp. *Va. Wildlife* 38(May):14–16.

*Ryan, D. D. 1974. Swamp "colors" filled in: more details on Swamp made known. *Richmond Times-Dispatch* (17 Mar.):B1 and B12.

*Sallinger, M. 1974. Civilization slowly intrudes on Dismal Swamp serenity. *Norfolk Ledger-Star* (19 Aug.):B4.

Stein, T. 1976. Where every day is like Halloween. *Norfolk Ledger-Star* (29 Oct.):C1.

Still, W. G. 1937. *Dismal Swamp.* New music orchestra series. The New Music Soc., San Francisco, Calif. A jazz composition produced by one of America's black musicians, William Grant Still.

*Thomas, B. 1970. Dismal delight. *Travel.* 133(Jan.):48–50.

*Troubetzkoy, U. 1970. Moonshadow on the Dismal Swamp. *Va. Wildlife* 31(5):8–9.

*_____. 1976. A look at Virginia—1607. *Va. Wildlife* 37(7):9–13.

*Turner, T. 1945. Whose business is fighting, preventing fires. *Portsmouth (Va.) Star* (14 Oct.).

*U.S. Army, Corps of Engineers, Norfolk District. 1970. *Great Bridge lock.* Information pamphlet.

*_____., and Dept. Interior, U.S. Fish and Wildlife Service. 1976. Dismal Swamp Canal and Refuge. Information pamphlet with maps. This provides the most concise, accurate introduction for the casual visitor.

*Whitehead, D. R. 1965. Prehistoric maize in southeastern Virginia. *Science* 150: 881–883.

*Williamson, M. and V. Weggel. 1972. Dismal Swamp threatened. *Mountain Laurel* (Sierra Club) 7(4).

*Willis, R. A. 1973. The Great Dismal Swamp. *Va. Clubwoman* 45(Apr.): 4–7.

*Wiseman, J. 1975. Chesapeake's scenic waterways. *Va. Wildlife* 36(7):10–11.

_____. 1976. That dark and dismal place. *Va. Wildlife Federation Record* 21 (August):10.

3. Dismal Swamp Study Reports and Summaries
A. Dismal Swamp Study Reports

*Federal Highway Admin. 1973. Report on ascertainment of potential public transportation system information. Rail-air-highway facilities. October. 6 pp. and appendix (correspondence).

*Schnack, C. D. 1973. Social, economic, and public management data. U.S. Dept. Interior, Bur. Sport Fish. and Wildlife, Div. Realty. Boston, Mass. 8 pp.

*U.S. Dept. Interior, Bur. Outdoor Recreation. 1974. The Great Dismal Swamp and Dismal Swamp Canal. A report on recreational potential. 53 pp.

*U.S. Dept. Interior, National Park Service, Northeast Region. 1973. Dismal Swamp and Canal historical and cultural data. Philadelphia, Pa. 11 pp.

B. Summaries and Comprehensive Reports Pertaining to the Dismal Swamp Study:

*Cahill, C. 1974. Great Dismal Swamp plan. *Amer. Forests* 80(12):18–21.

*Kirk, P. W., Jr. 1974. VWF endorses preservation of Great Dismal Swamp. *Va. Wildlife Federation Record* 19(5):1, 10–11.

*Shields, R. H. 1974a. Summary report and tentative recommendations of the secretary of the interior regarding preservation and management of the Great Dismal Swamp and Dismal Swamp Canal (P.L. 92–478). Dismal Swamp Study Coordinator, U.S. Fish and Wildlife Service, Boston, Mass. 02109. 4 June. 23 pp. (Also see "Summary of remarks received.")

*_____. 1974b. Statement of Robert H. Shields, Dismal Swamp Study Coordinator, U.S. Fish and Wildlife Service, at the public hearing at the Sheep School auditorium, Elizabeth City, North Carolina, and continued at the Suffolk High School auditorium, Suffolk, Virginia, June 24 and

25 respectively, regarding recommendations for preservation and management of the Great Dismal Swamp Canal. 17 pp.

*_____ . 1976. Recommendations of the secretary of the interior regarding a preservation and management program for the Great Dismal Swamp and Dismal Swamp Canal in Virginia and North Carolina (P.L. 92–478). 12 pp. (Differs little from 1974a above, but includes some clarification.)

*U.S. Dept. Interior, Fish and Wildlife Service. 1976. The Great Dismal Swamp and Dismal Swamp Canal. A report to the United States Congress from the secretary of the interior regarding actions taken and recommendations made pursuant to Public Law 92–478 (Dismal Swamp Study). June. 147 pp. and Addendum 33 pp. (This is the most recent comprehensive report on the Swamp cited, bringing together summaries of all Dismal Swamp substudy reports, pertinent discussions and management recommendations.)

[Editor's note: A complete set of the Dismal Swamp Study reports, summaries, and comprehensive reports, plus numerous newspaper clippings and other miscellaneous items, are available for inspection at the Old Dominion University Office of Dismal Swamp Programs. Group tours of the Swamp can also be arranged through this office.]

SCIENTIFIC AND TECHNICAL LITERATURE CONCERNING THE DISMAL SWAMP AREA

Paul W. Kirk, Jr., Harold G. Marshall, and Peter C. Stewart

In 1837 Edmund Ruffin, editor and proprietor of the *Farmers' Register*, wrote a rather colorful yet informative account of observations made during a visit into the Dismal Swamp. He included a description of Lake Drummond and travel along Jericho Ditch, with comments on the abundance of bears. This type of article about the Swamp, making general observations on the natural history and describing current events, has been common in books, newspapers, and periodicals from that time to the present. Many such articles have scientific value, particularly when they provide the only details of a biota and environmental conditions that have subsequently changed. Nevertheless, most of these references have been segregated in the preceding essay due to their overriding historical importance or popular appeal; the present bibliography stresses the more technical works characterized by a well-defined data base and organizational style. In a few cases where this distinction seems arbitrary the work has been listed in both bibliographies; duplicate listing is denoted here by an asterisk (*). It is recommended that serious biological investigators peruse both lists for pertinent information.

About two-thirds of the references listed in this article are concerned primarily with biology, including limnology, and most of the remaining third deal with some aspect of the geology of the Swamp and its immediate vicinity. Several of the the geological papers make little or no specific reference to the Dismal Swamp, but are considered important to a full appreciation of the Swamp's underlying stratigraphy and the historical development of geological concepts concerning the Swamp area. Of special significance are studies pertaining to the hydrology and mineral resources of the region, whose manipulation or exploitation might markedly affect the future of the Dismal Swamp and the Dismal Swamp Canal.

The hydrology of the coastal plain province, which includes the Dismal Swamp, has been investigated intensively by Sanford (1912), Cedarstrom (1941–47), the Virginia Bureau of Water Resources (1960–72), and the U.S. Geological Survey (1972a and b), including the recent open file report by Lichtler and Walker (1974), reprinted here in modified form. Investigators concerned with qualitative, quantitative, and economic aspects of the waters of the Swamp area should keep abreast of the latest publications from the Virginia Bureau of Water Resources. These and other useful documents are listed in the Virginia State Library's pamphlet *Virginia state publications (in print)*, available in most libraries. Topological maps of the U.S. Geological Survey (1902–54) and remote sensing data such as Carter's (1974) Dismal Swamp Study report, also reproduced in this volume, have application to hydrology as well as to other geological and ecological problems. A more recent report by Carter et al, (1977) contains several color photographs of the Swamp's vegetation, including LANDSAT digital classifications in winter and spring seasons. The U.S. Army Corps of Engineers' (1974) contribution to the Dismal Swamp Study (P.L. 92–478) likewise is basic to an appreciation of the demands on surface waters of the Swamp and probably groundwaters of the Norfolk aquifer as well. Reports on sand and gravel deposits (Wentworth 1930) and the distribution of permeability (Brown et al. 1972) give further insight into actual and potential groundwater supplies. Reports like those by Darton (1896) and Sabet (1975), emphasizing deep wells of the vicinity and the location of "fossil" water, relate to economic and ecological considerations in part by suggesting alternatives to industrial or domestic usage of the vital Norfolk aquifer. These studies also provide a larger data base for other research into geological history, natural resources, and pollution-disposal problems of the area, thus helping to spare the Swamp from possible subtle intrusions.

Just as any disturbance of the Dismal Swamp Canal must now be preceded by a detailed impact statement by the U.S. Army Corps of Engineers (e.g., 1975), future decisions affecting land use in the Dismal Swamp area will probably take an environmental geologic approach like that by Teifke (1973). In addition to its obvious significance as a source of lockage water, game, and timber, the Dismal Swamp area has long been recognized and catalogued as a potential source of agricultural land and of minerals, including marl, sand, gravel, and peat (e.g., Rogers 1884; Shaler 1886a and b, 1891; Watson 1907, 1912; Wentworth 1930; McGill 1936; Pharr and Calver 1963; Stuckey 1965). Special attention is called to the recent Dismal Swamp substudy report by Trent (1974), which emphasizes the Refuge lands surrounding Lake Drummond.

The mantle of peat and decaying vegetation that comprises the Dismal Swamp formation, in places 18 feet thick (Wieland 1897), has attracted the attention of foreign as well as American scientists. Lesquereux (1852) pointed out similarities in the vegetation and process of peat accumulation in the Dismal Swamp and European moors, and commented on the Swamp's large tulip and magnolia trees ("100 to 150 feet high"), maples, and conifers. Lesquereux's paper was presented to the German Geological Society by Edouard Desor, who also had an interest in the region (1852). The British geologist Lyell (1845) used the Swamp to illustrate the mechanism of coal formation, as did the American investigators Thiessen (1913) and White (White and Thiessen 1913). Numerous works list the Dismal Swamp peat as a natural resource and give estimates of its extent (e.g., Davis 1909, 1914; Soper and Osbon 1922; Dachnowski-Stokes 1933; Cameron 1973), but relatively few since Nicol (1837) and Osbon (1919) have provided detailed descriptions of the material. The analysis of amino acids in Dismal Swamp peat by Swain et al. (1959) and of soil profiles by Obenshain and Henry (1959) represent the kinds of thorough chemical investigations that are needed.

The earliest comprehensive scientific treatise concerning Dismal Swamp soils is the well-known *Essay on calcareous manures* by Ruffin (1852), although colonial farmers, including George Washington, and even primitive man apparently had some interest in the agricultural potential of this area (Whitehead 1965b). Lapham and Lyman (1905) produced the first of many U.S. Dept. of Agriculture surveys, maps, and interpretations of soils in the counties comprising the Dismal Swamp (Perkins et al. 1928; Devereux et al. 1936; Simmons and Shulkcum 1945; Shearin et al. 1957; Henry et al. 1959; U.S.D.A., Soil Conservation Service, 1971–1972c). As a part of the recent Dismal Swamp Study, the Soil Correlation Unit of the U.S.D.A. produced a comprehensive account of the Dismal Swamp soils that includes a detailed classification (1974). Other general treatments of this subject are by Wingo (1949), Drinkard (1950) and Henry (1970).

The most generally useful works on post-Miocene stratigraphy and morphology of the Dismal Swamp area are those developed by Oaks, Coch, and others in the period 1962–74, but older investigations and general summaries of coastal plain geology include some useful data, in addition to having historical significance. Before the turn of the century Shaler focused on geological processes, including sea level changes in the region (1890, 1895), and the confusing complex of terraces and shorelines of the North Carolina–Virginia Coastal Plain afterwards became the subject of conflicting accounts (Johnson 1907, Clark and Miller 1906, Clark et al. 1912, Stephenson 1912, Wentworth 1930, Cooke 1930a–1935, Roberts 1950, Spangler and Peterson 1950,

Moore 1956). The comparatively recent findings of Harrison et al. (1965) also formed an important basis for later, now widely accepted, conclusions by Oaks and Coch, and by Whitehead. The latter's extensive palynological studies (1965a–1973) may be regarded as geological or botanical, depending upon one's point of view, and are among the most valuable contributions to knowledge of the Swamp's more recent developmental history (about 12,000 years ago to present), including the formation of Lake Drummond. Other detailed palynological work in Swamp area has been done by Robeson (1928), Cooke, Lewis and others (1928–34) and Vick (1961).

Studies of fossil diatoms, molluscs, and other fauna have provided invaluable clues to the identity of various strata (e.g. Woolman and Boyer 1898, Richards 1936, McLean 1966). A monograph by R. S. Spencer, entitled "The fauna and paleoecology of the marine Pleistocene (Sangamon) of southeastern Virginia," will be published in the near future. Paleontologists should also scan the list of publications by E. W. Berry (pp. 99–104), T. A. Conrad (pp. 178–183) and others in Roberts's comprehensive bibliography (1942). The latter publication is the most complete guide available to older literature on the geology of Virginia. Among the many items included are two abstracts of the 1911 Dismal Swamp Symposium, a history of geologial thought in Virginia, and biographic sketches of prominent Virginia geologists, which should interest science historians. Hoffer's (1968) bibliography begins where Roberts's ends, and lists geological references through 1949.

The work of Harrison et al. (1959), previously mentioned, and of R. S. Davis et al. in this volume are noteworthy in being among the few chemical investigations of the Swamp to utilize relatively modern, precise analytical techniques. Preliminary instrumental analyses of the Swamp's soil, water, and atmosphere have been made by Maier et al. (1974), Copeland et al. (1974), Rosevear and Diefenderfer (1974) and Diefenderfer (1975). The continued development of such studies is essential to monitor and accurately quantify the subtle chemical interactions of the Swamp and the adjacent urban community.

Botanical studies of the Swamp are predominantly taxonomic, dealing with the vascular flora, although many of these include descriptive comments on the environment. Massey's (1961) bibliography of the Virginia flora is useful in locating some of the more obscure papers. Many floristic notes and short papers are scattered in the scientific journals (e.g., Chickering 1873, 1877; McCarthy 1884; Hollick 1890; Harper 1901; Coville 1911; Grimes 1922; Harville 1964; Meanley 1968a, 1969a). The more useful comprehensive works include floras of southeastern Virginia or of much broader regions (Fernald 1935–47, Small 1964, Radford et al. 1968), in addition to those pertaining more specifically to the Dismal Swamp (Palmer 1899, Kearney 1901, Waters et al. 1974, Musselman et al. 1976). Kearney's (1901) often cited work presents results of a botanical survey conducted in the summer of 1898. This is a remarkably complete study of vegetational composition in the southeastern Virginia Coastal Plain. He also relates various floral assemblages to soil characteristics and geographical conditions of the region.

Considering the important historical role the Swamp has played in the forest products industries, there are relatively few extensive published reports concerning forestry and forest ecology of the area. Ward (1877), Hollick (1912a), and particularly Dean (1969) provide useful summaries, and the recent Dismal Swamp Study report by the U.S.D.A. Forest Service (1974) includes a large foldout map showing forest types. Akerman (1923) and Little (1959) are concerned only with one of the more important species, Atlantic white cedar. Considerably more information can be found in unpublished manuscripts, including Master's theses by Old Dominion University students (Walker 1972, Janszen 1974, Messmore 1975), and reports prepared for the Union Camp Corporation such as those by Sharon Miller dealing with methods of cutting red maple (1958–65). Special mention is due the recent reports by Dabel (1976), Day (1976), and Dabel and Day (1977), as these are the first to provide estimates of biomass. Other process studies in progress will focus on energy flow and nutrient cycling.

Patterson's rather general works on Bryophytes of southeastern Virginia are among the very few published papers treating the lower plant groups of the Swamp exclusive of phytoplankters. Accounts of slime molds, lichens, and aquatic fungi are very preliminary in nature, consisting of abstracts and unpublished student reports (Gammon et al. 1973, Gammon 1974a and b, Folman 1974, Tillery 1975). Undoubtedly there are other unpublished data on a variety of scientific topics in the files of college professors; in Virginia principally at Old Dominion University, the Collge of William and Mary, and the Virginia Polytechnic Institute and State University.

The phytoplankton composition of Lake Drummond has been reported in considerable detail (Poore 1971, Poore and Marshall 1971, Marshall and Poore 1972a and b, Marshall 1976 and this volume). Zooplankton in the intracoastal waterway (Hillard 1974) and in Stumpy Lake just east of the presently delimited Dismal Swamp (Hernandez 1973) have also been studied intensively, but less has been written concerning the zooplankton in Lake Drummond and the system of ditches within the Swamp proper (Marshall 1974 and this volume, Anderson et al. 1975).

Comments by numerous naturalists over the past 150 years include reference to Lake Drummond. Many of these early accounts provide an apparent paradox in relating the influence of canal construction to the size and depth of the lake (see Marshall and Robinson, this volume). Further ecological appraisals of the lake with comments on the water dynamics associated with the natural drainage system are presented by Wilder (1970), Ramsey, Hinkle, and Benander (1970), and the C. T. Main report (1971), among others. Although written for the general public, the books by Russell (1895) and Stansbury (1925) offer the scientist glimpses of the lake in an earlier perspective.

Reports of the fish populations in Lake Drummond include some popular accounts listed in the preceding bibliographic essay, a few significant semitechnical papers listed here (Roseberry and Bowers 1952, de Rageot 1970–71, Andrews 1971), and a number of published and unpublished technical works (Jordan 1890, Raney 1950, Massman 1953, Brady 1969, Wilder 1970, Jenkins 1975, Russell 1976). Principal fishes in the intracoastal waterway are listed in the U.S. Army Corps of Engineer's (1975) impact statement. Jordan (1890), making collections from various river basins in Viriginia and North Carolina, offers one of the first accounts of fish from the Dismal Swamp area. He collected during August, when water levels were low in several creeks bordering the Swamp, Jericho Ditch, the Feeder Ditch, and Dismal Swamp Canal. The resulting frequently encountered snags made seining difficult in the ditches and canals, and impossible in Lake Drummond. However, he stated that the gar (*Lepisosteus osseus*) and bowfin (*Amia calva*) reach a very large size in the lake. An appraisal of fish populations in Lake Drummond over 60 years later by Roseberry and Bowers (1952) showed gar and bowfin still present, together with large crappie; these comprise the major predatory fishes. The lake was overrun with small crappie, shiners, stunted bullhead catfish, and other forage types, including fliers. Their three-day study using gill nets revealed the apparent failure of a 1947 stocking program by local fishermen to establish the bluegill sunfish. Roseberry and Bowers concluded that high acidity of the lake was not conducive to the development of bass and bluegills. Andrews (1971) further reviews the fish populations in the lake, ditches, and canals, pointing out a predominance of sunfishes (Centrarchidae) with the flier most abundant.

In addition to the tall tales and folk literature about snakes in the Dismal Swamp, there are a few scattered factual accounts of reptiles and amphibians in this area. The distributional study by Wood (1954) confirms that only three poisonous snakes occur in the Swamp, the cottonmouth, copperhead, and canebrake rattler. The checklist by Delzell in this book is the most complete to date for the Swamp, exceeding by many species those of Brady (1927) and Meanley (1973*b*) but showing much overlap with Carroll's (1950). The paper by Wood et al. (1955) is noteworthy for its in-depth treatment of a single species, the dusky salamander. Generally the most useful identification manuals are regional in scope, but for making some determinations using field characteristics, the color illustrations in *Virginia Wildlife* magazine articles are useful (e.g., Mitchell 1976, 1977; also see bibliography following Delzell's checklist).

Occurrence records are probably more complete for birds than for other groups of vertebrates in the Swamp, due in great measure to the efforts of Brooke Meanley in the period 1962–73. Meanley is one of the more prolific writers on the Swamp, and his works include general treatments (1973a and b) and articles on plants (1968a, 1969a) and mammals (1971a) in addition to numerous ornithological papers. Other thorough studies of Dismal Swamp birds have been done by Murray (1932–69), and shorter papers by Fisher (1895), Daniel (1902), Richardson (1926), Webb and Wetherbee (1960).

Published studies on mammals are more numerous than on any other animal group, but are scattered over a long period of time and are seldom comprehensive. For example, many are concerned with a single species, such as the yellow bat (de Rageot 1955) or lemming mouse (Taylor 1974). Most are taxonomic acounts, although a few are in-depth treatments of ecology and natural history (Wilson 1953, 1954; also see Paschal et al. in this volume). Although many of the more important scientific works concerning mammals are listed here, their number precludes discussion. The reader is referred instead to Handley's extensive review in this volume for a thorough examination of these and other sources.

Aquatic, crawling, and flying insects in the Swamp all deserve careful study, as they are important food sources for many fishes, herptiles, birds, shrews, and other mammals. Aquatic Coleoptera in the lake, ditches, and interior pools have been studied principally by Matta (1973), who reports on these and other aquatic insect groups in the present volume. Other works on Coleoptera are by Matta (1974, 1976), Matta and Michael (1976) and Michael and Matta (1977). The Clarks (1937–51) and Baldwin (1969) concentrated on butterflies, Banks (1904) and Pechuman (1973) on pesky flies, and the regional monograph of Battle and Turner on biting gnats (1971). Gurney's (1963) is a more general paper which emphasizes insects. Other invertebrates in the Swamp having received attention are land snails (Old and de Rageot 1956) and ticks (Garrett 1974), portions of the latter also being included in this volume.

The references mentioned in this article should provide entry into major areas of published scientific and technical literature concerning the Dismal Swamp through January 1978, although this is not as complete an accounting of unpublished manuscripts, such as Swamp fire reports, planting and logging records, and works in progress. As a final comment, particular attention is called to the Dismal Swamp Study report prepared by the Refuge staff (U.S. Dept. Interior 1974). This 49-page report is a well-written summary of scientific information on the Swamp, more comprehensive than the excellent one by Meanley (1973*b*), but unfortunately not nearly so readily available. The mimeographed report describes the developmental history and ecology, defines the communities that warrant management consideration, makes recommendations for limited public use of the Swamp, and includes abbreviated checklists of the various plant and animal groups present. With a little expansion, plus inclusion of some good-quality illustrations, this report could function as an introductory text on the subject. In its present form, it offers a valuable introduction to the Swamp for new investigators, regardless of their specialty, and may enlarge the perspective of others already working there. (Owing to its general content and emphasis on public interest in the Swamp, the June 1976 comprehensive report on P.L. 92-478 is cited as the last reference in the preceding essay [Stewart et al.].)

REFERENCES CITED AND SUPPLEMENTAL BIBLIOGRAPHY

Abert, S. T. 1876. Report on a survey of a line to connect the waters of the New and Cape Fear rivers in North Carolina, and of a line to connect the waters of Norfolk harbor in Virginia with the Cape Fear River at or near Wilmington in North Carolina. *U.S. Eng. Dept.* 35:2–38. (Abs. *Amer. J. Sci.,* ser. 3, 12:149.)

Akerman, A. 1923. The white cedar of the Dismal Swamp. *Va. Forestry Publ.* 30:1–21. Charlottesville.

Anderson, K. B., E. F. Benfield, and A. L. Buikema, Jr. 1975. Zooplankton of the Dismal Swamp waters. *Va. J. Sci.* 26:52. (Abs.)

Andrews, J. D. 1971. Fish for beauty in the Dismal Swamp (one man's view of the Swamp). *Va. J. Sci.* 22:5–13.

Anon. 197[?]. A study of some physical, chemical and biological characteristics of a Dismal Swamp ditch and Lake Drummond. (MS, Dismal Swamp Natl. Wildlife Refuge, Suffolk.)

Anon. 1974. *A checklist of North Carolina mammalian species.* N.C. Wildlife Resources Comm., Raleigh. 21 pp.

Bailey, J. W. 1946. *The mammals of Virginia.* Publ. by the author. Williams Printing Co., Richmond. 416 pp.

Baldwin, J. T., Jr. 1969. Insects—mostly butterflies—of Dismal Swamp. *Va. Wildlife* 30(9):11, 14–16.

Banks, N. 1904. The "yellow-fly" of the Dismal Swamp. *Entomol. News* 15: 290–291.

Bartsch, P. 1901. A trip to the Dismal Swamp. *Osprey* 5:35–37, 55–56, 67–69. (Reprinted in *Wood Thrush,* 1949–50, 5:12–20.)

Battle, F. V., and E. C. Turner, Jr. 1971. A systematic review of the genus *Culicoides* (Diptera: Ceratopogonidae) of Virginia. *Va. Polytech. Inst. and State Univ. Res. Bull.* 44. 129 pp.

Berry, E. W. 1909. A Miocene flora from the Virginia Coastal Plain. *J. Geol.* 17:19–30. Compares this to Dismal Swamp flora.

Brady, M. 1927. Notes on the reptiles and amphibians of the Dismal Swamp. *Copeia* 162:26–29.

Brady, P. M. 1969. The sport fishery of Lake Drummond in the Dismal Swamp of Virginia. Master's Thesis Va. Polytech. Inst. and State Univ. 112 pp.

———. and C. D. Wilder. 1968. Fish population investigation of Lake Drummond. *Va. J. Sci.* 19:176 (Abs.)

Braun, E. Lucy. 1950. *Deciduous forests of eastern North America.* McGraw-Hill, New York. 596 pp. Dismal Swamp forest types described pp. 290–295, 471. Hafner 1964 reprint available.

Brimley, C. S. 1905. A descriptive catalogue of the mammals of North Carolina, exclusive of the Cetacea. *J. Elisha Mitchell Sci. Soc.* 21:1–32.

———. 1945. The mammals of North Carolina. *Bull. Dept. Agric.* 18 pts., 36 pp. (also published in 18 parts in *Carolina Tips,* Carolina Biol. Supply, 1944–46. 39 pp.).

Brown, P. M., J. A. Miller, and F. M. Swain. 1972. Structural and stratigraphic framework, and spatial distribution of permeability of the Atlantic Coastal Plain, North Carolina to New York. *U.S. Geol. Survey, Prof. Pap.* 796. 79 pp.

Cameron, Cornelia C. 1973. Peat. Pp. 505–513 *in* D. A. Brobst and W. P. Pratt (eds). United States mineral resources. *U.S. Geol. Survey Prof. Pap.* 820.

Carpenter, M. 1973. *The black bear in Virginia.* Va. Comm. Game and Inland Fisheries, Richmond. 22 pp.

Carroll, R. P. 1935. The Dismal Swamp trip. *Claytonia* 21:31.

———. 1950. Amphibia and retiles. Pp. 195–211. In *The James River Basin: past, present and future.* Va. Acad. Sci., Richmond.

Carter, Virginia. 1974. The Dismal Swamp: remote sensing applications. U.S. Geol. Survey, Natl. Center, Reston, Va. 22092. March. 19 pp. A Dismal Swamp Study report, P.L. 92–478.

Carter, Virginia. Mary Keith Garrett, Lurie Shima, and Patricia Gammon. 1977. The Great Dismal Swamp: management of a hydrologic resource with the aid of remote sensing. *Amer. Water Resources Assn. Bull.* 13:1–12.

Cedarstrom, D. J. 1941. Ground-water resources of the southeastern Virginia Coastal Plain. *Va. Geol. Survey, Circular* 1. 11 pp.

_____. 1943. Chloride in ground water in the coastal plain of Virginia. *Va. Geol. Survey, Bull.* 58. 36 pp.

_____. 1945a. Geology and ground-water resources of the coastal plain in southeastern Virginia. *Va. Geol. Survey, Bull.* 63. 384 pp.

_____. 1945b. Structural geology of Southeastern Virginia. *Amer. Assoc. Petrol. Geol. Bull.* 29(1):71–95. Includes contours on gravity anomalies passing through the Swamp.

_____. 1946a. Genesis of ground waters in the coastal plain of Virginia. *Econ. Geol.* 41:218–245.

_____. 1946b. Chemical composition of ground water in the coastal plain of Virginia. *Va. Geol. Survey, Bull.* 68. 62 pp.

_____. 1947. Resume of Virginia coastal stratigraphy. *Va. Acad. Sci. Proc.* (1946–47):96–97. (Abs.)

Chappell, Dorothy L. 1971. Kearney on the Dismal Swamp. *Newsletter, Flora Comm. Va. Acad. Sci.* 5(2):9–11.

*Chickering, J. W. 1873. The flora of the Dismal Swamp. *Amer. Nat.* 7(Sept.): 521–524.

_____. 1877. A botanical trip in Virginia. *Field and Forest* 3(1):1–4.

Clark, A. H. 1937. Surveying the butterflies of Virginia. *Sci. Monthly* 45: 256–265.

Clark, A. H., and Leilia F. Clark. 1939. Butterflies of a wood road at Suffolk, Virginia. *Entomol. News* 50:1–5.

_____. 1951. The butterflies of Virginia. *Smithsonian Misc. Coll.* 116(7):1–239.

Clark, W. B., and B. L. Miller. 1906. A brief summary of the geology of the Virginia Coastal Plain. Pp. 11–24 *in* H. Ries. The clay deposits of the Virginia Coastal Plain. *Va. Geol. Survey, Geol. Series, Bull.* 2. Briefly describes Jurassic through Pleistocene.

Clark, W. B., B. L. Miller, E. W. Berry, and T. L. Watson. 1912. The physiography and geology of the coastal plain province of Virginia. *Va. Geol. Survey, Geol. Series, Bull.* 4. 274 pp. A comprehensive study of the Tertiary and later periods.

Climpson, J. T. 1973. Summary report of Dismal Swamp, summer 1973. (MS, Dismal Swamp Natl. Wildlife Refuge, Suffolk.)

Coch, N. K. 1965. Post-Miocene statigraphy and morphology, inner coastal plain, southeastern Virginia. U.S. office of Naval Research, Geography Branch, Contract NONR 609 (40), Task Order NR 388-064, Tech. Rpt. 6. Ph.D. Diss. Yale Univ. 97 pp.

_____. 1971. Geology of the Newport News South and Bowers Hill quadrangles, Virginia. *Va. Div. Mineral Resources, Rpt. Inv.* 28. 26 pp.

Coch, N.K., and R. Q. Oaks, Jr. 1966. Itinerary to post-Miocene stratigraphy and morphology, southeastern Virginia. 29th annual reunion friends of the Pleistocene. Chesapeake, Va. 12 pp. (unpublished).

Cocke, E. C. 1928. The history of the vegetation of the Dismal Swamp as determined by fossil pollen analysis. Master's Thesis Univ. Virginia. 43 pp.

———. 1930. The study of fossil pollen from the Dismal Swamp of Virginia. *Proc. Va. Acad. Sci.* (1930–31):29. (Abs.)

———. 1931. Pollen analysis of Dismal Swamp peat. Ph.D. Diss. Univ. of Virginia. 96 pp.

———. 1932. Further study of fossil pollen from Dismal Swamp peat. *Proc. Va. Acad. Sci.* (1932–33):39. (Abs.)

———. 1934. Fossil pollen and diatoms found in Dismal Swamp peat. *Proc. Va. Acad. Sci.* (1933–34):35. (Abs.)

Cocke, E. C., I. F. Lewis, and Ruth Patrick. 1934. A further study of Dismal Swamp peat. *Amer. J. Bot.* 21:374–395.

Cooke, C. W. 1930a. Pleistocene seashores. *J. Washington Acad. Sci.* 20:389–395. Background data on geology of Swamp area.

———. 1930b. Correlation coastal terraces *J. Geol.* 38:577–589. Background information on geology of the Swamp area.

———. 1931. Seven coastal terraces in the southeastern states. *J. Washington Acad. Sci.* 21:503–513. Evaluates the "Dismal Swamp Terrace" of Wentworth 1930.

———. 1933. Pleistocene changes of sea level. *J. Washington Acad. Sci.* 23:109–110. (Abs.)

———. 1935. Tentative ages of Pleistocene shore lines. *J. Washington Sci.* 25:331–333.

Copeland, G. E., A. R. Bandy, G. Maier, and E. C. Kindle. 1974. Interpretation of air quality data for a 30-day experiment at Deep Creek, Virginia. *Va. J. Sci.* 25:90. (Abs.)

Coville, F. V. 1911. The recent excursion into the Dismal Swamp. *Science* 33(857):871–872. (Abs.) (Also see Humphreys, 1911a and b.)

Dabel, Claire V. 1976. Four plant community types in the Great Dismal Swamp: aboveground biomass and litter. *Va. J. Sci.* 27:55 (Abs.)

Dabel, Claire V., and F. P. Day, Jr. 1977. Structural comparisons of four plant communities in the Great Dismal Swamp, Virginia. *Bull Torrey Bot. Club.* 104:352–360.

Dachnowski-Stokes, A. P. 1933. Peat deposits in U.S.A.—their characteristic profiles, and classification. *Handb. der Moorkunde* 7. 140 pp. Brief compilation of other published data.

Daniel, J. W. 1902. Summer birds of the Great Dismal Swamp. *Auk* 19:15–18.

Darton, N. H. 1896. Artesian well prospects in the Atlantic Coastal Plain region. *U.S. Geol. Survey, Bull.* 138. 228 pp. Includes Norfolk, Nansemond, and Princess Anne counties.

———. 1902a. Description of the Norfolk quadrangle. *Geol. atlas of United States, Norfolk folio,* no. 80. U.S. Geol. Survey. 5 pp. (2 maps. 1 sheet illus.)

———. 1902b. Catalog of photographs belonging to the Geological society of America. *Geol. Soc. Amer. Bull.* 13:377–474. Includes Dismal Swamp photos.

———. 1905. Preliminary list of deep borings in the United States. *U.S. Geol. Survey, Water-Supply Pap.* 149, 2d ed. 175 pp. (See also entries under the heading "Wells . . .," *in* J. K. Roberts, 1942, pp. 664–666.)

Davis, C. A. 1909. Peat resources of the United States exclusive of Alaska. *U.S. Geol. Survey, Bull.* 394:62–69. (Also see Humphreys 1911*a* and *b*, Roberts 1942).

———. 1914. Origin and formation of peat. *U.S. Bur. Mines, Bull.* 38:165–186.

Day, F. P., Jr. 1976. Ecosystem studies in the Great Dismal Swamp: a preliminary report. *Va. J. Sci.*: 27:55 (Abs.)

*Dean, G. W. 1969. Forests and forestry in the Dismal Swamp. *Va. J. Sci.* 20: 166–173.

de Rageot, R. H. 1955. A new northernmost record of the yellow bat, *Dasypterus floridanus. J. Mamm.* 36:456.

———. 1957. Predation of small mammals in the Dismal Swamp, Virginia. *J. Mamm.* 38:281.

———. 1964. The golden mouse. *Va. Wildlife* 25(2):10–11.

———. 1970–71. The Dismal Swamp fish. *Living Wilderness* 34(Winter):37–39.

Desor, E. 1852. Post-Pliocene of the southern states and its relation to the Laurentian of the north and the deposits of the valley of the Mississippi. *Amer. J. Sci.,* ser. 2, 14:49–59.

Devereux, R. E., E. Shulkcum, and G. W. Patteson. 1936. Soil survey of Nansemond County, Virginia. *U.S. Dept. Agric., Soil Survey Series* 1932, no. 6. U.S. Govt. Print. Off., Washington. 39 pp.

Diefenderfer, A. J. 1975. Chemical evidence of man's intrusion into the Dismal Swamp ecosystem. *Va. J. Sci.* 26:69. (Abs.)

Drinkard, A. W. 1950. Agriculture. Pp. 335–385 in *The James River Basin: past present and future.* Va. Acad. Sci., Richmond.

EROS Data Center. LANDSAT I and other images of the Dismal Swamp and vicinity (e.g., see endpapers, this volume). Sioux Falls, S.D. 57198.

Fernald, M. L. 1935. Midsummer vascular plants of southeastern Virginia. *Contrib. Gray Herbarium Harvard Univ.* 109. 68 pp. Reprinted from *Rhodora* 37.) (For complete listing of M. L. Fernald in Virginia, see A. B. Massey [1961], pp. 229–231.)

———. 1936. Plants from the outer coastal plain of Virginia. *Contrib. Gray Herbarium Harvard Univ.* 115. 68 pp. (Reprinted from *Rhodora* 38.)

———. 1937. Local plants of the inner coastal plain of southeastern Virginia. *Contrib. Gray Herbarium Harvard Univ.* 120. 137 pp. (Reprinted from *Rhodora* 39.)

———. 1938. Noteworthy plants of southeastern Virginia. *Contrib. Gray Herbarium Harvard Univ.* 123. 106 pp. (Reprinted from *Rhodora* 40.)

———. 1939. Last survivors in the flora of Tidewater Virginia. *Contrib. Gray Herbarium Harvard Univ.* 128. 82 pp. (Reprinted from *Rhodora* 41.)

———. 1940. A century of additions to the flora of Virginia. *Contrib. Gray Herbarium Harvard Univ.* 133. 161 pp. (Reprinted from *Rhodora* 42.) This records an occurrence of the silky camellia, *Stewartia malacondendron L.,* p. 466.

———. 1941. Another century of additions to the flora of Virginia. *Contrib. Gray Herbarium Harvard Univ.* 139. 164 pp. (Reprinted from *Rhodora* 43.)

———. 1942. The seventh century of additions to the flora of Virginia. *Contrib. Gray Herbarium Harvard Univ.* 145. 124 pp. (Reprinted from *Rhodora* 45.)

———. 1943. Virginia botanizing under restrictions. *Contrib. Gray Herbarium Harvard Univ.* 149. 120 pp. (Reprinted from *Rhodora* 45.) This account includes comments on the dwarf trillium *T. pusillum* Michaux (Salisbury), pp. 396–397.

———. 1945. Botanical specialties of the Seward forest and adjacent areas of southeastern Virginia. *Contrib. Gray Herbarium Harvard Univ.* 156. 98 pp. (Reprinted from *Rhodora* 47.)

———. 1947. Additions to and subtractions from the flora of Virginia. *Contrib. Gray Herbarium Harvard Univ.* 163. 88 pp. (Reprinted from *Rhodora* 49.)

Fernald, M., and L. Griscom. 1935. Three days of botanizing in southeastern Virginia. *Contrib. Gray Herbarium Harvard Univ.* 107. 52 pp. (Reprinted from *Rhodora* 37.)

Fisher, A. K. 1895. Occurrence of *Helinaia swainsoni* in the Dismal Swamp, Virginia. *Auk* 12:307.

Folman, J. 1974. Aquatic fungi of Lake Drummond and associated ditches. (MS, Old Dominion Univ. 5 pp.)

Gammon, Patricia T. 1974a. Variation in species composition and distribution of Myxomycetes from a forested area to an urban area with reference to air pollution. (MS, Old Dominion Univ. 9 pp.)

———. 1974b. Preliminary species list of Myxomycetes of the Great Dismal Swamp. (MS, Old Dominion Univ. 2 pp.)

Gammon, Patricia T., M. Huff, and P. W. Kirk, Jr. 1973. Slime molds of the Great Dismal Swamp and Tidewater. *Va. J. Sci.* 24:136. (Abs.)

Garrett, Mary Keith 1974. The ecology of the dominant tick species in the northwestern portion of the Dismal Swamp National Wildlife Refuge. Master's Thesis Old Dominion Univ. 31 pp.

Grimes, E. J. 1922. Some interesting plants of the Virginia Coastal Plain. *Rhodora* 24:148–152.

Gurney, A. B. 1963. A brief look at the Dismal Swamp and its natural history, especially insects. *J. Washington Acad Sci.* 53:57–63.

Hack, J. T. 1957. Submerged river system of Chesapeake Bay. *Geol. Soc. Amer. Bull.* 68:817–830.

Handley, C. O., Jr., and C. P. Patton. 1947. *Wild mammals of Virginia.* Va. Comm. Game and Inland Fisheries, Richmond. 220 pp.

Handley, C. O., Jr., and C. O. Handley, Sr. 1950. Mammals. Pp. 235–276 in *The James River Basin: past, present and future.* Va. Acad. Sci., Richmond.

Harper, R. W. 1901. A midsummer journey through the coastal plain of the Carolinas and Virginia. *Contrib. U.S. Natl. Herbarium* 5:408, 472, 547.

Harrison, W., R. J. Malloy, G. A. Rusnak, and J. Terasmae. 1965. Possible late Pleistocene uplift, Chesapeake Bay entrance. *J. Geol.* 73:201–229.

Harvill, A. M., Jr. 1964. *Magnolia grandiflora* in Gray's manual range. *Rhodora* 66:159. Notes occurrence just east of the present Swamp.

Henry, E. F. 1970. Soils of the Dismal Swamp of Virginia. *Va. J. Sci.* 21:41–46.

Henry, E. F., J. Chudoba, and H. C. Porter. 1959. Soil survey, Norfolk County, Virginia. *U.S. Dept. Agric., Soil Survey Series* 1953, no. 5. U.S. Govt. Print. Off., Washington. 53 pp.

Hernandez, J. E. 1973. A zooplankton study of Stumpy Lake, Virginia Beach, Virginia. Master's Thesis Old Dominion Univ. 54 pp. Although not in the Dismal Swamp as presently delimited, this lake embodies some characteristics of the nearby Swamp.

Hillard, O. C. 1974. Observations on the distribution and composition of zooplankton in portions of the Intra-coastal Waterway, Virginia. Master's Thesis Old Dominion Univ. 83 pp.

Hoffer, F. B. 1968. Bibliography of Virginia geology and mineral resources. 1941–49. *Va. Div. Mineral Resources, Info. Circ.* 14. 58 pp.

Hollick, A. 1890. Notes on the autumn flora of southeastern Virginia. *Mem. Torrey Bot. Club* 2:54–56.

*_____.1912a. The Dismal Swamp of Virginia. *Amer. Forests* 18(July):431–434.

_____. 1912b. Some features of the Dismal Swamp of Virginia. *J. New York Bot. Garden* 13:53–56.

_____. 1925. The Dismal Swamp of Virginia. *J. New York Bot. Garden* 26:227–230.

Holmes, H. B., Jr. (See Virginia Bur. Water Resources, 1960, 1961a and b.)

Humphreys, W. J. 1911a. Recording secretary's account of the 73rd meeting of the Washington Acad. of Sciences (Symposium on Dismal Swamp). *J. Wash. Acad. Sci.* 1:104. (Abs.)

_____. 1911b. Recording secretary's account of the 73rd meeting of the Washington Acad. of Science (Symposium on Dismal Swamp). *Science,* n.s., 33(858):909–910. A more detailed account than in the above reference.

Janszen, T. A. 1974. Studies on the causes of tree distribution in a forest type in the Dismal Swamp National Wildlife Refuge. Master's Thesis Old Dominion Univ. 32 pp.

Jenkins, R. E., L. A. Revelle, and T. Zorach. 1975. Records of the black-banded sunfish, *Enneacanthus chaetodon,* and comments on the southeastern Virginia ichthyofauna. *Va. J. Sci.* 26:128–134.

Johnson, B. L. 1907. Pleistocene terracing in the North Carolina Coastal Plain. *Science,* n.s., 26:640–642.

Jordan, D. S. 1890. Report of explorations made during summer and autumn of 1888 in the Alleghany region of Virginia, North Carolina, and Tennessee, and in western Indiana, with an account of the fishes found in each of the river basins of these regions. *Bull. U.S. Fish Comm.* 8:97–173.

Kearney, J. 1838. In relation to the survey from the southern debouche of the Dismal Swamp to Winyaw Bay. *Petersburg* (Va.) *Farmers' Register* 6(7):408–411.

*Kearney, T. H. 1901. Report on a botanical survey of the Dismal Swamp region. *Contrib. U.S. Natl. Herbarium* 5:321–550.

Lamb, R. 1885. A map of the Great Dismal Swamp of Virginia and the surrounding country with two geological cross-sections. *Virginias* 6:33. Applicable to topological and drainage studies.

Lapham, J. E., and W. S. Lyman. 1905. Soil survey of Perquimans and Pasquotank counties, North Carolina. *U.S. Dept. Agric., Soil Survey Rpt.* U.S. Govt. Print. Off., Washington. 22 pp.

Lesquereux, H. H. 1852. Ueber die Torfbildung im grossen Dismal-Swamp. *Zeitschrift Deutsch. Geol. Ges.* 4:695–697. (Paper actually presented by E. Desor; this paper is also published in *Deutsch. Naturf. Versamml. Bericht.,* 1852, pp. 172–173.)

Levy, G. F. 1975. Research opportunities in the Great Dismal Swamp. *Va. J. Sci.* 26:81. (Abs.) (See also Anon. 1976 in preceding essay by Stewart et al.)

―――. 1976a. Letter of intent: establishment of a new center. Center for Dismal Swamp Education and Research. Old Dominion Univ. 57 pp. (unpublished).

―――. 1976b. Report of the operations of the Office of Dismal Swamp Programs from May 1975–June 1976. Old Dominion Univ. 20 pp. (unpublished).

―――. 1976c. Feeder Ditch trail. Office of Dismal Swamp Programs. Old Dominion Univ. 4 pp. (unpublished). Working paper on development of an interpretive trail.

―――. 1977. Report of the operations of the Office of Dismal Swamp Programs from July 1976–June 1977. Old Dominion Univ. 24 pp. (unpublished). A continuing series of annual reports.

Levy, G. F., and T. A. Janszen. 1974. Studies on the relationships between microtopophic and pedological factors and tree distribution in the Dismal Swamp. *Va. J. Sci.* 25:73. (Abs.)

Levy, G. F., R. L. Ake, R. S. Spencer, et al. 1972. An integrated study of the Northwest River and its watershed. *Va. J. Sci.* 23:112. (Abs.) (Also in *Va. Water Resources Res. Center Bull.* 49:16, 18.)

Lewis, I. F., and E. C. Cocke. 1929. Pollen analysis of Dismal Swamp peat. *J. Elisha Mitchell Sci. Soc.* 45:37–58.

Lewis, J. B. 1928. Wildlife of the Dismal Swamp. *Game & Fish Conservationist* (Va.) 8(Nov.–Dec.):95–98.

Lichtler, W. F., and P. N. Walker. 1974. Hydrology of the Dismal Swamp, Virginia–North Carolina. U.S. Geol. Survey, Water Resources Div. Open File Rpt. 74–39. 200 West Grace St., Richmond, Va. 23220. 50 pp. A Dismal Swamp Study report, P.L. 92–478.

Little, S. 1959. Silvical characteristics of Atlantic white cedar. *U.S. Dept. Agric., Forest Service, Northeastern Forest Expt. Station, Pap.* 118. 16 pp.

Lohman, Carol C., and G. F. Levy. 1971. A study of the vegetation in some Dismal Swamp openings. *Va. J. Sci.* 22:106. (Abs.)

*Lyell, C. L. 1845. *Travels in North America in the years 1841–1842: with geological observations on the United States, Canada and Nova Scotia.* v. 1, 251 pp. v. 2, 221 pp. Wiley & Putnam, New York. (Pagination is different in the London edition.)

McCarthy, G. 1884. The August flora of the Dismal Swamp and vicinity. *Amer. Nat.* 18(3):288–290.

McGill, W. M. 1936. Outline of the mineral resources of Virginia. *Va. Geol. Survey, Bull.* 47(ed. ser. no. 3). 79 pp.

McLean, J. D., Jr. 1966. Miocene and Pleistocene foraminifers and Ostracoda of southeastern Virginia. *Va. Div. Mineral Resources, Rpt. Inv.* 9. 123 pp.

Maier, G. F., G. E. Copeland, and A. R. Bandy. 1974. Evaluation and interpretation of air concentration data obtained with the Old Dominion University mobile air pollution laboratory in the Dismal Swamp area. *Va. J. Sci.* 25:80. (Abs.)

Main, C. T., Inc. 1971. Dismal Swamp study 1659-25. Charles T. Main Engineers, Inc., 1301 E. Morehead St., Charlotte, N.C. 34 pp. (Prep. by W. P. Taylor.)

Marshall, H. G. 1974. Zooplankton populations in Lake Drummond, Dismal Swamp, Virginia. *Va. J. Sci.* 25:66. (Abs.)

_____. 1976. The phytoplankton of Lake Drummond, Dismal Swamp, Virginia. *Castanea* 41(1):1-9.

Marshall, H. G., and W. H. Poore. 1972a. Phytoplankton composition at Lake Drummond in the Dismal Swamp, Virginia, summer 1970. *Castanea* 37:59-67.

_____. 1972b. Lake Drummond of the Dismal Swamp: 1. Phytoplankton composition. *Va. J. Sci.* 23:72-76.

Martin, J. 1835. *A new and comprehensive gazeteer of Virginia, and the District of Columbia.* Moseley & Tompkins, Printers, Charlottesville. 529 pp.

Massey, A. B. 1961. Virginia flora. *Va. Agric. Expt. Sta. Tech. Bull.* 155. 258 pp. Blacksburg. Includes early records of the vascular plant collections in Virginia.

_____. 1969. *Virginia ferns and fern allies*, 4th ed. Coop. Ext. Service, Va. Polytech. Inst. and State Univ., publ. 273. 63 pp. There are additional records in earlier and later editions.

Massman, W. H. 1953. A tentative list of fishes from the Dismal Swamp area. Va. Fisheries Lab Bull. 10 Dec. (unpublished).

Matta, J. F. 1971. Distribution aspects of aquatic Coleoptera in the Dismal Swamp. *Va. J. Sci.* 22:99. (Abs.)

_____. 1973. The aquatic Coleoptera of the Dismal Swamp. *Va. J. Sci.* 24:199-205.

_____. 1974. The aquatic Hydrophilidae of Virginia (Coleoptera: Polyphaga). *Va. Polytech. Inst. and State Univ. Res. Bull.* 94. 44 pp.

_____. 1976. The Haliplidae of Virginia (Coleoptera: Adephaga). *Va Polytech. Inst. and State Univ. Res. Bull.* 109. 26 pp.

Matta, G. F., and A. G. Michael. 1976. A new subspecies of *Acilius* from the southeastern United States. *Entomol. News.* 87:11-16.

Meanley, B. 1962. Feeding behavior of the redwinged blackbird in the Dismal Swamp region of Virginia. *Wilson Bull.* 74(1):91-93.

_____. 1968a. Notes on Dismal Swamp plants. *Atlantic Nat.* 23(2):78-82.

_____. 1968b. Birds of the Great Dismal Swamp. *Atlantic Nat.* 23(3):141-142.

_____. 1968c. Singing behavior of the Swainson's warbler. *Wilson Bull.* 80(1): 12-17.

_____. 1969a. The wild camellia and dwarf trillium in the Dismal Swamp. *Atlantic Nat.* 24(1):19-20.

———. 1969*b*. Swainson's warbler in the Dismal Swamp. *Atlantic Nat.* 24(4): 204–208.

———. 1969*c*. Notes on Dismal Swamp birds. *Raven* 40(3):47–49.

———. 1969*d*. Pre-nesting and nesting behavior of the Swainson's warbler. *Wilson Bull.* 81(3):246–257.

———. 1970*a*. A million robins and 10,000 pine siskins in the Dismal Swamp. *Atlantic Nat.* 25(1):40.

———. 1970*b*. The Wayne warbler in the Great Dismal Swamp. *Atlantic Nat.* 25(3):116–117.

———. 1971*a*. Great Dismal Swamp mammals. *Atlantic Nat.* 26(1):17–18.

———. 1971*b*. Natural history of the Swainson's warbler. *N. Amer. Fauna* 69: 1–90.

———. 1973*a*. *Swamps, river bottoms and canebrakes.* Barre publishers, Barre, Mass. 142 pp.

———. 1973*b*. *The Great Dismal Swamp.* Audubon Nat. Soc. Cent. Atlantic States, Washington, D.C. 48 pp. All factors considered, the most generally useful concise introduction to the vegetation and fauna of the Swamp, for scientist and layman alike.

———. 1973*c*. Additional notes on Dismal Swamp birds. *Raven* 44:3–4.

———. 1973*d*. Notes from the Dismal Swamp, spring 1973. *Atlantic Nat.* 28 (3):119–120. (Also see U.S. Army Corps of Engineers, 1975.)

Meanley, B., and J. S. Webb. 1961. Distribution of winter redwinged blackbird population on the Atlantic coast. *Bird-Banding* 32:94–97.

Merriam, C. H. 1895*a*. Revision of the shrews of the American genera *Blarina* and *Notiosorex*. *N. Amer. Fauna* 10:5–34. (Also see Humphreys 1911*a* and *b*.)

———. 1895*b*. Synopsis of the American shrews of the genus *Sorex*. *N. Amer. Fauna* 10:57–100.

———. 1896. Revision of the lemmings of the genus *Synaptomys*, with descriptions of new species. *Proc. Biol. Soc., Washington* 10:55–64.

———. 1897. Description of a new muskrat from the Great Dismal Swamp, Virginia. *Proc. Biol. Soc., Washington* 11:143.

———. 1898. Life zones and crop zones of the United States. *U.S. Dept. Agric., Div. Biol. Survey, Bull.* 10. 79 pp. + maps.

Messmore, J. A. 1975. Application of satellite data and Lars data processing techniques to mapping vegetation of the Dismal Swamp. Master's thesis, Old Dominion Univ. 67 pp.

Messmore, J. A., G. E. Copeland, G. F. Levy, and R. N. Blais. 1975. Application of ERTS imagery and the LARS system to vegetational mapping of the Dismal Swamp. *Va. J. Sci.* 26:65. (Abs.)

Michael, A. G., and J. F. Matta. 1977. The Dytiscidae of Virginia (Coleoptera: Adephaga) (subfamilies: Laccophilinae, Colymbelinae, Dytiscinae, Hydaticinae, and Cybistrinae). *Va. Polytech. Inst. and State Univ. Res. Bull.* 124. 53 pp.

Miller, G. S., Jr., and R. Kellog. 1955. List of North American recent mammals. *U.S. Nat. Mus. Bull.* 205. 954 pp.

Miller, Sharon R. 1958. Working plan: methods of cutting in red maple stands in the Dismal Swamp with emphasis on commercial thinnings. Woodlands Res. Dept., Union Bag–Camp Paper Corp.

_____. 1961. Establishment report: methods of cutting in red maple stands in Dismal Swamp with emphasis on commercial thinnings. Woodland Res. Dept., Union Bag-Camp Paper Corp.

_____. 1965. Progress report: methods of cutting in red maple stands in Dismal Swamp with emphasis on commercial thinnings. Woodland Res. Dept., Union Bag-Camp Paper Corp.

Mitchell, J. C. 1976. Turtles of Virginia. *Va. Wildlife* 37(6):17–21.

_____ 1977. Salamanders in Virginia. *Va. Wildlife* 38(6):16–19.

Moore, Julie H. 1974. Report on the botanical survey of the proposed Pasquotank Reservoir. J. N. Pease Associates. (MS.)

Moore, W. E. 1956. *Pleistocene terraces south of the James River, Virginia.* Va. Acad. Sci. Guidebook, 1956 fieldtrip.

Murray, J. J. 1932. Wayne's warbler, an addition to the Virginia avifauna. *Auk* 49:487–488.

_____. 1940. The faunal zones of the southern Appalachians. *Va. J. Sci.* 1:53.

_____. 1948. The Great Dismal Swamp. *Raven* 19:14.

_____. 1950. Birds. Pp. 213–233 in *The James River Basin: past, present and future.* Va. Acad. Sci., Richmond.

_____. 1965. The Great Dismal Swamp. Pp. 249–257 *in* O. S. Pettingill, Jr. (ed). *The bird watcher's America.* 1974. Apollo ed., Thomas Y. Crowell Co., New York, publ. by arrangement with McGraw-Hill, New York.

_____. 1969. The birds of the Dismal Swamp. *Va. J. Sci.* 20:158–165.

Musselman, L. J., D. L. Nickrent, and G. F. Levy. 1976. A contribution towards a vascular flora of the Great Dismal Swamp. *Rhodora.* 79: 240–268.

Nansemond Refuge. 197[?]. Refuge land-acquisition–biological-reconnaissance report. Naval Transmitting-Facility–Portion, Town of Driver, Nansemond Co., Va. (MS, Dismal Swamp Nat. Wildlife Refuge, Suffolk).

Nicol, A. 1837. The peat soils of Scotland, compared with the juniper soil of the Dismal Swamp. *Petersburg* (Va.) *Farmers' Register* 4(9):528–529.

Oaks, R. Q., Jr. 1964. Post-Miocene stratigraphy and morphology, outer coastal plain, southeastern Virginia. U.S. Office of Naval Research, Geography Branch, Contract NONR 609(40), Task Order NR 388-064, Tech. Rpt. Ph.D. Diss. Yale Univ. 240 pp.

Oaks, R. Q., Jr., and N. K. Coch. 1963. Pleistocene sea levels, southeastern Virginia. *Science* 140:979–983.

_____. 1973. Post-Miocene statigraphy and morphology, southeastern Virginia. *Va. Div. Mineral Resources, Bull.* 82. 135 pp.

Oaks, R. Q., Jr., N. K. Coch, J. E. Sanders, and R. F. Flint. 1974. Post-Miocene shorelines and sea levels, southeastern Virginia. Pp. 53–87 in R. Q. Oaks, Jr., and J. R. Dubar (eds). *Post-Miocene statigraphy, central and southern Atlantic Coastal Plain.* Utah State Univ. Press, Logan. (Also see Sanders et al. 1962.)

Oaks, R. Q., Jr., and W. H. Rodgers, Jr. 1973. Ground magnetic survey, outer coastal plain, southeastern Virginia. *Va. Minerals* 19(1):6–9.

Obenshain, S. S., and E. F. Henry. 1959. Chemical characteristics of profile samples of soils of Norfolk county, Virginia. *Va. Agric. Ext. Sta. Res. Rpt.* 25.

Old, W. E., Jr. and R. H. de Rageot. 1956. Land snails of Nansemond, Norfolk and Princess Anne counties, Virginia. *Va. J. Sci.* 7:87–90.

Omohundro, R. E. 1971a. The Dismal Swamp operation. *J. Amer. Vet. Med. Assoc.* 158:1891–92. (Abs.)

_____. 1971b. The Dismal Swamp operation. *J. Amer. Vet. Med. Assoc.* 159: 1564–66. Re: hog cholera epizootic.

Osbon, C. C. 1919. Peat in the Dismal Swamp, Virginia and North Carolina. *U.S. Geol. Survey, Bull.* 711–C:41–59.

_____. 1921. Classification and formation of peat and related deposits. *J. Amer. Peat Soc.* 14(1):37–44. General account.

Packard, R. L. 1969. Taxonomic review of the golden mouse, *Ochrotomys nuttalli*. *Univ. Kansas Mus. Nat. Hist., Misc. Pub.* 51:373–406.

Palmer, W. 1899. Ferns of the Dismal Swamp, Virginia. *Proc. Biol. Soc. Washington* 13:61–70.

_____. 1902. The log fern. *Fern Bull.* 10:37–41.

Paschal, J. E., Jr. 1973. A simulation model of *Peromyscus leucopus* in an area of the Great Dismal Swamp. Master's Thesis Old Dominion Univ. 43 pp.

Patterson, P. M. 1951. Bryophytes of Virginia; III. Collections made in southeastern Virginia by Bayard Long. *Rhodora* 53:117–128.

_____. 1953. Virginia Bryophytes collected by Bernard Mikula. *Va. J. Sci.* 4:125–128.

Pearson, T. C. 1893. In the Great Dismal Swamp. *Ornithologist and Oologist* 18:26.

Pechuman, L. L. 1973. Horse flies and deer flies of Virginia (Diptera: Tabanidae). *Va. Polytech. Inst. and State Univ. Res. Bull.* 81. 92 pp.

Penfound, W. T. 1952. Southern swamps and marshes. *Bot. Rev.* 18:413–446. General account.

Perkins, S. O., W. D. Lee, G. B. Shivery, and S. F. Davidson. 1928. Soil survey of Camden and Currituck counties, North Carolina. *U.S. Dept. Agric., Soil Survey Series* 1923, no. 2. U.S. Govt. Print. Off., Washington. 56 pp.

Pharr, R. F., and J. L. Calver. 1963. Mineral industries and resources of Virginia (map). *Va. Div. Mineral Resources,* Charlottesville.

Poore, W. H., Jr. 1971. Phytoplankton composition at Lake Drummond in the Dismal Swamp, Virginia. Master's Thesis Old Dominion Univ. 83 pp.

Poore, W. H., Jr., and H. G. Marshall. 1971. Seasonal study of the phytoplankton at Lake Drummond in the Dismal Swamp, Virginia. *Va. J. Sci.* 22:107. (Abs.)

_____. 1972. Lake Drummond of the Dismal Swamp: I. Phytoplankton composition. *Va. J. Sci.* 23:72–76.

Radford, A. E., H. E. Ahles, and C. R. Bell. 1968. *Manual of the vascular flora of the Carolinas*. Univ. North Carolina Press, Chapel Hill. 1183 pp.

Ramsey, E. W., K. R. Hinkle, and L. E. Benander. 1970. Waters of the Dismal Swamp. *Va. J. Sci*. 21:81–83.

Raney, E. C. 1950. Freshwater fishes. Pp. 151–194 in *The James River Basin: past, present and future*. Va. Acad. Sci., Richmond.

Reid, J. H. 1952. *Report on Dismal Swamp*. Camp Mfg. Co., Franklin, Va. 19 pp.

Rhoads, S. N., and R. T. Young. 1897. Notes on a collection of small mammals from northeastern North Carolina. *Proc. Acad. Nat. Sci*. Philadelphia (1897):303–312.

Richards, H. G. 1936. Fauna of the Pleistocene Pamlico formation of the southern Atlantic Coastal Plain. *Geol Soc. Amer., Bull*. 47:1611–1656.

Richardson, R. 1926. Black-throated green warbler in the Dismal Swamp. *Auk* 43(4):552–553.

Roberts, J. K. 1942. *Annotated geological bibliography of Virginia*. Alderman Library, Charlottesville. 726 pp. This includes a history of geological thought and biographical sketches of geologists in Virginia; also abstracts of 1911 Wash. Acad. Sci. Symposium on Dismal Swamp, pp. 209 (C. A. Davis) and 556 (E. W. Shaw).

———. 1950. The Triassic and coastal plain. Pp. 465–481 in *The James River Basin: past, present and future*. Va. Acad. Sci., Richmond.

Robeson, J. M., Jr. 1928. A study of fossil pollen as found in peat from the Dismal Swamp area of Virginia and North Carolina. Master's Thesis Univ. of Virginia. 35 pp.

Rogers, W. B. 1884. *A reprint of annual reports and other papers, on the geology of the Virginias*. D. Appleton and Co., New York. 832 pp. Includes "Report of geological reconnaissance of the State of Virginia, 1835" and "Some observation on the tertiary marl of lower Virginia."

Rogers, W. S., and R. S. Spencer. 1968. Pleistocene geology of Princess Anne County, Virginia. *Southeastern Geol*. 9:101–114. Briefly reviews Pleistocene concepts, but is primarily concerned with groundwater hydrology east of the Swamp, involving Triassic strata.

———. 1969. Sedimentary model for the Nansemond formation (Pleistocene) of Virginia. Geol. Soc. Amer., Southeastern Section, Abstracts, p. 70.

Roseberry, D. A., and R. Bowers. 1952. Under the cover of Lake Drummond. *Va. Wildlife* 13(8):21–23.

Rosevear, P., and A. J. Diefenderfer. 1974. Chemical analysis of the Dismal Swamp waters. *Va. J. Sci*. 25:82. (Abs.)

*Ruffin, E. 1837. Obervations made during an excursion to the Dismal Swamp. *Petersburg* (Va.) *Farmers' Register* 4(9):513–521.

———. 1852. *Essay on calcareous manures*, 5th ed. J. W. Randolph, Richmond. 493 pp. [First published in 1832, 242 pp.]

Russ, W. P. 1973. The rare and endangered terrestrial vertebrates of Virginia. Master's Thesis Va. Polytech. Inst. and State Univ. 339 pp.

Russell, I. C. 1895. *Lakes of North America*. Ginn & Co., New York. 125 pp. Lake Drummond discussed.

Russell, S. C. 1976. Food habits of *Ictalurus natalis, Centrarchus macropterus* and *Perca flavescens* in Lake Drummond, Dismal Swamp, Virginia. Master's Thesis Old Dominion Univ. 25 pp. and appendices.

Sabet, M. A. 1975. Vertical electrical resistivity soundings to locate ground water resources; a feasibility study. *VPI Water Resources Research Center Bull.* 73. 64 pp.

Sanders, J. E., R. F. Flint, N. K. Coch, and R. Q. Oaks, Jr. 1962. Preliminary report on the geology of southeastern Virginia and adjacent coast and continental shelf, with remarks on sediment sampling techniques using vibro-drilling methods. Ann. Rpt. Contract NONR 609(40). NR 388–064. Geography Branch, Office of Naval Research. 45 pp.

Sanford, S. T. 1912. Underground water resources of the coastal plain province of Virginia. *Va. Geol. Survey, Bull.* 5. 361 pp.

Shaler, N. S. 1886a. The swamps of the United States. *Science* 7:232–233.

_____. 1886b. The national survey of resources of the southern states. *Indus. South* 6(25 Mar.):133–135. Dismal Swamp mentioned in connection with soils.

_____. 1890. General account of the fresh-water morasses of the United States, with a description of the Dismal Swamp District of Virginia and North Carolina. *U.S. Geol. Survey, Ann. Rpt.* 10(pt.1):261–339. Swamp specifically treated pp. 313–339.

_____. 1891. The origin and nature of soils. *U.S. Geol. Survey, Ann. Rpt.* 12 (pt. 1):213–345. Photo of Dismal Swamp canebrake facing p. 312.

_____. 1895. Evidences as to changes in sea-level. *Geol. Soc. Amer. Bull.* 6:141–166.

Shaw, E. W. 1911. See Humphreys (1911a and b) and Roberts (1942) for abstracts of Shaw's remarks on the geography and geology of the Swamp which were presented at the Wash. Acad. Sci. Symposium on the Dismal Swamp. For a résumé of these remarks see Stansbury (1925, pp. 221–226).

Shearin, A. E., J. P. Covington, and J. H. Vaden. 1957. Soil survey of Pasquotank County, North Carolina. *U.S. Dept. Agric., Soil Survey Series* 1949, no. 3. U.S. Govt. Print. Off., Washington. 58 pp.

Simmons, C. S., and E. Shulkcum. 1945. Soil survey of Princess Anne County, Virginia. *U.S. Dept. Agric., Soil Survey Series* 1939, no. 3. U.S. Govt. Print. Off., Washington. 56 pp.

Small, J. K. 1964. *Ferns of the southeastern states.* Hafner, New York. 517 pp.

Smith, E. R., J. B. Funderberg, Jr., and T. L. Quay. 1960. *A distributional list of the Recent mammals of North Carolina.* N.C. Wildlife Resources Comm. 19 pp.

Smith, W. C., and D. McDavid. 1935. Heavy mineral suites from some Virginia sediments. *Va. Acad. Sci., Proc.* (1934–35):67–68 (Abs.)

Sonenshine, D. E., and Mary K. Garrett. 1972. Ecological factors affecting the survival of two species of ticks in the Dismal Swamp. *Va. J. Sci.* 23:117. (Abs.)

Soper, E. K., and C. C. Osbon. 1922. The occurrence and uses of peat in the United. States. *U.S. Geol. Survey, Bull.* 728. 207 pp.

Spangler, W. B., and J. J. Peterson. 1950. Geology of the Atlantic Coastal Plain in New Jersey, Delaware, Maryland and Virginia. *Amer. Assoc. Petrol. Geol.* 34(pt. 1):1–99. Cretaceous, Tertiary and Quaternary covered: includes schematic representation of Pleistocene terraces.

Spencer, R. S.1970. Geology of the outer coastal plain—Chesapeake, Norfolk, Virginia Beach, Guidebook: Pt. 1, 11th Annual Field Conf., Atlantic Coastal Plain Geological Assoc., pp. 1–32.

———. 1978. The fauna and paleoecology of the marine pleistocene (Sangamon) of southeastern Virginia. *J. Paleontol, Mem. Ser.* (under review).

Spencer, R. S., and W. S. Rogers. 1970. The Miocene-Pleistocene uncomformity in Norfolk County, Virginia. *Va. J. Sci.* 20:19–21.

*Stansbury, C. F. 1925. *The lake of the Great Dismal.* Albert and Charles Boni Publ. Co., New York. 238 pp. (Pages 221–226 are a résumé of E. W. Shaw's remarks at the Wash. Acad. Sci. Symposium on the Dismal in 1911.)

Stephenson, L. W. 1912. The coastal plain of North Carolina. *N.C. Geol. Survey* 3:266–290.

Stephenson, L. W., C. W. Cooke, and W. C. Mansfield. 1933. *Chesapeake Bay region.* Internatl. Geol. Cong. 16, Washington, D.C. Guide Book 5. 49 pp. July 17 trip is the Dismal Swamp.

Stevens, C. E., Jr. 1946. Dismal Swamp notes. *Raven* 17:59–60.

Stuckey, J. L. 1965. *North Carolina: its geology and mineral resources.* Dept. Conserv. Devel., N.C. State Univ., Raleigh. 550 pp.

Swain, F. M., A. Blumentals, and R. Millers. 1959. Stratigraphic distribution of amino acids in peats from Cedar Creek Bog, Minnesota, and Dismal Swamp, Virginia. *Limnol. Oceanog.* 4:119–127.

Taras, M. A. 1971. American woods: Atlantic white cedar. *U.S. Dept. Agric., Forest Service.* FS-225. 8 pp.

Taylor, J. W. 1974. The Dismal Swamp lemming mouse. *Va. Wildlife* 35 (5):27.

Teifke, R. H. 1973. Geologic studies, coastal plain of Virginia. *Va. Div. Mineral Resources, Bull.* 83(Pts. 1 and 2):1–101 (concern Cretaceous through Miocene); (Pt. 3):107–153 (concerns Pleistocene, Holocene and environmental geology).

Thiessen, R. 1913. Microscopic study of coal. *U.S. Bur. Mines, Bull.* 38. 390 pp.

Tillery, J. T. 1975. Lichen survey of the Great Dismal Swamp. (MS, Old Dominion Univ. 10 pp.)

Trent, V. A. 1974. Mineral resource potential of the Lake Drummond area, Great Dismal Swamp, Virginia–North Carolina. U.S. Dept. Interior, Geol. Survey. 29 Pp., map, and geol. profile. A Dismal Swamp Study report, P.L. 92–478.

True, F. W. 1891. The puma, or American lion: *Felis concolor* of Linnaeus. *Ann. Rpt. Natl. Mus.* (1888–89):591–608. (also see Humphreys, 1911*a* and *b*).

U.S. Army, Corps of Engineers, Norfolk District. 1974. The Dismal Swamp Canal as related to the Great Dismal Swamp study, P.L. 92–478. Norfolk, Va. February. 63 pp. and map. A Dismal Swamp Study report P.L. 92–478.

_____. 1975. Albemarle and Chesapeake Canal and the Dismal Swamp Canal routes of the Atlantic Intracoastal Waterway, Virginia and North Carolina (maintenance dredging): final environmental impact statement. September. Norfolk, Va. 140 pp. Includes seasonal checklist of Tidewater Virginia birds by B. Meanley.

U.S. Army Corps of Engineers, North Atlantic Div. (e.g., 1973). Water Resources Development in Virginia. 72 pp. plus foldout map. This annual report briefly describes projects involving the Dismal Swamp Canal.

U.S. Dept. Agric., Forest Service, Southeastern Area State and Private Forestry. 1974. Report on ascertainment of present and potential forest product use. 9 pp. and addendum 4 pp. and large fold-out map showing forest types. A Dismal Swamp Study report, P.L. 92–478.

U.S. Dept. Agric., Soil Conservation Service. 1971. General soil map and interpretations, Perquimans County, North Carolina. Raleigh, N.C. (unpublished).

_____. 1972a. General soil map and interpretations, Camden County, North Carolina. Raleigh, N.C. (unpublished).

_____. 1972b. General soil map and interpretations, Gates County, North Carolina. Raleigh, N.C. (unpublished).

_____. 1972c. General soil map and interpretations, Currituck County, North Carolina. Raleigh, N.C. (unpublished).

U.S. Dept. Agric., Soil Conservation Service, Soil Correlation Unit. 1974. Report on ascertainment of soil types and agricultural information. Northeast Technical Service Center, USDA, Upper Darby, Pa. February. 13 pp. and map. A Dismal Swamp Study report P.L. 92–478.

U.S. Dept. Interior, Bur. Sport Fish. and Wildlife, Northeast Region, Dismal Swamp National Wildlife Refuge. 1974. Developmental history and ecology of the Dismal Swamp with recommendations for public ownership and management. Suffolk, Va. March. 49 pp. A Dismal Swamp Study report, P.L. 92–478. An outstanding general summary.

U.S. Geological Survey. 1902. Norfolk quadrangle, Virginia–North Carolina, topographic map surveyed in 1888–91 by W. R. Atkinson and R. M. Towson.

_____. 1945. Lake Drummond quadrangle, Virginia–North Carolina, topographic map surveyed in 1940 by C. W. Buckley, L. S. Howe, Jr., and J. W. Pumpelly.

_____. 1954. Lake Drummond quadrangle, Virginia–North Carolina, topographic map of 1940 revised from aerial photographs in 1954.

_____. 1972a. Water resources data for Virginia, 1971. Richmond. 305 pp.

_____. 1972b. Aeromagnetic map of southeastern Virginia. U.S. Geol. Survey open-file report.

Usher, J. W. 1974. Morphological considerations of mistletoe parasitism of red maple in the Dismal Swamp. *Va. J. Sci.* 25:74. (Abs.)

Vick, A. R. 1961. Some pollen profiles from the coastal plain of North Carolina. Ph.D. Diss. Syracuse Univ. 99 pp.

Virginia Bureau of Water Resources. 1960. Chemical character of surface waters of Virginia, August 1958–February 1960. Bull. 23. 59 pp. (By

H. B. Holmes, Jr.) Earlier bulletins on this topic, and other publications listed below, are available from the Bureau, 11 S. 10th St., Richmond, Va. 23219, and Box 1846, University Station, Charlottesville, Va. 22903.

_____ . 1961*a*. Surface water supply of Virginia James River Basin, 1956–1960. Bull. 25. 278 pp. (By H. B. Holmes, Jr.) (Earlier bulletins on this topic available from the Bureau; see 1960, above.)

_____ . 1961*b*. Surface water supply of Virginia Chowan and Roanoke River basins, 1956–1960. Bull. 26. 306 pp. (By H. B. Holmes, Jr.) (Earlier bulletins on this topic available from the Bureau; see 1960, above.)

_____ . 1969–71. *James River Basin, comprehensive water resources plan*, v. 1–4 (Planning Bull. 213–216) plus addendum (Planning Bull. 269) Richmond. (See esp. v. 1, Planning Bull. 213, 1969, Introduction. 193 pp.; also v. 3, Planning Bull. 215, 1970, Hydrologic analysis. 369 pp.; v. 2 concerns economic base and v. 4 water requirements and problems.)

_____ . 1970. Groundwater of southeastern Virginia. *Va. Dept. Conserv. Econ. Devel., Planning Bull.* 261. 54 pp. plus foldout maps showing aquifers.

_____ . 1972. *Chowan River-Dismal Swamp comprehensive water resources plan*, v. 1–4 (Planning Bull. 237P–240P) plus addendum (Planning Bull. 263) Richmond. (See esp. v. 1, Planning Bull. 237P, Introduction; also v. 3, Planning Bull. 239P. Hydrologic analysis, 173 pp.; v. 2 concerns economic base and v. 4 water requirements and problems.)

Walker, S. 1959. Cytotaxonomic studies of some American species of *Dryopteris. Amer. Fern J.* 49:104–112.

Walker, Susan W. 1972. Plant succession in the Great Dismal Swamp of Virginia. Master's Thesis Old Dominion Univ. 52 pp.

Walker, Susan W., and G. F. Levy. 1972. An ordination of plant succession in the Great Dismal Swamp of Virginia. *Va. J. Sci.* 23:123. (Abs.)

Ward, L. F. 1877. Timber trees of the Dismal Swamp. *Field and Forest* 3: 29–31.

Waters, S. B., Rebecca D. Bray, and G. F. Levy. 1974. A taxonomic survey of the spring vascular flora of the Nansemond County, Virginia, portion of the Great Dismal Swamp. *Castanea* 39:82–95.

Watson, T. L. 1907. *Mineral resources of Virginia.* Virginia-Jamestown Exposition Comm. J. P. Bell Co, Lynchburg, Va. 619 pp.

_____ . 1912. Economic products of the Virginia Coastal Plain. *Va. Geol. Survey, Bull.* 4:223–272. Peat in the Swamp considered.

Webb, J. S., and D. K. Wetherbee. 1960. Southeastern breeding range of the brown-headed cowbird. *Bird-Banding* 31(2):83–87.

*Webster, N. B. 1875. On the physical and geological characteristics of the Great Dismal Swamp, and the eastern counties of Virginia. *Amer. Nat.* 9(May):260–262.

Wells, B. W. 1942. Ecological problems of the northeastern coastal plain. *Bot. Rev.* 8:533–561. General account.

Wentworth, C. K. 1930. Sand and gravel resources of the coastal plain of Virginia. *Va. Geol. Survey, Bull.* 32. 146 pp.

White, C. D., and R. Thiessen. 1913. The origin of coal. *U.S. Bur. Mines, Bull.* 38. 390 pp. Dismal Swamp receives significant attention.

Whitehead, D. R. 1965a. Palynology and Pleistocene phytogeography of unglaciated eastern North America. Pp. 416–432 *in* H. E. Wright, Jr., and D. G. Frey (eds). *The Quaternary of the United States.* Princeton Univ. Press, Princeton, N.J.

*———. 1965b. Prehistoric maize in southeastern Virginia. *Science* 150:881–883.

———. 1967. Studies of full-glacial vegetation and climate in southeastern United States. Pp. 237–248 *in* E. J. Cushing and H. E. Wright, Jr. (eds). *Quaternary paleoecology.* Yale Univ. Press, New Haven.

———. 1972. Developmental and environmental history of the Dismal Swamp. *Ecol. Monographs* 42:301–315.

———. 1973. Late-Wisconsin vegetational changes in unglaciated North America. *Quaternary Res.* 3:621–631.

Whitehead, T. 1893. *Virginia: a handbook giving its history, climate, and mineral wealth; its educational, agricultural, and industrial advantages.* Everett Waddey Co., Richmond. 341 pp. Lake Drummond mentioned as a unique feature.

Whitford, L. A. 1958. Phytoplankton in North Carolina lakes and ponds. *J. Elisha Mitchell Sci. Soc.* 74:143–157.

Wieland, G. R. 1897. The depth of peat in the Dismal Swamp. *Amer. J. Sci.,* ser. 4, 4:76. Peat 10 feet thick; vegetable matter 18 feet.

Wilder, C. D., Jr. 1970. A preliminary ecological survey of the water resources and land use patterns of the Dismal Swamp area of Virginia. Project Termination report, OWRR project A-020-VA. Va. Polytech. Inst. and State Univ. 56 pp.

Wilder, C. D., Jr., P. M. Brady, G. M. Simmons, S. E. Neff, and L. A. Hart. 1969. A preliminary ecological survey of water resources and land use patterns of the Dismal Swamp area of Virginia. Proj. Completion Rpt., OWRR project A-020-VA. Va. Polytech. Inst. and State Univ. 4 pp.

Wilson, K. A. 1953. Raccoon predation on muskrats near Currituck, North Carolina. *J. Wildlife Mgt.* 17:113–119.

———. 1954. The role of mink and otter as muskrat predators in northeastern North Carolina. *J. Wildlife Mgt.* 18:199–207.

Wingo, A. L. 1949. *Virginia's soils and land use,* v. 31(8). Baughman Co., Richmond. 323 pp.

Wood, J. T. 1954. The distribution of poisonous snakes in Virginia. *Va. J. Sci.* 5:152–167.

Wood, J. T., F. G. Carey, and R. H. de Rageot. 1955. The nesting and ovarian eggs of the dusky salamander, *Desmognathus f. fuscus* Rad., in southeastern Virginia. *Va. J. Sci.* 6:149–153.

Woolman, L., and C. S. Boyer. 1898. Fossil mollusks and diatoms from the Dismal Swamp, Virginia and North Carolina. Indication of the geological age of the deposits; with note on the diatoms by Charles S. Boyer. *Proc. Acad. Nat. Sci.,* Philadelphia, 50:414–429.

Zon, R. 1911. See Humphreys, 1911a and b.

INDEXES

AUTHOR INDEX

Akerman, A., 382
Allen, G. M., 313
American Ornothologists' Union, 264
Anderson, K. B., 382
Anderson R. R., 93
Andrews, J. D., 383
Arber, E. 318, 328
Ariza, J. F., 304, 307, 316, 317, 326, 331
338, 340, 341, 342, 343, 345, 346, 348,
351, 364
Arnold, R., 301, 363
Asdell, S. A., 282, 291

Bailey, J. W., 306, 308, 309, 311, 312, 328,
329
Bailey, V., 327, 328
Baldwin, J. T., Jr., 200, 384
Bandy, A. R., 188
Banks, N., 200, 219, 384
Bartsch, P., 261, 303, 314, 315, 323, 324,
331
Bassett, J. S., 299, 361
Battle, F. V., 200, 209, 218, 384
Beatty, R. C., 298
Beaven, G. F., 93
Benander, L. E., 383
Bendell, J. F., 282, 291, 292
Berkeley, D., 58, 60, 359
Berkeley, E., 58, 60, 359
Berry, E. W., 381
Bethge, H. 178
Beverley, R., 298, 319
Bishop, W. H., 62, 64, 333, 363
Blair, W. F., 248
Bobb, M., 205
Bolte, J. R., 240
Bottoms, E., 46, 58, 360
Bouyoucos, G. J., 103
Bowers, R., 383
Boyd, J. F., 65
Boyd, W. K., 59, 71, 299, 300, 319, 330,
331, 343, 344, 347, 361
Boyer, C. S., 381

Brady, M., 244, 248
Brady, P. M., 383
Braun, E. L., 32
Bray, J. R., 104
Brimley, C. S., 302, 303-4, 306, 313, 314,
319, 325, 329, 337, 341, 342, 346
Brown, A. C., 65, 66, 185, 365
Brown, P. M., 145, 379
Buell, M. F., 121, 277
Burt, W. H., 282, 288
Butts, C., 53
Byrd, W., 59, 63, 299, 361

Cain, R. L., 121
Caldwell, H., 68
Caldwell, J. R., 46
Calver, J. L., 379
Cameron, C. C., 380
Carpenter, M., 337, 339
Carroll, R. P., 244, 284
Carter, V., 2, 91, 189, 262, 379
Catlin, L. E., 364
Cedarstrom, D. J., 379
Chapman, J. G., 67, 361
Chen, K. L., 130
Chickering, J. W., 366, 381
Citron, H., 48
Clark, A. H., 200, 384
Clark, F. H., 287
Clark, L. F., 200, 384
Clark, W. B., 8, 380
Clayton, J. (1694), 297, 318, 319, 349
Clayton, J., 298, 319
Clymer, B. C., 240
Coch, N. K., 4, 5, 7, 8, 10, 12, 13, 16, 18,
25, 27, 28, 44, 97, 142, 147, 148, 151,
153, 167, 380, 381
Cocke, E. C., 3, 8, 14, 17, 25, 27
Code of Federal Regulations, 188
Coffey, P. E., 188
Cohen, A. D., 20
Conrad, T. A., 381
Cooke, C. W., 380, 381

Copeland, G. E., 381
Coville, F. V., 381
Craig, A. J., 31
Cross, C. B., Jr., 360
Cross, E., 360
Cumming, W. P., 297, 319
Cummings, E. G., 364
Curtis, J. T., 104

Dabel, C. V., 382
Dachnowski-Stokes, A. P., 380
Daniel, J. W., 384
Darton, N. H., 8, 379
Darwin, C., 47, 53
Davis, C. A., 380
Davis, H. J., 362
Davis, M., 304, 351, 362
Davis, R. S., 381
Day, F. P., Jr., 382
Dean, G. W., 94, 101, 382
Delzell, D. E., 383
De Rageot, R. H., 315, 383, 384
Desor, E., 380
Devereux, R. E., 4, 380
Dice, L. R., 304, 322, 323
Dickson, D. R., 46
Diefenderfer, A. J., 381
Downing, S. C., 347
Drinkard, A. W., 380
Duke, A., 366
Dunn, J. B., 304, 333, 340, 341, 343, 348, 351

Eaton, W. P., 302, 304, 307, 317, 333, 340, 348, 351, 364
Eberhardt, L. L., 292
Eisenlohr, W. S., Jr., 80
Ellenberg, H., 105
Emery, K. O., 37, 38
Emmerson, J. C., Jr., 66, 360, 365
Evans, A. M., 132
Evans, J., 330

Fairbanks, H., 50
Fall, H. C., 206, 207
Federal Register, 188
Ferleger, H. R., 65
Fernald, M. L., 381
Fisher, A. K., 261, 302, 303, 307, 308, 311, 313, 314, 317, 318, 320, 324, 327, 329, 340, 345, 348, 351, 367, 384

Fitzpatrick, J. C., 59, 65, 360
Flint, O. S., 205
Flint, R. F., 27
Folman, J., 382
Force, P., 297, 319
Ford, A., 47, 48, 50
Foreman, A. S., 63
Forrester, J. W., 278, 279
Freeman, Harriet E., 364
French, N. R., 291
Freston, T. E., 67, 361
Frey, D. G., 31, 39, 172

Gains, W. R., 67, 301, 365
Gall, F., 14
Gammon, P. T., 382
Garrett, M. K., 46, 154, 166, 278, 291, 384
Garrison, L. E., 37, 38
Goldman, E. A., 320, 341
Golley, F. B., 277, 293
Great Britain Naval Office Returns, 358
Griffin, J. B., 44
Grimes, E. J., 381
Griscom, L., 264
Grosenbaugh, L. R., 103
Gupta, T. R., 80
Gurney, A. B., 200, 206, 215, 384

Hall, E. R., 308, 324
Hall, F. R., 80
Hallock, C., 301, 340, 344, 345, 347
Handley, C. O., Sr., 20, 306, 329
Handley, C. O., Jr., 20, 278, 306, 308, 315, 321, 325, 329, 333, 337, 346
Hariot, T., 297
Harlan, R., 324
Harper, R. W., 381
Harrison, W. R., 18, 31, 151, 381
Harriss, F. L., 298, 318, 319
Hart, A. B., 65
Harvill, A. M., Jr., 381
Hatch, M. H., 207
Hemming, J., 47
Henry, E. F., 3, 4, 102, 380
Hernandez, J. E., 382
Herrman, A., 299, 344
Hibben, F. C., 46, 48
Hill, D., 44n, 319, 339, 352
Hillard, O. C., 179, 382
Hillel, D., 120
Hilsenhoff, W. L., 207

Hinkle, K. R., 383
Hodge, F. W., 48
Hoffer, F. B., 381
Hollick, A., 367, 381, 382
Hollister, N., 308, 326
Holmes, W. H., 53
Hooker, W. A., 240
Hooper, E. T., 320, 321
Howard, J. H., 70, 362
Howell, A. B., 325
Howell, A. H., 317, 319, 320, 321
Hranicky, W. J., 44, 46
Hrbacek, J., 178
Hughes, C. 366
Hungerford, H. B., 205
Hunter, A., 300, 301, 307, 315, 326, 333, 340, 343, 347, 364

Jackson, D., 59, 360
Jackson, H. H. T., 308, 311, 312
Jackson, W. B., 282, 288, 291
Janszen, T. A., 124, 382
Jenkins, R. E., 383
Jennings, J. D., 46
Johnson, B. L., 380
Johnson, E., 204
Jolly, G. M., 292
Jordan, D. S., 383

Kaye, C. A., 21
Kearney, J., 382
Kearney, T. H., 3, 27, 64, 101, 184, 367, 382
Kelson, K. R., 308, 324
Kowal, N. E., 278, 279

Lancaster, J. L., Jr., 240
Lantz, D. E., 329
Lapham, J. E., 4, 380
Larson, J. S., 80
Leakey, L. S. B., 47
Lesquereux, H. H., 380
Levy, G. F., 94, 103, 105, 155, 156, 171, 184, 201, 223, 237, 262, 277
Lewis, I. F., 3, 14, 17, 25, 27, 381
Lewis, J. B., 303, 307, 311, 312, 315, 317, 319, 326, 331, 333, 340, 341, 342, 343, 345
Lichti-Federovich, S., 31
Lichtler, W. F., 90, 98, 102, 171, 184, 379
Lindsey, A. A., 103

Little, S., 115, 382
Longfellow, H. W., 68, 362
Lorant, S., 297
Lyell, C., 300, 366, 380
Lyman, W. S., 4, 380

McAlpin, B. W., 135
McAvoy, J. M., 46
McCarley, H., 277
McCarthy, G., 381
McCary, B. C., 44, 46, 58, 360
McGill, W. M., 379
McGinnies, W. G., 109
McIlwain, W. B., 261
McKnight, F., 58, 366
McLean, J. D., Jr., 146, 381
MacMillan, E. L., 240
Maier, G. F., 381
Main, C. T., 156, 159, 161, 162, 170, 171, 173, 383
Manton, I., 130
Marambaud, P., 361
Marshall, H. G., 154, 169, 170, 171, 173, 174, 178, 179, 184, 200, 202, 382, 383
Martof, B. S., 248
Massey, A. B., 381
Massman, W. H., 383
Matta, J. F., 200, 206, 207, 208, 215, 216, 384
Meanley, B., 94, 95, 101, 244, 248, 266, 278, 306, 314, 315, 316, 318, 330, 331, 338, 339, 343, 346, 381, 383, 384, 385
Merriam, C. H., 303, 308, 314, 316, 324, 326
Messmore, J. A., 382
Metzgar, L. H., 288
Michael, A. G., 200, 207, 215, 384
Miller, B. L., 8, 380
Miller, G. S., Jr., 313, 314, 315
Miller, P. R., 188
Miller, S., 5, 382
Mitchell, J. C., 244, 384
Moore, T., 67, 362
Moore, W. E., 8, 381
Morrison, R. H., 68, 69, 70, 365
Morton, C. V., 135
Mueller-Dombois, D., 104-5
Mulloy, W. J., 298
Murray, J. J., 261, 264, 299, 304, 307, 317, 331, 337, 338, 340, 342, 343, 346, 348, 351, 384

Muscalus, J. A., 67, 365
Musselman, L. J., 101, 131, 135, 137, 382

Needham, J. G., 203, 204
Nelson, E. W., 316
Nelson, R. F., 337, 346, 348, 351, 364
Nelson, W. E., 46, 47
Newman, W. S., 18, 38
Nicholson, A. J., 288
Nicol, A., 380

Oaks, R. Q., Jr., 4, 5, 7, 8, 10, 12, 13, 16,
    18, 25, 28, 44, 97, 102, 141, 142, 146,
    147, 148, 150, 151, 152, 153, 154
Obenshain, S. S., 380
Ogden, J. G., 37
Old, W. E., Jr., 384
Olmstead, F. L., 363
Olsen, J., 299, 306, 338, 349
Oosting, H. J., 93
Osbon, C. C., 3, 8, 14, 17, 380
Osgood, W. H., 322, 323, 324

Packard, R. L., 303, 324
Painter, F., 46, 58, 360
Palmer, W., 127, 129, 261, 382
Paradiso, J. L., 312
Paschal, J. E., Jr., 323, 324, 384
Patterson, P. M., 382
Patton, C. P., 306, 308, 325, 329, 333, 337,
    346
Pearson, T. G., 261, 264
Pechuman, L. L., 200, 209, 210, 219, 384
Penfound, E. T., 102
Perino, G., 48
Perkins, S. O., 4, 380
Peterson, J. J., 380
Peterson, R. L., 347
Pharr, R. F., 379
Platt, J. R., 278
Pollard, C. L., 367
Poore, W. H., Jr., 169, 171, 173, 174, 178,
    200, 382
Pugh, J. F., 66, 360

Quimby, G. I., Jr., 50

Radford, A. E., 105, 381
Ramsey, E. W., 102, 383
Raney, E. C., 383
Redfield, A. C., 38
Reid, J. H., 97

Reid, R., 60, 61, 62, 65, 365
Rhoads, S. N., 302, 307, 308, 309, 311,
    315, 317, 319, 321-29, 333, 340, 341,
    343, 345, 348
Richards, E. V., 337
Richards, H. G., 381
Richardson, R., 384
Ripperton, L. A., 188
Ritchie, J. C., 31
Ritchie, W. A., 50
Roberts, C. H., 207
Roberts, J. K., 380
Robeson, J. M., Jr., 381
Robinson, W. W., 154, 170, 179, 383
Rogers, W. B., 7, 14, 379
Rood, J. P., 287
Roseberry, D. A., 383
Rosevear, P., 381
Ross, H. H., 206
Rountrey, W. F., 261, 265
Ruffin, E., 63, 184, 299, 300, 331, 332,
    341, 342, 344, 345, 378, 380
Rusnak, G. A., 38
Russell, E. W., 114
Russell, I. C., 383
Russell, S. C., 383

Sabet, M. A., 379
Sanders, J., 27
Sanford, S. T., 379
Schwartz, K., 64
Sealander, J. A., Jr., 289, 293
Seher, J. S., 93
Shaler, N. S., 2, 3, 4, 5, 7, 40, 301, 302,
    317, 331, 333, 350, 351, 367, 379, 380
Shearin, A. E., 4, 380
Sheppe, W., 288, 291
Shulkcum, E., 17, 380
Simmons, C. S., 17, 380
Sisson, R. F., 47
Small, J. K., 127, 129, 132, 380
Smith, C. N., 239
Smith, D. G., 91
Smith, E. R., 306
Snow, D. R., 48
Snyder, D. R., 288
Sonenshine, D. E., 223, 237, 239, 278, 291
Soper, E. K., 380
Spangler, P. J., 207
Spangler, W. B., 380
Spencer, R. S., 381
Squires, W. H. T., 304

Stansbury, C. F., 303, 306, 307, 309, 312, 313, 315, 317, 318, 319, 320, 321, 326, 327, 329, 330, 331, 336, 337, 340-46, 348, 351, 364, 383
Stasink, W. N., Jr., 188
Stephenson, L. W., 380
Stewart, P. C., 64, 66, 385
Stewart, W. H., 70, 71, 302, 366
Stickel, L. F., 282, 290
Stone, A., 209
Stowe, H. B., 69, 70, 362
Street, F., 364
Strother, D. H., 333, 343, 361, 363
Stuckey, J. L., 379
Sutton, H., 306, 366
Swain, F. M., 380
Swem, F. G., 361
Swift, D. J. P., 20
Sykes, P., Jr., 261

Taylor, J. W., 326
Taylor, W. C., 63, 129, 130
Teale, E. W., 326
Teifke, R. H., 379
Thiessen, R., 380
Thom, B. C., 39
Thomas, R. D., 130
Tillery, J. T., 382
Tinling, M., 59, 61
Traver, J., 58
Trent, V. A., 379
Troubetzkoy, U., 299, 306, 339, 348, 366
True, F. W., 345
Tueller, P. T., 93
Tugwell, P., 240
Turner, E. C., Jr., 200, 209, 218, 384

Underwood, L. M., 129
U.S. Army, Corps of Engineers, 170, 171, 379, 383
U.S.D.A., 102
U.S.D.A., Forest Service, 382
U.S.D.A., Soil Conservation Service, 380
U.S. Dept. Commerce, 102
U.S. Dept. Health, Education, and Welfare, 188
U.S. Dept. Interior, 81, 95, 385
U.S. Fifth Circuit Court of Appeals, 188
U.S. Geological Survey, 159, 379
U.S. Public Health Service, 164
U.S. Weather Bureau, 143

Vick, A. R., 381
Virginia Bureau of Water Resources, 379
Virginia State Air Pollution Control Board, 188

Wade, R. 63
Wagner, F. S., 129, 130
Wagner, W. H., Jr., 129, 130, 132, 135
Walker, E. M., 204
Walker, P. N., 90, 98, 171, 379
Walker, S. W., 102, 103, 129, 130, 131, 132, 137, 155, 166, 184, 262, 277, 382
Warbach, O., 282, 290
Ward, L. F., 382
Waters, R. S., 337
Waters, S. B., 101, 382
Watson, T. L., 379
Webb, C. H., 47, 48, 50
Webb, J. S., 384
Weber, J. A., 264
Webster, A. B., 366
Wecker, S. C., 288
Wells, B. W., 102
Wentworth, C. K., 8, 25, 379, 380
Wertenbaker, T. J., 330, 347, 350
Westfall, M. J., Jr., 203, 204
Wetherbee, D. K., 384
Wetzel, R. M., 325
Wherry, E. T., 129
White, C. D., 380
White, E., 365
Whitehead, D. R., 17, 18, 21, 27, 29, 31, 39, 44, 46, 49, 57, 97, 101, 102, 141, 142, 146, 147, 148, 150, 151, 152, 153, 154, 167, 380, 381
Whittaker, R. H., 123
Wieland, G. R., 380
Wilder, C. D., Jr., 383
Wilkerson, J. C., 366
Williams, F. T., 66, 360
Williams, L. B., 14
Wilson, F., 70
Wilson, H., 364
Wilson, K. A., 305, 307, 309, 312, 315, 318, 320, 323, 326-29, 337, 340-44, 348, 384
Wingo, A. L., 380
Wobber, F. J., 93
Wood, J. T., 244, 383, 384
Woolman, L., 381
Worth, J. J. B., 188

Wright, L. B., 59, 60, 316

Yarborough, B. H., 366
Young, F. N., 206, 207
Young, R. T., 302, 305, 307, 308, 309,

311, 315, 317, 319, 321-29, 333, 340,
341, 343, 345, 348
Young, S. P., 345

Zimmerman, J. R., 206

ORGANISM INDEX

See subject index for common names. Page numbers followed by t refer to tables; page numbers in *italics* refer to illustrations.

Ablabesmyia, 202, 218
Acer rubrum, 95, 101, 106, 124, 262
Acilius fraternus dismalus, 207, 216
  mediatus, 201, 207, 216
Acris gryllus gryllus, 250
Aedes canadensis, 201, 209, 218
  vexans, 218
Agabetes accuductus, 201, 207, 216
  aeruginosus, 202, 207, 216
  gagates, 207, 216
  stagninus, 207, 216
Agkistrodon contortrix contortrix, 258
  piscivorus piscivorus, 259
Amblyomma americanum, 222, 223, 226-37,
    229t, 231t, 232t, 234-36t, 240, 241
Ambystoma opacum, 251
Amia calva, 383
Amphibia, 245-46
Amphiuma means means, 251
Anax junius, 203, 211
Anchistea virginica, 127
Anolis carolinensis carolinensis, 254
Anomalagrion hastatum, 204, 212
Arthrodesmus, 129
  incus extensus, 174
Artiodactyla, 347-52
Arundinaria, 95
Asimina triloba, 112
Asterionella formosa, 169, 174, 175, 178, 180
Athripsodes transversus, 206, 215
Aves (checklist), 272-76; *see also individual*
    species under common names in subject
    index

Bacillariophyceae, 176
Belostoma flumineum, 213
  testaceum, 201, 205, 213
Berosus aculeatus, 208, 217
  exiguus, 208, 217
  infuscatus, 202, 208, 217
  peregrinus, 208, 217

Bidessonotus inconspicuus, 201, 206, 216
  pulicaris, 206, 216
Blarina brevicauda, 305, 310t
  brevicauda, carolinensis, 309
  brevicauda churchi, 309
  brevicauda kirklandi, 309
  brevicauda telmalestes, 303, 308-9, 311
  carolinensis, 305, 311
Bosmina, 169
  longirostris, 178, 179
Bos taurus, 349-51
Bufo americanus americanus, 248
  quercicus, 248
  terrestris, 248
  woodhousii fowleri, 248

Caborius, 206, 215
Calopteryx maculatus, 204, 212
Campephilus principalis, 261
Canis familaris, 228
  lupus lycaon, 330-31
Capra hircus, 352
Carex, 97
Carnivora, 330-47
Carphophis amoenus amoenus, 257
Carpinus caroliniana, 115-
Castor canadensis canadensis, 20
  canadensis carolinensis, 319-20
Cerotina truncona, 200, 206, 215
Chamaecyparis thyoides, 95, 101, 124, 262
Chaoborus punctipennis, 202, 209, 218
Chauloides pectinicornis, 201, 205, 214
Chelydra serpentina serpentina, 252
Chironomidae, 218
Chironomus, 202, 208, 218
Chiroptera, 313-15
Chlorophyceae, 176-77
Chlorophyta, 176-77
Chlorotabanus crepuscularis, 210, 219
Chrysemys concinna concinna, 253
  floridana floridana, 254

Chrysemys concinna concinna (cont.)
  picta picta, 253
  rubriventris rubriventris, 254
  scripta scripta, 253
Chrysophyceae, 176
Chrysophyta, 176
Chrysops brimleyi, 209, 219
  cinticornis, 209, 219
  flavidus, 209, 219
  hinei, 209, 219
  macquarti, 209, 219
  niger, 209, 219
  pikei, 209, 219
  reicherti, 209, 219
  univattatus, 209, 219
  upsilon, 209, 219
  vittatus floridanus, 209, 219
  vittatus vittatus, 209, 219
Clemmys guttata, 253
Closterium, 169, 174, 175
  gracile, 174
  lineatum, 174
Coleoptera, 200, 206, 215
Coluber constrictor constrictor, 258
Condylura, 303
  cristata parava, 312
Copelatus caelatipennis princeps, 207, 216
  glyphicus, 201, 207, 216
Coptotomus interrogatus interrogatus, 201,
    207, 216
Corethrella, 209
Corydalidae, 214
Corynorhinus macrotis, 315
Cosmarium, 169, 175
Crotalus horridus atricaudatus, 259
Cryptotis parva parva, 305, 310t, 311
Culicoides, 200, 218
  debilipalpis, 209, 218
  furens, 209, 218
  stellifer, 209, 218
Culiseta melanura, 209, 218
Cyanophyta, 177
Cymbiodyta blanchardi, 202, 208, 217
  vindicata, 208, 217

Dasyhelea, 209, 218
Dermacentor variabilis, 222, 223, 226-41,
    229t, 231t, 232t, 234t, 235t, 236t
Desmidiacea, 177
Desmognathus fuscus auriculatus, 251
Diachlorus ferrugatus, 210, 219
Diadophis punctatus punctatus, 257

Didelphis virginiana virginiana, 307
Dineutus carolinus, 202, 207, 217
  discolor, 202, 207, 217
Diptera, 208-10, 217-19
Dryopteris, 127
  atropalustris, 127, 132, *133*, *134*, 135, 137
  X *australis*, 131
  celsa, 127-32, *128*, 135, *136*, 137
  celsa x *cristata*, 131
  celsa x *clintoniana*, 131
  celsa x *goldiana*, 131
  celsa x *intermedia*, 131, 132, 137
  celsa x *ludoviciana*, 131
  celsa x *marginalis*, 129, 131
  celsa x *spinulosa*, 131, 135, 137
  clintoniana, 129, 130, 137
  cristata, 129, 135
  goldiana, 129, 130, 131, 132, 137
  goldiana x *intermedia*, 132
  goldiana x *marginalis*, 129
  intermedia, 127, 131, 132
  X *leedsii*, 129, 131
  ludoviciana, 130, 137
  separabilis, 127
  X *separabilis*, 131, 132, 137
  spinulosa, 131, 132, 135
Dytiscidae, 200, 216
Dytiscus fasciventris, 201, 207, 216

Elaphe obsoleta obsoleta, 258
Enallagma, 201, 204
  durum, 204, 212
Enochrus cinctus, 208, 217
  consortus, 208, 217
  ochraceus, 201, 208, 217
  sublongus, 208, 217
Ephemeroptera, 203, 211
Epiaeshna heros, 201, 203, 211
Eptesicus fuscus fuscus, 313-14
Ericaceae, 262
Erythemis semplicicollis, 201, 204, 211
Euastrum bidentatum, 175
Eucorethra underwoodi, 209, 218
Euglenophyta, 177
Eumeces fasciatus, 254
  inexpectatus, 255
  laticeps, 255
Eunotia pectinalis, 175
Euphagus carolinus, 269
Eurycea bislineata cirrigera, 252

Fabria inornata, 201, 206, 215

Fagus grandifolia, 95
Farancia abacura abacura, 257
  erythrogamma erythrogamma, 257
Felis concolor couguar, 344-45
  rufus floridanus, 345-47
Forcipomyia, 208, 218
Fragilaria crotonensis, 174, 175
Fraxinus, 101, 105, 124
  americana, 105
  caroliniana, 105
  pennsylvanica, 105
Frustulia rhomboides, 175

Gastrophyrne carolinensis, 250
Gelastocoris oculatus, 205, 214
Gerris canaliculatus, 205, 214
  marginatus, 205, 214
  nebularis, 202, 205, 213-14
Glaucomys volans volans, 319
Gomphaeschna antilope, 204, 211
  furcillata, 204, 211
Gomphus exilus, 204, 211
Gyrinidae, 217
Gyrinus borealis, 207, 217
  elevatus, 207, 217
  frosti, 207, 217

Haemaphysalsis leporispalustris, 228, 241
Haliplidae, 200
Haliplus fasciatus, 206, 216
  leopardus, 215
  puntatus, 215-16
Hebrus burmeisteri, 205, 214
Helocombus bifidus, 208, 217
Hemiptera, 205, 212-14
Hesperocorixa brimleyi, 205, 212
  interruptus, 205, 212
  nitida, 201, 205, 212
Heterodon platyrhinos platyrhinos, 257
Hoparius planata, 201, 207, 216
Hybomitra hinei, 210, 219
  lasiophthalma, 210, 219
Hydacticus bimarginatus, 207, 216
Hydraena, 208, 217
Hydraenidae, 217
Hydrobius tumidus, 202, 208, 217
Hydrocanthus iricolor, 207, 216
Hydrochara obtusatus, 201, 208, 217
Hydrochidae, 217
Hydrochus, 208, 217
Hydrometra hungerfordi, 201, 205, 213
Hydrophilidae, 217

Hydrophilus triangularis, 208, 217
Hydroporus, 202
  carolinus, 201, 206, 216
  clypealis, 206, 216
  lobatus, 201, 206, 216
  niger, 206, 216
  venustrus, 201, 207, 216
Hyla cinerea cinerea, 248
  crucifer crucifer, 248
  femoralis, 249
  squirella, 249
  versicolor versicolor, 249
Hypnum, 321

Ilex, 92, 95
  glabra, 95, 262, 340
  opaca, 95, 106, 124, 262
Insectivora, 307-12
Ixodes scapularis, 228, 241

Juncus, 321, 322, 325, 327, 328
  setaceus, 325

Kinosternon subrubrum subrubrum, 253

Laccophilus fasciatus rufus, 206, 216
  maculosus maculosus, 206, 216
Laccornis difformis, 201, 207, 216
Lagomorpha, 315-16
Lampropeltis getulus getulus, 258
  triangulum elapsoides, 258
Lasionycteris noctivagans, 313
Lasiurus borealis borealis, 314
  cinereus cinereus, 314
  intermedius floridanus, 314-15
  ega, 315
Leiolopisma laterale, 254
Lepisosteus occeus, 383
Leptocella pavida, 206, 215
Leptophlebia austrinus, 203, 211
Lestes disjunctus, 204, 212
Libellula cyaenae, 204
  flavida, 204, 212
  incesta, 204, 211
  semifasciata, 202, 204, 212
Limnaoedus ocularis, 249
Limnephilus, 206, 215
Liquidambar styraciflua, 95, 106, 124, 262
Liriodendron tulipifera, 95
Lorinseria areolata, 127
Lutra canadensis lataxina, 342-44
Lygosoma laterale, 254

Magnolia virginiana, 95, 109, 262
Mansonia perturbans, 209, 218
Marsupialia, 307
Melosira, 175, 178
  distans, 178
  granulata, 174, 175, 178
  Herzogii, 178
  italica, 178
  polymorpha, 178
Mephitis mephitis nigra, 342
Microtus, 327, 342
  pennsylvanicus nigrans, 302-3, 305, 310t, 327
  pennsylvanicus pennsylvanicus, 327
  pinetorum, 305, 310t
  pinetorum pinetorum, 328
Molanna uniophila, 200, 206, 215
Mus musculus, 305, 310t, 329-30
Mustela frenata noveboracensis, 341
  vison mink, 341-42
Myocastor coypus bonariensis, 330
Myotis keenii septentrionalis, 313
  lucifugus lucifugus, 313

Natrix erythrogaster erythrogaster, 255
  rigida, 256
  sipedon sipedon, 256
  taxispilota, 255
Navicula, 174
Necturus punctatus punctatus, 251
Neuroptera, 205, 214
Notonecta irrorta, 201, 202, 205, 213
  raleighi, 205, 213
  uhleri, 201, 205, 213
Nycticeius humeralis humeralis, 314
Nyssa aquatica, 95, 101, 262
  biflora, 262
  sylvatica, 95, 101, 105, 124

Ochrotomys nuttalli nuttalli, 228, 277, 279, 282t, 285, 287, 288, 290, 294, 303, 304, 305, 310t, 323-24
Odocoileus virginianus virginianus, 228, 347-49
Odonata, 203-4, 211-12
Oecetis cinerascens, 206, 215
  inconspicua, 206, 215
Oedogonium, 175
Ondatra zibethicus, 326
  zibethicus macrodon, 303, 326
Onoclea sensibilis, 127
Opheodrys aestivus, 258

Ophisaurus attenatus longicaudus, 255
  ventralis, 255
Orontium, 97
  aquaticum, 97
Orthoptera, 200
Oryzomys, 342
  palustris, 305, 310t
  palustris palustris, 320, 327
Osmunda cinnamomea, 127
  regalis, 127
Oxydendrum arboreum, 97, 124

Pachydiplax longipennis, 204, 207, 212
Paracymus subcupreus, 208, 217
Paratendipes, 208, 218
Pelocoris femoratus, 201, 202, 205, 213
Peltodytes dunavani, 201, 206, 215
  muticus, 206, 215
  oppositus, 206, 215
Peridinium limbatum, 174
  westii, 174
Peromyscus, 303, 324, 342
  gossypinus, 304, 305, 310t
  gossypinus gossypinus, 321-22, 323
  leucopus, 304, 305, 310t
  leucopus leucopus, 228, 238, 277-96, 281t, 282t, 321, 322-23
Persea borbonia, 95, 106, 124, 262
Pinnularia, 175
Pinus serotina, 95, 101, 105, 262
  taeda, 95, 101, 105, 124
Pipistrellus subflavus subflavus, 313
Plathemis lydia, 212
Platycentropus, 201, 206, 215
Pleoctus rafinesquii, 314
  rafinesquii macrotis, 315
Plethodon cinereus cinereus, 251
  glutinosis glutinosis, 252
Polypodium polypodioides, 127
Procyon lotor lotor, 228, 340-41
Pseudacris brimleyi, 249
  triseriata feriarum, 249
Psorophora ferox, 209, 218
Pyrrhophyta, 177

Quercus, 95, 101
  alba, 124
  laurifolia, 115
  michauxii, 262
  nigra, 95, 262
  velutina, 124

Rana catesbeiana, 250
  clamitans melanota, 250
  utricularia, 250
  virgatipes, 250
Ranatra australis, 205, 213
  buenoi, 201, 205, 213
  drakai, 205, 213
  kirkaldyi, 205, 213
Rattus alexandrinus, 328, 329
  frugivorus, 328, 329
  norvegicus, 304, 328, 329
  rattus, 328-29
  rattus rattus, 328
Reithrodontomys, 321
  humulis, 305, 310t
  humulis humulis, 320-21
Reptilia, 246-47
Rhantus calidus, 207, 216
Rodentia, 317-30

Sagittaria, 97
Scalopus aquaticus aquaticus, 311-12
Scaphiopus holbrooki holbrooki, 247
Sceloporus undulatus hyacinthinus, 254
Scenedesmus opoliensis, 174
  quadricauda, 174
Scirpus, 95
  olneyi, 327
Sciurus, 317, 318
  carolinensis carolinensis, 317-18
  niger niger, 318
Sialis americana, 205, 214
Sigara, 205, 212
Sigmodon hispidus virginianus, 324
Simulidae, 218
Simulium, 209, 218
Siren lacertina, 251
Smilax laurifolia, 95
Sorex longirostris, 305, 310t
  longirostris fisheri, 303, 307-8, 309
Sphagnum, 33, 34, 36
Staurastrum, 169, 174, 175
  paradoxum, 174
Stereochilus marginatus, 252
Sternothaerus odoratus, 252
Storeria dekayi dekayi, 256
  occipitomaculata occipitomaculata, 256
Suphisellus, 207, 217

Surirella, 174
Sus scrofa, 347
Sylvilagus floridanus mallurus, 228, 315-16
  palustris palustris, 316
Synaptomys cooperi helaletes, 303, 305, 310t, 324-26
  cooperi stonei, 325
  helaletes, 325

Tabanidae, 200, 218-19
Tabanus arr, 210, 219
  americanus, 210, 219
  atratus atratus, 210, 219
  fulvulus, 210, 219
  fusconervosus, 210, 219
  lineola, 210, 219
  melanocerus, 210, 219
  nigrovittatus, 210, 219
  petiolatus, 210, 219
  pumilus, 210, 219
  sparus milleri, 210, 219
  trimaculatus, 210, 219
  zythicolor, 210, 219
Tabellaria fenestrata, 175
Tamias striatus fisheri, 317
Taxodium distichum, 95, 101, 170, 186, 262
Terrepene carolina carolina, 253
Tetragoneuria cynosura, 201, 204, 212
Thamnophis sauritus sauritus, 256
  sirtalis sirtalis, 256
Thermonectus basillaris, 201, 207, 216
  ornaticollis, 216
Trichoptera, 200, 206, 214-15
Triplocerus gracile, 175
Tropisternus blatchleyi blatchleyi, 201, 208, 217
  collaris striolatis, 201, 208, 217
  lateralis nimbatus, 208, 217
  natator, 208, 217
Typha, 95, 327

Ulmus americana, 101, 115
Urocyon cinereoargenteus cinereoargenteus, 331
Ursus americanus americanus, 331-40
Uvarus lacustris, 206, 216

Virginia valeriae valeriae, 257

SUBJECT INDEX

Page numbers in *italics* refer to figures; page numbers followed by t refer to tables.

Abolitionism, 69

Aborigines, bola utilization, 44-56, 45t

Academy of Natural Sciences, Philadelphia, 302

Aerial photography, 80-100
  ecological community identification, 95, 97
  ERTS data, 82, 87t, 88, 90
  for field inspection, 80
  hydrologic data, 90-91, 98
  monitoring potential, 97
  NASA data, 82, 84-86t, 88, *96*
  theme extraction, 91-92, 98
  U.S. Forest Service, 94
  U.S.G.S. data, 82, 87t, 88
  vegetation mapping, 91-97, *94, 96*
  wetlands extraction, 91, *92, 93*

Africa, bola utilization, 47

Agriculture, 62-65. *See also specific products*

Air pollution. *See* Atmospheric hydrocarbons

Albemarle River Valley, 20

Albemarle Sound, 20, 25

Alexandrine rat, 328-39

American elm, 115, 116t, 118t

American Museum of Natural History, 302, 304

American notes (Dickens), 69

American Robin, 266, 268

American toad, 248

American Woodcock, 266, 268, 269

Amphibians
  checklist, 245-46
  distribution, 247-52
  literature, 383-84

Aquatic insects, 200-221
  abundance, 202, 203-10t
  distribution, 203-10t
  general considerations, 202-10
  habitat, 201-2, 203-10t
  literature, 203-10t
  seasonal factor, 203-10t

  summary, 203-10t

Aquatic plants, 29, 31-33, 95

Aransas National Wildlife Refuge, 74, 77

Archaeology, 44-54, 45t
  literature, 360

Archaic period, 44, 45t, 46, 49, 53, 54

Arrowheads, 97

Artifacts, 45t, 57-58. *See also specific periods and objects*
  cultural, 361

Ash, 101, 105-13t, 107t, 110t, 111t, 115, 116t, 118t, 120, 123, 124

Atlantic white cedar (juniper), 60, 92, 95, 101, 106, 107t, 109, 110t, 114-16t, 119-24, 262, 269

Atlatls, 46

Atmospheric hydrocarbons, 188-99
  concentration, 192-*97, 193,* 194t, *195,* 196t
  gas chromatography, 191-93, *192*
  research methodology, 189-*92, 190, 191*
  seasonal factor, 194, 198
  wind direction factor, 192-94

Bachman's Warbler, 264

Badger Ditch Road, tick population, 223, 229t

Bailey, Vernon, 304

Bald cypress, 116t, 170, 186, 262

Bald Eagle, 266

Bannerstones, 46

Barlowe, Arthur, 297

Barred Owl, 263

Bartsch, Paul, 302

Bats, 313-15

Bay, 95, 101, 106, 107t, 109-13t, 110t, 111t, 116t, 118t-21, 123, 124, 262

Bear, 301, 302, 330, 331-40
  kill, *339*

Beaver, 20-21, 24, 301, 317, 319-20

Beaver dams, 20-21

Beech, 95, 97, 116t, 118t, 124

Beech-hemlock-birch assemblage, 29, 32

Belostomatid, 213

Bibliographical material, 358-77, 378-402. *See also* Author Index

Big brown bat, 313-14

Big Entry Ditch, 161

Birds, 261-76
  abundance, 267t
  checklist, 272-76
  fauna analysis, 262-66
  literature, 384
  migration period, 266, 268-70t
  migratory, 74
  roosts, 268
  species number, 262

Black-and-White Warbler, 264, 268

Black bear, 331

Blackbirds, 266, 268, 269

Black-crowned Night Heron, 263

Black Duck, 263

Black gum, 95, 105-11t, 107t, 110t, 113t, 116t, 118t, 120-24

Black oak, 117t, 118t, 124

Black racer, 258

Black rat, 328-29

Black rat snake, 258

Black-throated Blue Warbler, 268

Black Vulture, 263

Black willow, 117t

Bluebirds, 266

Blue-gray Gnatcatcher, 266

Blue-winged Teal, 263

Blue-winged Warbler, 268

Bobcat, 301, 345-47

Bobolink, 268

Bobwhite, 262

Bola, 44-46, 45t
  in Africa, 47
  construction, 46-47
  contemporary use, 47
  in Dismal Swamp area, 49-54, 50t, *51, 52,* 53t
  Eskimo use, 47-48
  manufacture, 53
  in North America, 47-49, 50, 53
  origin, 47
  in South America, 47
  use, 46, 47-49

Bola weights, 46-54, 50t, *51, 52,* 53t

Botany. *See also* Vegetation; *individual species*
  literature, 381-82

Boundary dispute, 58

Briars, 95

Brimley's chorus frog, 249

Broad-headed skink, 255

Brown-headed Cowbird, 264, *265*

Brown rat, 328

Brown Thrasher, 268

Brown water snake, 255

Bullfrog, 250

Bulrushes, 95

Buntings, 262

Butler, Ben, 64

Butterflies, 200

Byrd, William, 58-59, 63, 65, 360, 361

Caddisfly, 214

Calvert Formation, 146

Camp, A. L., 62

Canada Warbler, 268 ·

Canal Bank Motel, groundwater quality, 164, 165t

Canal projects, 60, 64-66, 155

Cane, 95, 97, 101

Canebrake rattlesnake, 259

Carabid beetles, 233, 239

Carnivores, 301

Carolina bay, 39

Carolina Wren, 266

Carpenter frog, 250

Catbird, 268

Cats, 330

Cattails, 95

Cattle, 301, 302, 349-51

Cedar, 102, 115

Chemical analysis, literature, 381

Chesapeake Bay Bridge-Tunnel, peat deposits, 18

Chestnut, 262

Chipmunk, 317

Chlorophyceans, 174

Choptank Formation, 146

Chrysophyceans, 174

Chuckatuck, 57

Chuck-will's-widow, 266

Churchland Flat, 11, 18, 152

Cinnamon fern, 127

Civilization, 39-41

Cladocerans, 169, 178, 179

Climate, 17, 31-33, 35, 37-38, 41, 98, 143, 152
Clinton's fern, 129
Colonial exploration, 58-59
Columbia Formation, 8
Common Crow, 263, 268
Common Flicker, 268
Common Nighthawk, 268
Common snapping turtle, 252
Common snipe, 266
Computer model, white-footed mouse population, 277-96
Conservation, 74-79, 80-81. *See also* Wetlands management
Cooters, 253, 254
Coots, 263
Copepods, 169, 179, 187
Copperhead, 258-59
Corapeake Canal, 161, 184
Cormorants, 263
Cotton mouse, 321-22
Cottonmouth, 259
Cotton rat, 324
Cotton-tail rabbit, 228
Cowbird, *265*
Creepers, 248
Cretaceous Period, 143, *145*, 152
Crows, 263, 268
Cultural chronology, 45t
Cyanophyceans, 174
Cypress, 60-62, 95, 101, 109, 116t, 170, 186, 262
Cypress-gum assemblage, 29, 34, 36, 40, 41
Cypress Swamp, 157-59, *158*
bola finds, 49

Damselfly, 212
Daniel, W. J., Jr., 302, 303, 305
Dark Swamp forest, 101
Deep Creek Swale, 5, 142, 147, 148, 151, 153
Deer, 228, 240, 301, 311, 347-49
Desert Road, aquatic insects, 211
Desmids, 169, 174, 175
Diamond Springs Scarp, 10
Diaries of George Washington, 1748-1770, The, 360
Diatoms, 169, 174, 175
Dickens, Charles, *American notes,* 69
Dismal Swamp

age, 28
area, 1-4
developmental history, 25-43
developmental synthesis, 35-39, *37*
extent, 1-4
location, 14, 25, *26*
morphology, 2-7, *3, 6, 15,* 142
origin theories, 152-54
physiography, 142
prehistory, 28
preservation, 166-67
remote sensing research area, 83, *84*
survival, 40
Dismal Swamp Canal, 8, 65-66, 155, 171-72, 184
dredging, 3, 8
locks, 161
peat, 17
plankton composition, 173, 175
spoil banks, 5
surface-water outflow, 159, 161, 168
surface-water quality, 162, 163t
Dismal Swamp Land Company, 59-62, 65
Dismal Swamp National Wildlife Refuge, 103
Dismal Swamp Peat, 1, 4-8, *6,* 12-21, *15, 19,* 25, 27, 29, 151
age, 18, *19*
base of peat, 16
burn, 39
character changes, 37-38
definition, 12-13
developmental synthesis, 36-38
distribution, 12-13, 27
forest stands and, 106-9, 107t, 108t, 113-15, 119-24
formation mechanisms, 18, 20-21, 27, 152-53
hydrology and, 167
losses, 40-41
origin, 17-18
oxidation, 40
pollen analysis, 17, 18, 27, 29-*35, 30, 34,* 37
radiocarbon dating, 151
stratigraphic relations, 13-16
survival, 40-41
thickness, 13-16, 25
water movement in, 162, 164
Dismal Swamp Programs, Office of, 337

Dismal Swamp Terrace, 27-29
Dismal Town
  tick population, 223, 226, 236t
  white-footed mouse population, 278
Ditches. *See also specific constructions*
  aquatic insects, 201-2
Ditching, 5, 155
  forest dynamics and, 102, 114
Dobsonfly, 214
Dogs, 228, 240
Dog tick, 222-43
Domestic cattle, 349-51
Domestic goat, 352
Domestic hog, 347
Drainage, 1, *2*, 3, 5, 16, 18, 21, 28, 32,
  36, *89*, 90, 152-53, 155, 159, 167,
  170-72. *See also* Groundwater; Hy-
  drology; Surface water
Dred . . . (Stowe), 69-70
Drummond, William, 58
Ducks, 263
Dwarf waterdog, 251

Eagle, 262, 266
Earth Resources Technology Satellite
  (ERTS), 80-81
  aerial photography, 82, 87t, 88, 90
  hydrologic data, 80, 90-91, 98
  Multispectral Scanner, 81
  theme extraction, 91-92, 98
East Ditch, 172, 186
Eastern big-eared bat, 315
Eastern Bluebird, 266
Eastern box turtle, 253
Eastern chipmunk, 317
Eastern cottonmouth, 259
Eastern cottontail, 315-16
Eastern earth snake, 257
Eastern garter snake, 256
Eastern glass lizard, 255
Eastern harvest mouse, 320-21
Eastern hognose snake, 257
Eastern kingsnake, 258
Eastern long-eared myotis, 313
Eastern mole, 311-12
Eastern mud snake, 257
Eastern mud turtle, 253
Eastern narrow-mouthed toad, 250
Eastern painted turtle, 253
Eastern Phoebe, 266
Eastern pipistrelle, 313
Eastern ribbon snake, 256

Eastern slender glass lizard, 255
Eastern spadefoot, 247
Eastern worm snake, 257
Ecological communities, aerial photog-
  raphy, 95, 97
Education, federal land management
  and, 77-79
Egrets, 263
Elizabeth River, 142
Elm, 101, 115, 116t, 118t
Environmental education, 77-79
Environmental Protection Agency, 188
Eskimo, bola utilization, 47-48
Euglenophyceans, 174
Evening bat, 314
Evening Grosbeak, 269
Evergreen briar, 95
Evergreen shrub-bog community, 95,
  101, 262
Exploration, colonial, 58-59

Fancy fern, 127
Farming. *See* Agriculture; *specific products*
Federal land management, 74-79
  wetlands, 80-81
Feeder Ditch, 161, 171, 184, 187
  groundwater quality, 164, 165t
  plankton composition, 173, 175, 179
  redredging, 184
Fentress Rise, 10, 11, 18, 20, 25, 142,
  147, 148, 151-53
  Archaic sites, 44, 46
Ferns, 127-39, *128, 133, 134, 136*
Figgins, J. D., 302
Finches, 269
Fires, 14, 27, 40, 61, 102, 121
Fish, literature, 383
Fish Crow, 263, 268
Fisher, A. K., 302, 303
Five-lined skink, 254
Flickers, 268
Florida cooter, 254
Flying squirrel, 319
Forest communities, 101-24. *See also spe-*
  cific stands
  origin, 102
Forest dynamics, 101-26, 261-62
  climax-pattern hypothesis, 123
  cluster analysis, 109-22, 110t, 111t,
    113t, 114t, 116-17t, 118t
  isolated sapling stands, 121-22
  isolated tree stands, 119-20

Forest dynamics *(cont.)*
  mineral soils stands, 106-9, 107t, 108t, 115, 121-24
  peat soils stands, 106-9, 107t, 108t, 113-15, 119-24
  research methodology, 102-5
  research results, 106-22
  research stands, 103-5, *104*
  salt effect, 114
  sapling clusters, 120-21
Forest products industry, 60-63, 65, 102, 119-24, 262
Forests, 27, 36. *See also individual species and assemblages*
  aerial photography, 92-97, *94, 96*
  literature, 382
Fossil pollen. *See* Pollen analysis
Fowler's toad, 248
Foxes, 330, 331
Fox Sparrow, 268
Fox squirrel, 318
Frogs, 247-50
Fruit rat, 328-329

Garter snake, 256
Gas chromatography, 191-*93, 192*
Gaut, J. H., 302
Geese, 263
Geology, 1-24, 25, 27, 28, 35, 143, 146-51, *145. See also specific formations*
  literature, 379-81
  setting, 7-12
  strata, 6, 7-*12, 9, 11, 13*
Glencoe diary . . ., 360
Glossy water snake, 256
Gnatcatcher, 266
Goats, 347-52
Goldenclub, 97
Goldenclub-composite-fern subzone, 33
Golden mouse, 228, 277, 323-24
Goldies' woodfern, 129, 130, 137
Grass-limnophyte subzone, 33, 97
Gray Catbird, 268
Gray fox, 331
Gray squirrel, 317-18
Gray treefrog, 249
Gray wolf, 330-31
Great Black-backed Gull, 263
Great Blue Heron, 263
Great Bridge Formation, 7-10, 147, 150t
Greater siren, 251
Great short-tailed shrew, 308-9, 311

Grebs, 263
Green anole, 254
Green frog, 250
Green treefrog, 248
Green-winged Teal, 263
Gristmill, 60
Ground skink, 254
Groundwater, 98, 153-55, *154*
  inflow, 162, 164
  level, 164
  quality, 164, 165t
Gulls, 263
Gums, 95, 97, 101, 105-13t, 107t, 110t, 111t, 116t, 118t, 120-23, 124, 262

Half Way House, 66, 67
Hamburg Ditch, 159, 161, 162
  aquatic insects, 202, 218
  bola finds, 49
  peat, 12
Hardwoods, 32, 36, 41. *See also individual species*
Hares, 315-16
Harvest mice, 320
Hawks, 263
Hazelton Scarp, 10
Hemp culture, 59
Henry, Patrick, 65
Hermit Thrush, 269
Herons, 263
Herring Gull, 263
Hickory Scarp, 10, 142
Historic periods, 44, 45t
History of Nansemond County, Virginia (Dunn), 304
Hoary bat, 314
Hognose snake, 257
Hogs, 301, 347
Holly, 95, 97, 106-13t, 107t, 110t, 111t, 116t, 118t, 121-24, 262
Holocene Epoch, 18, 20, 143, 147, 150t, 151
Honeysuckle, 95
Hooded Merganser, 263
Hooded Warbler, 266
Hotels, 66
House mouse, 329-30
Hummock forest, 95
Hunting, 364-65
  with bola, 46-54
  missiles, 46
Hunting dogs, 228, 240

Hydrocarbons. *See* Atmospheric hydrocarbons
Hydrology, 140-68
    literature, 379
    systems modification, 155
Hydrology research
    area description, 140-42, *141*
    climate, 143
    physiography, 142
    remote sensing applications, 80, 90-91, 98
    topography, 142
Hypsithermal interval, 21, 41

Ilex—pond pine association, 92, 95
Inca, bola utilization, 47
Indian legends, 362
Indians, 39, 57
    bola utilization, 44-56
Indiantown Creek, 16, 142
Indigo Bunting, 262
Insects. *See also* Aquatic insects; *individual species*
    literature, 384
Interior Ditch, 186
In the shadow of the pines (Howard), 70
Intracoastal Waterway, 40, 171
Iron ore, 53
Ironwood, 115, 116t, 124
Ivory-billed Woodpecker, 261, 264

Jack pine, 31
Jefferson, Thomas, 65
Jericho Ditch, 60, 159, 161, 172, 184, 186
    aquatic insects, 218
    forest dynamics, 114
    peat, 16
    plankton composition, 173-75
    surface-water quality, 162, 163t
Jericho Ditch Road
    aquatic insects, 212-14, 217
    tick population, 223, 229t
June berry, 118t
Juniper, 60-62

Kearney, Thomas, 64
Kempsville Formation, 9, 10
Kentucky Warbler, 264
Killdeer, 266
Kingsnake, 258
Knickerbocker, Lake Drummond engraving, 67

Lady of the Lake (Williamson), 67
"Lake, The" (Poe), 68
Lake Drummond, 25
    aquatic insects, 202, 212, 214, 218
    bottom contours, 183-87, *185*
    drainage, 170-72
    engraving, 67
    Feeder Ditch, 66
    forest dynamics, 115, 119
    general features, 169-73, 179-80
    geology, 10, 16, 25
    hotel, 66
    inflow, 159, 161, 170-71
    lake level, 98, 170
    log fern finds, 131, 135
    morphology, 5, 7
    nutrients, 173
    origin, 38-39, 153-54
    outflow, 162
    peat substrate, 186
    plankton composition, 169-82
    radiocarbon dating, 154
    spillway, 5
    storage capacity, 170
    substrate, 183-87, *185*
    surface area, 170
    surface-water quality, 162, 163t
    water characteristics, 172-73, 179-80
    water depth, 170
    water temperature, 173
"Lake of the Dismal Swamp, The" (Moore), 67-68
Land companies, 59-62, 65
Land management, 74-79, 80-81
Land-of-Promise Ridge, 11
    Archaic sites, 46
LANDSAT, 81
Late Jurassic Period, 143
Laurel oak, 115, 116t, 118t
Lawson, John, 298
Lawson's history of North Carolina, 298
Least shrew, 311
Legends, 362-63
Lemming vole, 324-26
Lesser short-tailed shrew, 311
Lewis, Fielding, 59
Light Swamp forest, 101
Limonene, 194t, *195*, 196t, *197*
Literature, 67-71, 358-75. *See also* Author Index
    amphibians, 383-84
    archaeology, 360
    articles, 364-66, 378

Literature *(cont.)*
  birds, 384
  botany, 381-82
  chemical analysis, 381
  fiction, 362
  fish, 383
  forests, 382
  geology, 379-81
  government records, 358-59
  historical scholarship, 365-66
  hydrology, 379
  insects, 384
  legends, 362-63
  letters, 59-60
  mammals, 384
  manuscript collections, 358
  memoirs, 363-64
  naturalists, 382-83
  newspapers, 360
  periodicals, 361-62
  poetry, 362
  reptiles, 383-84
  scientific, 366-67, 378-402
  sports, 364-65 .
  technical, 378-402
  travel accounts, 363, 364
Little Blue Heron, 263
Little brown myotis, 313
Little grass frog, 249
Little River, 16
Lizards, 254-55
Loblolly pine, 95, 97, 101, 105, 107-10t, 116t, 119, 123, 124
Log ferns, 127-39, *128, 133, 134, 136*
  distribution, 131, 132
  taxonomy, 129-30
Londonbridge Formation, *6,* 9, 10, *12,* 16, 17, 147, 148, 150t, 151
Lone star tick, 222-43
Long-tailed weasel, 341
Loons, 263
Louisiana Waterthrush, 268
Louisiana (Florida) woodfern, 130
Lundy, Benjamin, 69
Lunz, Robert, Jr., 304
Lynn Ditch Road, tick population, 223, 226, 229t, 230, 236t

McAtee, W. L., 303
Magnolia, 95, 262
Maize (corn) pollen, 39, 57

Mallards, 263
Mammals, 297-357
  biological surveys (1890s), 302-3
  biological surveys (20th century), 303-7
  exploration period, 297-98
  first impressions, 299-300
  late colonial period, 298
  literature, 384
  post–Civil War period, 301-2
  pre–Civil War period, 300-301
  settlements period, 297-98
  species, 307-52
Man, 39-41, 57-73
  bola utilization, 44-56, 45t
Many-lined salamander, 252
Maples, 95, 101, 262
Maps, 2, 3, *4,* 5
Marbled salamander, 251
Marsh, 95, 97
  aquatic insects, 202
Marsh rabbit, 316
Marsh rice rat, 320
Marsupials, 307
Martins, 266
Meadow vole, 327
Merganser, 263
Merriam, C. Hart, 302, 303
Mesic forest, 95, 97
Mice, 228, 310t, 317, 320-24
Middle Ditch, 114
Migratory birds, 74
Mineral soils, forest stands, 106-9, 107t, 108t, 115, 121-24
Mink, 341-42
Miocene Epoch, 7, 8, *145,* 146, 150t, 152
Moles, 307, 311-12
Moss Swamp, bola finds, 49
Mountain lion, 344-45
Mouse, 228
Muskrat, 301, 320, 326-27, 340-41, 343

Nansemond Formation, 7, 8
Nansemond Indians, 57
Narrow chain fern, 127
National Aeronautics and Space Administration, aerial photography, 82, 84-86t, 88, *96*
National Wildlife Refuge System, 74-79
Naturalists, literature, 383
Nelson, Thomas, 59
Nelson, William, 59

Newland Canal, 162
New Lebanon Company, 61, 65
Newport News City Park, tick research,
    223, *224*, 226, 230, 231t, 232t, 234-
    36t, 241-42
Nighthawk, 268
Nonmethane hydrocarbons, 192-*97*, *193*,
    194t, 196t
Norfolk aquifer, 98, 162, 164, 166, 167
Norfolk Formation, 6, 8-*11*, 16, 17, 147-
    51, *149*, 150t, 153, 154
    hydrology, 167-68
North American bola utilization, 47-50,
    53
Northern black racer, 258
Northern brown snake, 256
Northern fence lizard, 254
Northern red bat, 314
Northern red-bellied snake, 256
Northern yellow bat, 314-15
Northern water snake, 256
Northern Waterthrush, 268
North Landing River, 20
Northwest River, 16, 20, 142, 152, 153
Norway rat, 328
Nuthatch, 266
Nutria, 320, 330

Oak fern, 127
Oak-hickory assemblage, 29, 33, 36, 38
Oaks, 95, 97, 101, 115, 116-18t, 124, 262
Oak toad, 248
Oceana Ridge, 10
Okefenokee Swamp, 20
Opossum, 307
O'Reilly, John Boyle, 70-71
Orontium-composite-fern subzone, 97
Otter, 342-44
Ovenbird, 266
Owls, 263
Oxidant control, 188
Ozone, 188-89, 198

Paleocene-Eocene rocks, 143, *145*, 146
Paleoecological studies, 27-35
Paleo-Indian period, 44, 45t
Paleozoic formations, 143
Palmer, T. S., 302
Palmer, William, 302, 303
Parula Warbler, 264, 268
Pasquotank River, 16, 20, 152
Pawpaw, 111-13t, 117t, 118t, 120

Peat deposits. *See* Dismal Swamp Peat
Pelican Island National Wildlife Refuge,
    74
Percy, George, 297
Peroxides, 189
Perrygo, Watson M., 304
Peters, H. S., 304
Phoebe, 266
Phytoplankton, 169, 174-78, 176-77t
    form variations, 175, 178
    research methodology, 173
    seasonal pattern, 174-75
Pileated Woodpecker, 263
α-Pinene, 193-96t, 194t, *195*
Pines, 95, 97, 101, 105, 107-10t, 116t,
    119, 123, 124
Pine Siskin, 269
Pine-spruce assemblage, 29, 31-32, 41
Pine vole, 328
Pinewoods treefrog, 249
Plankton, 169-82
    research methodology, 173-74
Plantation economy, 59-60
Pleistocene Epoch, 8, 10, 18, 21, 25, 27,
    28, 142, 146-51, 150t, 167
    artifacts, 44
Pliocene Epoch, 7, 8, 146-52, 150t
Pocomoke River Swamp, 93
Pocosin, 101
Poe, Edgar Allan, "The Lake," 68
Pollen analysis, 17, 18, 27, 29-*35*, *30*,
    34, 37-41, 49, 57
Pollen zones, 29, 31-34
    beech-hemlock-birch assemblage, 29,
        32
    cypress-gum assemblage, 29, 34, 36,
        40, 41
    oak-hickory assemblage, 29, 33, 36, 38
    pine-spruce assemblage, 29, 31-32, 41
Ponding, 17, 18, 20-21, 37
Pond pine, 101, 105
Poplar, 95, 97, 116t, 118t, 124
Portsmouth and Roanoke Railroad, 66
Portsmouth Ditch, 161, 186
Powells Point Ridge, 11
Powhatan Confederation, 57
Prairie Warbler, 266
Preble, E. A., 302
Precambrian formation, 143
Precipitation, 17, 37, 143, 144t, 152, 170
Prehistoric period, 57
Prentiss, D. W., 302

Princess Anne Rise, 11, 27
Prothonotary Warbler, 266
Public use policy, 74-79
Puma, 344-45
Pungo Ridge, 8, 11
    Archaic sites, 46
Purple Finch, 269
Purple Martin, 266
Pyrrhophyceans, 174

Rabbits, 228, 315-16
Raccoons, 228, 301, 326, 340-41
Radiocarbon dating, 18, 29, 32-35, 34
    Dismal Swamp Peat, 151
    Lake Drummond, 154
Railroad Road, aquatic insects, 211, 212,
    215-18
Railroads, 66
Rainbow snake, 257
Ralph, W. L., 303, 305
Rats, 317, 320, 324-26, 328-39
Rat snake, 258
Rattlesnake, 259
Reclamation projects, 63-65
Recreation, federal land management
    and, 75-79
Recreational Use of Conservation Areas
    Act, 76
Red ash, 105
Red-backed salamander, 251
Red bay, 95, 106, 107t, 109-13t, 110t,
    111t, 116t, 118t-20, 123, 124, 262
Red-bellied turtle, 254
Red-bellied water snake, 255
Red-cockaded Woodpecker, 266
Red Crossbill, 269
Red-eyed Vireo, 266
Red maple, 95, 101, 106-13t, 107t, 110t,
    111t, 116t, 118t-24, 262
Red-shouldered Hawk, 263
Red-tailed Hawk, 263
Remote sensing research, 80-100
    advantages and disadvantages, 80
    available data, 82, 84-86t, 87t, 88
    Dismal Swamp Study authorization,
        82
    ecological communities, 95, 97
    field inspection, 90
    future applications, 97-98
    hydrologic data, 80, 90-91, 98
    interpretation, 81
    monitoring potential, 97

study area, 88-89
theme extraction, 91-92, 98
vegetation mapping, 91-97, 94, 96
Reptiles
    checklist, 246-47
    literature, 383-84
Resurrection fern, 127
Rice culture, 60, 97
Rice rat, 320
Riddick Ditch, 184
Ring-billed Gull, 263
Ring-necked Duck, 263
River cooter, 253
River otter, 342-44
Rivers. See Drainage; specific features
Robins, 266, 268
Rogerson, Isaiah, 66
Roof rat, 328-29
Roper, John, 62
Rotifers, 169, 178
Rough green snake, 258
Royal fern, 127
Royster, Alphonso, 302, 303
Ruffin, Edmund, 63
Rufous-sided Towhee, 268
Rusty Blackbird, 269

St. Marys Formation, 146
Salamanders, 251-52
Salt effect, 114
Sand Bridge Formation, 6-14, 13, 16-18,
    28, 147, 148, 150t-53, 162, 164, 167
Sangamon interglacial, 28
Sassafras, 117t
Scarlet kingsnake, 258
Scarlet Tanager, 266
Sea level, 18, 20, 21, 27, 28, 37, 38, 41, 151,
    153
Sedges, 97
Sedley Formation, 6, 147, 150t
Sensitive fern, 127
Shingle production, 60-62, 65
    machinery for, 62
Shorebirds, 263
Shrews, 307-11, 310t
Silkworm culture, 60
Silver-haired bat, 313
Skinks, 254, 255
Skippers, 200
Skunk, 301, 342
"Slave in the Dismal Swamp, The"
    (Longfellow), 68-69

Slavery, 59, 60, 63, 68-70
Slimy salamander, 252
Smith, John, 328
Smithwick brothers, 302
Snakes, 255-59
Snipe, 266
Songbirds, 264, 268. *See also individual species and groups*
Sourwood, 97, 117t, 118t, 124
South America, bola hunting, 47
Southeastern five-lined skink, 255
Southeastern long-tailed shrew, 307-8
Southern copperhead, 258-59
Southern cricket frog, 250
Southern dusky salamander, 251
Southern flying squirrel, 319
Southern lemming vole, 324-26
Southern leopard frog, 250
Southern ringneck snake, 257
Southern toad, 248
Southern two-lined salamander, 252
Spanish oak, 117t
Sparrows, 266, 268
Spear-throwers, 46
Spleenwort hepatic, 211
Spotted turtle, 253
Spring creeper, 248
Squirrels, 301, 317-19
Squirrel treefrog, 249
Star-nosed mole, 312
Steamboats, 64, 66, 67
Stinkpot, 252
Stream cutting, 7, 8, 10, 152, 153
Stream gradients, 16, 20
Striped skunk, 342
Suffolk Scarp, 4, 5, 7, 8, 10, 25, 27-29, 38, 142, 147, 148, 151-53, 157, 158, 164, 167, 172
  Archaic sites, 46, 49
  formation, 28
  groundwater quality, 164, 165t
  hydrology, 168
  Indian settlements, 57
Surface water, 98, 154-55
  flow estimates, *157, 158*, 160-61t
  general considerations, 155-57
  inflow, 159, 168
  outflow, 159-62, 168
  profiles, *156*
  quality, 162, 163t
Surry Scarp, 147
Surveying, 58-59, 64

Swainson's Warbler, 264-66, 268
Swallow, 266
Swamp black gum, 101, 262
Swamp chestnut, 262
Swamp chestnut oak, 116t
Swamp magnolia, 95, 262
Swamp white oak, 118t
Swans, 263
Sweet bay, 109, 111t, 113t, 116t, 118t, 121, 124
Sweet gum, 95, 97, 106-13t, 107t, 110t, 111t, 116t, 118t, 121, 123, 124, 262
Sweet gum subzone, 33
Switch cane, 101

Tanager, 266
Tate, G. H. H., 304
Teals, 263
Thermal imagery, 98
Thrashers, 268
Thrush, 269
Ticks, 222-43
  abundance, 223
  density variation, 238-41
  distribution, 223, 237-38
  ecological factors, 239-42
  environmental studies, 227-28
  hosts, 228, 238-40
  inundation and, 237-40, 238t, 242
  molting, 233, 236t, 237, 242
  predatation, 233, 239, 240
  research methodology, 222-28
  species composition, 223, 228-30, 229t
  summer survival, 230-33, 231t, 232t
  survival studies, 226-27
  winter survival, 233, 234t, 235t
Toads, 247-50
Towhees, 268
Topography, *2-5, 3, 9, 11, 12, 13, 15*, 16, 25, 28, 142
Transportation, 64-67
Tree Swallow, 266
Truck farming, 64
Tupelo gum, 101, 262, *263*
Turkey, 264
Turkey Vulture, 263
Turtles, 252-54
Two-toed amphiuma, 251

Uncle Tom's cabin (Stowe), 70
Upland chorus frog, 249
Upper Cretaceous Period, 152

U.S.D.A., Bureau of Biological Surveys, 302, 304
U.S. Fish and Wildlife Service, 75, 88
U.S. forest Services, 94
U.S. Geological Survey
    aerial photography, 82, 87t, 88
    Autographic Theme Extraction System, 91, 98
    hydrologic studies, 90-91
    remote sensing research, 82
U.S. National Museum, 302, 303

Vegetation
    aerial photography, 91-97, *94, 96*
    in Archaic period, 49
Vireos, 266
Virginia chain fern, 127
Virginia Company, 59
Virginia opossum, 307
Vole, 327
Vultures, 263

Waders (birds), 263
Wagner's Warbler, 268
Walker, Thomas (Dr. John), 59
Warblers, 261, 264-66, *265*, 268
Washington, George, 59, 65, 97
    engraving, 67
Washington Ditch, 60, *156*, 172, 184, 186
    aquatic insects, 202, 211-16, 218
    bola finds, 49
    forest dynamics, 115
    groundwater quality, 164
    log ferns, 127, 129
    plankton composition, 173-75
    tick population, 223, 226, 229t, 230
Water. *See* Drainage; Groundwater; Hydrology; Surface water
Water ash, 105
Waterfowl, 74-76, 266
    hunting, 46-54
    production areas, 74-76
Water gum, 95, 116t, 118t
Water oak, 95, 116t, 118t, 262
Water resources management, 80-81
Water snakes, 255, 256
Water table, 33, 37-38, 41
    peat water movement, 162, 164
Waterthrush, 268
Wayne's Warbler, 261, 264, *265*
Weasel, 330, 341
Wetlands, aerial photography, 91, *92, 93*

Wetlands management, 80-81, 166-68
Whip-poor-will, 266
White ash, 105
White-breasted Nuthatch, 266
White cedar, 102
White-footed mouse, 228, 322-23
White-footed mouse population
    constants, 278, 279, 282t, 285, *286*, 292-93
    model format, 285, 287-92
    model formulation, 278-81t, *280*
    model incrementation, 285, *286*
    research methodology, 278-81
    research results, 282-85
    simulation vs. observed and estimated, 282-84t, *283*
    simulation model, 277-96
    study area, 278
    trapping, 281
    variables, 278-79, 281t, 285, *286*
White oak, 116t, 124
White-tailed deer, 228, 240, 301, 347-49
Whooping Crane, 74
Wicomico Terrace, 227
Wildcat, 345-47
Wildlife refuges, 74-79
William Byrd's natural history of Virginia, 298
Williams, Edward, 297
Williamson, Hugh, 65
Williamson, Thomas, *Lady of the Lake*, 67
Williamson Ditch Road, tick population, 223, 229t
Willow, 117t
Willow oak, 117t
Windsor Formation, *6*, 147, 150t
Winter Wren, 269
Wisconsin glaciations, 28
Wolves, 330-31
Woodcock, 266, 268, 269
Wood Duck, 263
Woodland period, 44, 45t
Woodland pools, aquatic insects, 201
Woodpeckers, 261, 263, 264, 266
Worm-eating Warbler, 264
Wren, 266, 269
Wright, William, 58
Writings of George Washington, 1745-1799, The, 360

Yellow-bellied turtle, 253
Yellow-fly, 200